Leo Walmsley was born at Shipley, Yorkshire, in 1892. During the First World War he served in the Royal Flying Corps, winning the Military Cross and being four times Mentioned in Despatches. Trained as a marine biologist he went on several scientific expeditions to Central Africa and wrote *Flying and Sport in East Africa* (1920).

His first books to attract general critical attention, the novels *Three Fevers* (1932) and *Phantom Lobster* (1933), were set among the fisher-folk of Robin Hood's Bay, which he called Bramble-wick, in his native Yorkshire. J. Arthur Rank bought the rights of *Three Fevers* for his first film production but, while Walmsley's work was praised by nearly every distinguished writer of the day – including T. E. Lawrence, Rebecca West, J. B. Priestley, and Compton Mackenzie – he never quite achieved the bestseller which would have provided financial stability.

Love in the Sun, the fictional account of his escape to Cornwall in the mid-1930s with his future wife, looked certain to break this pattern. It was published in 1939 to a storm of critical acclaim on both sides of the Atlantic. But the Second World War inter-vened and there was to be no bestseller. Walmsley moved to a hill farm in Wales with his growing family, but his marriage ended in divorce.

He published a volume of autobiography, *So Many Loves* (1944), and post-war novels included *Master Mariner*, *The Golden Waterwheel*, *The Happy Ending*, and *Sound of the Sea*. Then, in 1963, came the real-life sequel to *Love in the Sun*. Called *Paradise Creek* it tells of his return to the creek across the river from Fowey, and to the old army hut where he and his wife had made their home years before. And it tells of how, in Cornwall, Leo Walmsley was to find happiness again, before his death in 1966.

THE CORNISH LIBRARY
NUMBER SEVENTEEN

Love in the Sun

LEO WALMSLEY

ANTHONY MOTT LTD

LONDON

Published by Anthony Mott Limited 1983
50 Stile Hall Gardens, London W4 3BU

First published 1939
by William Collins

ISBN 0 907746 24 1

Printed in Great Britain by
Richard Clay (The Chaucer Press) Ltd

Affectionately to Ulric B. Walmsley

Who doth ambition shun,
And loves to live i' the sun,
Seeking the food he eats,
And pleas'd with what he gets.
Come hither, come hither, come hither :
Here shall he see,
No enemy,
But winter and rough weather.

—As You Like It

ST. JUDE is a seaport in South Cornwall. It lies near the mouth of a small river, the Pol, whose estuary, shut in on all sides by high land, affords a safe, deep-water anchorage to ships of considerable size. The town itself, while small, straggles along a mile and a half of waterfront, its main street widening out here and there into wharves and jetties. This street continues through the old town into a residential area of hotels, boarding-houses and modern villas, becomes a parade, and ends near the sea in public pleasure gardens, with a golf course extending along the coastline.

Once a market town, and a centre of the pilchard industry, St. Jude to-day owns neither market nor fishing fleet. Its commercial importance is due to its proximity to the chief china clay pits of South Cornwall, and to the loading facilities of its harbour: and in a lesser degree to its sheltered and sunny position, which makes it a favoured retreat for invalids, retired business men, and officers of the army and navy. There is little of historic interest in the town. The parish church has an early foundation, but it has been extensively "restored." There is a typically Cornish, granite-built town hall dating from the fifteenth century, and at the harbour mouth, the ruins of a fortification of the same period. The old houses are honestly built of granite, and roofed with slate. What beauty they may possess is largely spoilt by a gasometer, and the aggressive roofs and spires of two nonconformist chapels which rise among them and catch the eye from every viewpoint. The architecture of the residential area is chiefly Victorian.

Across the harbour from St. Jude, and connected to it by motor ferry, is the smaller and more compact town of Porthkerris, which, facing north-west, lacks the climatic attractions of its neighbour, and has not been developed as a health resort; although a modern baroque parish church, a methodist chapel, and a red brick and stucco coastguard station successfully break the colourful pattern of its slate roofs and massive cottage walls. Porthkerris too, was once a fishing port, and in the eighteenth and nineteenth, and even into the twentieth century, enjoyed a reputation (through that of the firm of Hoskins and Sons) as a shipyard. But the ships built were sailing ships, and, as we were to discover, the men of Porthkerris were no longer shipwrights or fishermen but labourers on the china-clay jetties of St. Jude, or simply unemployed and on the dole.

It was the afternoon of a Christmas day that I, a Yorkshireman and a stranger, arrived on foot in St. Jude, and, from one of those quays that break its straggling main street, had my first view of its harbour. That view was not specifically attractive. It did not encourage the hope that I was near the end of my peculiar quest: least of all did it suggest the beginning of a great adventure. The weather was muggy, and unseasonably mild. A sabbatarian quiet hung over that part of the town through which I had passed. The shop blinds were drawn. The pubs were closed, and if I had seen tinsel and Christmas decorations through the windows of the cottages, I had heard few voices and met few people. To save money, I had spent the previous night on the floor of a deserted coastguard look-out, and since breakfasting on a stale Cornish pasty, I had tramped the best part of twenty miles along a rough cliff path, the last six of them with a blister the size of a walnut on one foot.

I was tired and hungry. Yet I was far from being unhappy or discouraged. I had escaped from an awkward fix: I had, successfully it seemed, burnt my boats behind me. St. Jude might not provide me with the final solution of my problems, but there was a drowsy peacefulness about it that I liked, and at least it had the merit of being three hundred miles distant from Bramblewick, as remote from the worrying life I had left as if indeed I was in a foreign country. Here, thank God, I knew no one, and no one knew me.

I stood leaning against the rails of what evidently was a boat landing quay, for there were steps, and a number of small boats were moored close by. The main physical features of the harbour and its boundaries were fairly comprehensible, although from my present view-point the china-clay jetties, which lie along the more restricted estuary of the Pol, were hidden by a twist in the estuary itself. The true harbour began where, almost opposite me, this estuary broadened; and ended where, to southward, the hilly land of the east shore narrowed in towards that of St. Jude. This made a stretch of water that was almost land-locked, a mile long and at least half a mile broad. I could not see the actual harbour mouth. But I could see Porthkerris; and, tracing the line of the east shore, I could see that it continued inland to form a fairly wide creek, running parallel to the Pol, and divided from it by another hill formation. My map informed me that this creek bore the curious name of Pill, that it was nearly a mile in length, and that no road ran near its shores, so that it was virtually isolated except by water even from Porthkerris. From what I had seen of other Cornish harbours it seemed likely that the Pill would be used as a winter berth for yachts and other small craft. I could only see its mouth, however, and for the time I did no more than make a mental note that it might be worth exploring before I left St. Jude.

There was no activity in the harbour, and apart from three large cargo steamers moored close to the farther shore of the estuary, no ships. The steamers had evidently been laid-up for a considerable time. Their hulls were red with rust, the paint of their superstructures was blistered and cracked, and I could see grass growing from a pile of ashes and kitchen rubbish on the deck of the nearest one. Moored to the shore with innumerable ropes and wires that seemed to have grown like roots; rusty, dirty, and with no apparent sign of human occupation, those steamers, which from their names I recognised as belonging to a famous line that had paid record dividends before the great slump in shipping came, increased in a peculiar way my sense of detachment from the active world, and of the drowsiness of St. Jude. But suddenly there appeared round the stern of the nearest one a man rowing a small boat, and heading for my quay. He was (we were to discover later) one of the several longshoremen of the place who earn a living doing odd jobs on the wharves, running out ropes for incoming ships, ferrying sailors to and from the quays: and he must have thought I had some business on one of the steamers, for as he got near the quay he slewed his boat round and hailed me.

"Do you want to go aboard one of they ships, sir?"

I shouted, "No!" He pulled in to the steps, got out, and with the boat painter in his hand, came up to where I stood, eyeing me as though reluctant to abandon the idea of business, on a day when business was obviously bad. He was elderly, disreputable-looking. So was his boat, which had no paint on it, and was rotten in many places and mended haphazardly, with bits of box-wood, and untidy rope

lashings. There was at least six inches of water in her
bottom. But the man seemed good-natured, and having
quickly summed me up as a stranger to the place with a
possible curiosity as to its chief points of interest, he set
about describing the attractions of a trip by boat up the
River Pol, or up the Pill, or to Porthkerris, or down the
harbour to St. Jude castle. He would take me any of these
trips for a bob an hour and a glass of cider when we got back.
I told him I didn't care a damn for the beauties of the Pol
or the castle, but that I was here looking for a cottage or a
bungalow, or a house-boat or a laid-up yacht; and I asked
him if he knew of any such thing lying in a quiet part of the
river or one of its creeks, that I could rent cheaply for a few
months. He seized quickly on the word "yacht."

"Yacht?" he said. "You be looking for a yacht? Why,
there be plenty of laid-up yachts in Pill Creek. You ought
to see Joe Hoskins over at Porthkerris if you be wanting a
yacht. Whole of Pill foreshore belong he. Damned if he
ain't got an old schooner up there on the mud he be wanting
to sell or charter for somebody or other. You jump into my
skiff, sir. I'll take you to Joe Hoskins for a bob. You wait
till I bale 'e out."

There was something of the Ancient Mariner about the
old man; or I was too tired and overcome with the drowsiness of St. Jude to argue or resist. He made a pretence of
baling his wretched craft. I got in. He headed for Porthkerris. Gradually Pill Creek became clearer. It narrowed
quickly behind the hill that parted it from the Pol, and the
hill itself steepened almost into a cliff, covered for the most
part in heath and bracken, with occasional clumps of oak.
The east bank was not so steep, but it too, close to the shoreline, was uncultivated. There were too many twists in the
Creek itself for me to see the entire shore, but several laid-up

yachts and motor-cruisers were visible, and, about half-way up, was a three-masted ship, which my guide informed me was the schooner he'd spoken about. It would have a nice little cabin, of course, but he couldn't tell me whether Joe would want to let anybody live aboard. Joe was an obliging sort of chap, though, specially when he'd had a pint or two. It had been a bad day for Porthkerris when Joe's firm went smash.

A ship with a tolerably decent cabin was just the thing I wanted. My needs after all were simple enough; shelter, somewhere to sleep, something to cook on, seclusion; and security for a period long enough for me to write my Bramblewick book, the salvage of a not complete disaster. Then, if the book succeeded, I could face the world again. Dain and I would live the life we wanted to.

I would have questioned the old man for more details about the schooner, but he never stopped talking. I couldn't help thinking how different he, and all the other Cornishmen I had met, were from the dour men of Bramblewick. Words gushed from him, and in defence I listened only vaguely to the version he gave me of the story of the rise and fall of the firm of Hoskins and Sons, a story which with varying details we were to hear so many times. All that impressed me then was that the firm was bankrupt, that its interest in shipping and boats was chiefly that of caretakers and agents: so that I was prepared to find the senior member of the firm more human and approachable than if he had been a successful and opulent man of business. I was surprised all the same.

We avoided the little stone pier of Porthkerris where the ferry boats land, and rowed in alongside an old jetty, back of which were several stone and wooden buildings, one of them bearing a faded notice-board:

J. HOSKINS AND SONS,
SHIPWRIGHTS, SHIP-BREAKERS, SAILMAKERS,
BLOCKMAKERS, CHANDLERS, ETC.

On the jetty itself was an old-fashioned crane with a wooden boom, and the space between this and the buildings was filled with small boats, timber, ship's anchors, chains, tanks, spars, barrels, in indescribable confusion. Close by the crane, sitting on the stock of an anchor, was a small, white-haired man, in his shirt sleeves, chopping firewood. He took no notice of our arrival until my guide hailed him.

"Hey, Joe! Here's a gennelman be looking for a yacht."

Then Mr. Hoskins turned a pair of surprisingly blue eyes upon us and smiled wistfully.

"That be Joe Hoskins," my guide told me in a loud whisper. "You'll find Joe a nice obliging sort of chap. I'll wait here for you, sir, then if you want to go up Pill Creek and see that schooner, I'll be handy. I'll have 'e baled out again by time you'm ready."

During our voyage the water in the boat had risen ankle-deep. I paid him off, and climbing a ladder up the jetty wall I picked my way through the confusion of things to Mr. Hoskins, who had got up to his feet. I told him what I wanted. He listened silently until I made a direct inquiry about Pill Creek, and the craft laid up there. Then he said quietly, with a curiously unassuming air:

"Oh, yes. All foreshore of Pill Creek belongs we. But I don't know of any boats any one could live in. They laid-up boats all be covered with tarpaulins, and their cabins battened down, and all their gear stowed away on shore, and none of they belongs we. We only look after them and their moorings."

"What about the schooner?"

Mr. Hoskins smiled, this time with a gentle irony.

"Why—you'd find it quiet living on a boat like she all right. But she be for sale. I don't think her owner wants to let any one live on board her. She's not insured, and you might set fire to her. No. I reckons that what you want is a little bungalow, with a bit of garden and grow your own vegetables, and a bit of land to keep chickens or goats. I've got a place up Pill Creek would suit you if I hadn't gone and let it to someone else a while back. You'd find it quiet in Pill Creek, specially in winter-time."

I had no wish to see a bungalow that had been let to someone else; yet I had taken a great liking to Mr. Hoskins, and I was not without hope that the schooner might do, temporarily at least. I suggested, diffidently, for I was conscious that it was Christmas day, that I'd like to have a look up the Creek, and to my surprise Mr. Hoskins at once offered to take me. He had to go up in any case, he said, to look at some moorings.

"I only be chopping a bit of firewood," he said as he put on his coat. "Be nothing else to do these days," he added with a more ironic smile. "You don't want to buy a shipyard, do you?"

We got into a small boat moored at the jetty steps. I offered to row, and Mr. Hoskins sat in the stern, the terrier at once curling up at his feet. As we sheered off I glanced at the desolate shipyard, and said conversationally:

"Trade's bad, eh?"

His expression was wistful again.

"Trade? We've almost forgotten what a word like trade means in Porthkerris. Only word we know be bloody dole."

He waved his hand backwards to the yard.

"You wouldn't think ten years ago Hoskins be paying more than a hundred pounds a week in wages! Would you?"

"What—shipbuilding?"

"No." He pointed to the half-demolished hulk of a sailing ship, whose ribs stuck out of the water, close to the shore. "That be the last ship Hoskins built, *Amelia Hoskins*. My father built she for his brother Joe who had a nice little coal trade, but she got into a collision just before the War, and we bought her back for firewood, only damned if we can afford the labour to have her broken up. We gave up building real ships long before the War. We were building smacks and yachts and motor-boats when the War came. Then we started repairing sailing ships the old Garmuns had damaged with mines and torpedoes and guns. You wouldn't think that there'd be twelve sailing ships, all at the same time, moored off Porthkerris, waiting for repairs. You wouldn't think there was so much trade that we were working day and night with more than eighty men! We were coining money faster than the Royal Mint! If we'd only had the sense to retire then, we'd be living in a castle now instead of chopping firewood!"

For the second time within half an hour, only with more detail, I was to hear the story of the collapse of the firm of Hoskins and Sons; of how, towards the unguessed end of that post-war boom in shipping, when any craft, steam or sail, that could obtain a certificate of sea-worthiness, was earning enormous profits, a large foreign barque that had been severely damaged by a mine, and then by fire, was towed into St. Jude harbour. She was surveyed and pronounced repairable, and was bought by an English company as a speculation. Hoskins was given the contract for the job, the biggest in the history of the firm. She was too big to be brought alongside the yard. Hoskins purchased a

section of the Pill Creek foreshore, laid down a "slip,"
beached her, and began the job with a doubled staff of workmen.

Timber, iron, cordage, canvas, paint, the raw materials
of the shipbuilding trade were at a record scarcity and cost.
But the firm's credit was high. The job went merrily on.
The biggest difficulty was to find men, shipwrights, carpenters, blacksmiths, sailmakers, riggers, to share in that
vast pay-roll, which in fact was the firm's capital turned
liquid. That capital was not enormous. It went. Credit
was found to feed the weekly stream of cash. The job at
last was finished. But the owners had bargained on a
continuance of the trade boom, and that boom already was
collapsing. The money to meet the contract with Hoskins
and Sons could not be found until the ship itself earned it.
She was allowed to sail. She was lost on the first voyage,
before she had earned a penny, and whatever insurance was
paid precious little of it came back to Porthkerris to meet
the liabilities of the firm, which had no alternative but
bankruptcy.

I listened only vaguely to Mr. Hoskins's version of that
tragic story, with my mind half on my own problems, for
we had entered Pill Creek, and whenever I glanced over my
shoulder I could see the schooner for which I presumed we
were aiming. The creek was shallow. The tide was ebbing,
but it was neap, and there was water to float close up to the
east shore, which, by Mr. Hoskins's occasional directions, I
hugged. The shore itself was rocky, and for twenty feet
from water level made a precipitous cliff, on the edge of
which was a belt of oaks, and above this again hilly ground
covered with brambles and bracken. Ahead of us the line
of cliff suddenly ran out in a bluff, hiding temporarily what
lay beyond it.

"That be our south boundary," Mr. Hoskins said, pointing to the bluff. "But we had to buy all the land above it too. Landlord wouldn't sell what we wanted unless we bought the lot. Seven hundred quid we had to give 'e for it. Seven hundred quid! Wish I had a quarter of that for a Christmas present!"

We reached the bluff, but we had completely rounded it before I observed that we had come into the mouth of a little cove, the termination of a short steep valley with bracken and furze and brambles on one side of it, rough pasture on the other. A little stream ran down the valley, and a hundred yards or so before it entered the cove was a relatively level patch of cleared ground on which was a building I recognised as an army hut. For a moment I did not connect the hut with Mr. Hoskins's story. My mind was still on the schooner, and before I thought of questioning him he was talking again. I stopped rowing.

"This be the very place where we laid that ship. We had to wait for a big spring tide, of course. Her bows were almost to high-water mark and we had to cut down two oaks to clear her bowsprit. When tide be low you'll see the slip-blocks down to low-water mark. They blocks cost more than one hundred quid. That hut cost one hundred and fifty, and more than another fifty to fetch down from Salisbury. Had it for a workshop. Then we made it into a bungalow."

"And that's the place you've let?"

"Yes. I let it to a man with a wife and three kids, came along looking for work a while back. Fine place to look for work—Porthkerris! But he told me he'd got no home, and I was sorry for his wife and kids, so I said 'e could have it for half a crown a week, but damned if we've seen any of his money yet. We'd better go ashore. Maybe I'll get some rent from 'e now."

I turned the boat into the beach. We got out, and made the painter fast to a stone. Close to the stream a rough path climbed up towards the hut, which was built end on, and, as I soon perceived, with its nearer end on piles to set off the slope of the site. I did not feel too happy at what we were doing. I dare not let myself think of the place as a possibility, and deliberately I kept in my mind the fact that it was already tenanted. That its tenant was poor and owed rent, even to so kindly a person as Mr. Hoskins, put my sympathies on his side. Yet I could not blind myself to the fact that the cove, the valley with its little stream, the hut itself, were completely out of sight and sound of the harbour and town of St. Jude, that the place was virtually more isolated than anything I had yet seen on my quest. And Mr. Hoskins seemed bent on convincing me about the less obvious attractions, as he slowly led the way up the path, with the terrier close to his heels. He pointed up the right side of the valley.

"That all belongs we," he said. "Be more than nine acres altogether. Be a lovely little spring too close by hut. You've never tasted lovelier and cooler water, and it never runs dry. I've never seen such lovely early taties do grow hereabouts. I've never seen such beans and peas and onions and broccoli. I reckons this be a perfect place for any one be wanting to be quiet. You can't hear nothing all day but singing birds. Be like a garden of Eden!"

We drew near the hut, and Mr. Hoskins stopped talking. There was a door, reached by a flight of steps, for the piles on which the whole structure rested were here at least six feet high. We stopped at the bottom of these steps, and Mr.

Hoskins hesitated before ascending to the door. There he stopped again for an appreciable time before knocking. There was no answer. There was no detectable sound whatever from within the hut itself. He knocked again. Still there came no sound. Mr. Hoskins looked down at me and said:

"Be a queer thing. Don't seem to be any one at home. Hope he ain't been and murdered his wife and kids, and hanged himself."

It was a ghastly suggestion, and I was not surprised that Mr. Hoskins hesitated again before trying the handle, and then slightly opening the door. The terrier sniffed through the gap and growled.

"Be a queer thing," he repeated, looking down at me. "Door ain't locked."

He knocked once more, and gave a shout inside, "Any one in?"

Still there was no sound. I climbed up the steps, and Mr. Hoskins suddenly pushed the door wide open. The terrier, with its hair bristling, rushed inside. But we stood on the threshold, looking into a room that was exactly half of the entire hut. There were windows right and left, of the standard army hut type. The rafters and the roofing boards were bare. The walls, too, were mostly bare weather boarding, although in places some sheets of old plywood were nailed to the uprights, and at the far end a match-board partition reached from side to side, and there was a door leading into what evidently was the living part of the hut. The big room was empty but for an old mattress, a number of beer bottles and condensed milk tins. It was dirty, dilapidated, and there was a stale smell of beer, and tobacco and cooking, like that of a disreputable pub. Mr. Hoskins gave another shout. Then he said:

"Looks as though 'e's either done a murder and hanged himself, or done a moonlight flit. We'll have a look."

The terrier was sniffing at the old mattress. Mr. Hoskins called it to heel before we stepped in. Outside, the winter light was already fading. There was a gloom within that was accentuated by the sound of our footsteps as we walked over the bare wood floor towards the door of the partition. I don't think I would have been surprised then if Mr. Hoskins's first suggestion had proved correct; if we had found the corpses of the tenant's family on the floor, the tenant himself suspended by the neck from one of the perfectly-suited rafters. One glance through the partition door confirmed for him at any rate that his second conjecture was the right one. Except for the dirt, a broken chair, and another collection of beer bottles and condensed milk tins, the place was empty; and Mr. Hoskins expressed his feelings with a surprising heat.

"Damned if 'e ain't gone. Damned if 'e ain't—and 'e not paid a farthing of rent. Be a damned rascal 'e be. That's what comes of doing a christian kindness. Chap like 'e ought to be in prison."

He went on talking, but I scarcely listened to him. The door led into a corridor which continued through the remaining half of the hut to another entrance door at the far end. Immediately right and left were rooms, one of them containing a coal cooking stove. I left Mr. Hoskins and continued up the corridor. There was another room on the right. Two more on the left. They were all indescribably dirty. The ceiling of the one containing the stove was black with soot. There were signs of leakage in this, and the ceilings of all the others save the farther one on the right. The partition walls had been papered by some previous tenant. This mostly hung down in strips, but where the wood was bare it looked sound, the floors if filthy were not rotted.

The second entrance door was bolted on the inside. I opened it and stepped out. At this end, farthest from the creek, the floor of the hut was level with the ground. The brook ran parallel to the length of the hut, and within a couple of strides. Two old willows grew near to it and there were several little waterfalls and pools below them, choked with weeds, more bottles and tin cans, and strips of rusty corrugated iron. To the left, for the whole length of the hut, and reaching thirty yards up the north bank of the valley, was a neglected vegetable garden. Here, what was evidently a section of the fence of the whole property turned at right angles, and then followed the course of the brook upwards for two or three hundred yards before turning south along the crest of the hill. The fence was broken, and in the garden I saw the hoof pits and droppings of cattle. It was clear that the whole place was derelict.

Mr. Hoskins had joined me, still tirading against the absconded tenant. I questioned him about the hut, the garden, the spring, the actual extent of the property. He pointed to the fence, and told me that it continued over the crest of the hill for about 200 yards, then came down to the shore again close to the bluff. The cove itself belonged to the property down to low-water mark, and there was three-quarters of a mile of foreshore beyond, where the yachts and the schooner were moored. But the schooner had gone completely from my mind. I asked him to show me the spring. We crossed the brook. Not more than twenty yards from the hut there was a cavity in the bank from which there flowed a copious stream of clear water. I said nothing, for it would have been a mistake to show Mr. Hoskins how desperately excited I was. There was a rough

path leading up the hill, which, he explained, joined a path
which led to Porthkerris. We climbed the path to the
crest of the hill, where we came in sight of the harbour
and St. Jude, three-quarters of a mile away. I could see the
entire boundary of the property, and look down at the cove
and the hut, and follow the winding of the Pill among the
hills to the north.

That northward view, with the red bracken and the bare
oaks, and rocky outcrops of the opposite bank reflected in
the glassy creek, even in the fading winter light had a
spectacular beauty. But it was the little valley below that
made my heart beat fast. I could see that the hut, despite
its present dilapidation, could, with hard work and very little
cost, be made decently habitable: that the garden was not
beyond redemption: that the nearby land, thick though it
was with weeds and rubbish, could be cleared and trans-
formed with paths and grass and flowers. So could the
brook, with its little waterfalls and pools. And I saw, above
all, that this valley which Mr. Hoskins perhaps ironically,
perhaps with some secret thwarted yearning for romance,
had likened to an Eden, was secluded, as remote from the
outside world as a desert island, offering undisturbed peace,
yet near enough by boat to the indispensable amenities of
civilisation.

But it came upon me suddenly that the place might
offer something more than this: something that was not
far short of what Dain and I had dreamt of when we had
parted. Then, it was true, we had been obsessed chiefly by
the idea of escape, from a life which for both of us had
become intolerable. It was not merely that we had been the
acquiescent defendants in an amiable and "convenient"
action for divorce: that we had become the talk of the
village of Bramblewick: that the furnished cottage, where

ostensibly I had lived alone the past two years had become
the focusing point of many inquisitive eyes: that all our
expeditions together, along the shore, fishing, getting bait,
driftwood for my fire, were observed and discussed, that
the village boys shouted after us. This by itself I could have
stood. But my invention of a new sort of lobster pot, which
had I received enough financial backing might have revolu-
tionised the inshore fishing industry, and brought pro-
sperity to the coast and wealth to myself, had failed. I had
acquired a load of debts (including the heavy costs of
the divorce) which I saw no prospect of ever shifting,
certainly not out of my fishing partnership with Henry
and Marney and John Lunn. I owed for my gas and
my rent. And the owner of my cottage, a pious
Wesleyan spinster, had given me more than a hint that I
must soon quit. . . .

I thought now of our last night in Bramblewick. There
had been a fresh north-easterly breeze that morning. The
two local cobles had been unable to put to sea, but at low
tide Dain and I had set a long line on the scaurs, a mile south
of the village opposite a cove to which a bridle path came
down from the farm, where since summer she had been
living. By night, when we met again at the cove, the storm
had taken on a character typical of the coast, a persistent
north-east gale with intermittent squalls of snow and hail
during which the wind almost reached hurricane force. The
moon was full and between the squalls shone brilliantly.
On the hills rising behind the actual coastline the snow was
lying thick, and the vertical cliffs and the shore made a
dark space between them and the scaur ends where the seas
were thundering and breaking white. There was a wide-
mouthed cave in the cliff close by the cove, and we sheltered
here while a squall blew over. Then we made our way

seawards, fighting the gusts of wind, picking a way carefully through the treacherous drifts of spume that filled the hollows and crevices of the scaurs.

We had set the line close to low-water mark, and reaching the place we had to wait while the "run" of a big wave receded. Our nerves were keyed up. There was something exciting in the wind, in the thunder of the seas breaking on the scaur ends. The moon was so bright we could see the deep blue of them before they broke, the translucent green of each rearing crest at the moment of its fracture, the rainbow iridescence of the fine spray the wind blew shorewards. And to me there was something immeasurably exciting in the way Dain stood with her lean body arched against the wind, the moonlight flashing in her eyes. There was only one small codling on the line. It was dead. I gutted it, hooked it on my gaff, and we started shorewards. The tide was on the turn. Another squall was brewing. We reached the cave, and for a while we stood there, looking at the weather. Already the north end of the bay was hidden in a curtain of driving hail. Above, the white storm clouds reached to a stupendous height, and for a while were brightly lit by the moon. Then the moon was hidden as the storm advanced, and it was dark in our cave as though there was no moon at all.

We thought suddenly that we should make a fire. There was plenty of drift-wood lying about, and quickly we gathered some dry whins from the cliff edge of the cove. By the time the first pellets of hail were pattering on the shingle our fire was burning furiously, and we squatted down by it, feeding it with more whins and drift-wood. Then we thought of the fish, and I split it like a kipper with my knife, made a rough fork out of a stick, and started grilling it. The storm reached its climax. There was lightning, and several violent claps of thunder. The hail, yellow in the firelight, drove almost horizontally across the mouth of the cave. With the roar of the wind and the now invisible sea in our ears, we watched the grilling fish, and we talked and planned.

We were in love and we knew what we wanted. To have a little house close to the sea, a garden, a boat. We could not live in Bramblewick. We were both still friendly with the Lunns, but the Lunns themselves were, in the local meaning of the word, "foreigners," and, for a long time past, they had been considering "flitting" to the nearby port of Burn-harbour, where there was no dangerous bar to stop them fishing except in really violent weather. Besides I wanted to start my life afresh, to cut all the ties that had bound me, to this my native place, and surely there was in England some other place that could give us what we wanted. . . . But first I must write my book, I must make money, and pay off all my debts. We could not, anyway, get married until the decree had been made absolute. We must part for the time being, I to write my book, Dain to a temporary "job" she had got on a poultry farm in the Midlands: not that she had any deep interest in poultry farming, but because it was the only thing that offered.

I looked at the hut, with my heart pounding inside me. Wasn't it almost the very thing that we wanted? We'd imagined a fisherman's cottage, on a lonely beach, or perhaps on a little island. It would be primitive and dilapidated, and of course, unfurnished, but we'd have the excitement of putting it to rights, of furnishing it ourselves. Wasn't that hut almost as good as such a cottage? Wasn't the place almost as secluded as an island? It was out of sight of the real sea, but was there not an outweighing advantage in having a cove and a waterway one could use in all weathers? Why should we wait? Why should we remain parted. The granting of a decree nisi lays no such injunction on the defendants of a suit. It would take me at least six months to write my book. I could live in that place alone. But the job of putting it straight, of transforming it, looked too thrilling an adventure for us, as lovers, not to share it.

Mr. Hoskins had become silent again. I tried to keep my voice steady when I said:

"Well, that hut's much bigger than what I'm looking for, and it's in a pretty awful mess. Do you want to let it?"

He gave me a quick glance that was not devoid of suspicion.

"Yes. We're wanting to let it all right, providing we can get our money. We've had nothing but bad luck with that hut since we bought it. Other people who had it weren't much better. None of they stayed long enough to pay what it cost to make it into a bungalow. How are we to know we'll get our rent this time?"

"I'll pay in advance if I take it. How much do you want?"

"Couldn't let it under three bob a week!"

I gasped.

"Including the land?"

"Yes. Land be no good to we. But not the foreshore where they boats be moored. You can have the cove to low-water mark."

My voice must have trembled when I said:

"If I took it for a year, and paid you quarterly in advance, would you get some of the muck cleared out, and mend the roof and the fence, so as to keep the cattle out of the garden?"

He was thoughtful for a moment. Then:

"Why—that really be for my nephew Charley May to say. You see, he be manager of Hoskins since we be bankrupt. But I reckons he'll do all that when he sees the money."

Before leaving Bramblewick I had sold privately the last of my possessions, save a few necessary garments and a cheap watch. I had paid off all my small tradesmen's debts, leaving the gas and the rent (for in the past I had been a good customer to both parties concerned, and, although I had not consulted them in the matter, I knew they could not be seriously inconvenienced by waiting). My railway fare to Cornwall had been expensive. My capital now was less than twenty pounds: but there is something impressive in the sight of a wad of notes, and I was careful to let Mr. Hoskins see inside my pocket-book as I took it out. He looked embarrassed.

"Why—I'd rather not take any money from 'e," he said. "You'd better pay that to Charley, or I'll get into trouble. But I reckons you can have the hut. Charley will be glad enough to see some money, particularly when I tell him other tenants be done a moonlight flit. I reckons we'd better go and see Charley now. I'll come up to-morrow and look at they moorings."

Mr. Hoskins looked even more embarrassed. Then he added:

"If you just gave me a bob for a drink, I reckons that would be as good as a bargain. Money be damned scarce this Christmas."

It seemed a peculiar request for a landlord to make to a prospective tenant. Diffidently I offered him a half-crown, which he took and slipped into his waistcoat pocket as he led the way down to the cove. Perhaps he half-guessed my thoughts at that moment, for he said rather wistfully:

"Yes. Be a lovely little place. Be a lovely little place if you'm fond of flowers and birds. Be like a garden of Eden in summer time I tell 'e. No one to disturb 'e here. Be you married?"

The question surprised me, but I answered that I was.

2

ON THE WHOLE the Cornish are a delightful people, but they are inclined to talk too much, and they have a habit of promising you something and forgetting all about it as soon as your back is turned.

Charley May was like this, yet in other respects he was a complete contrast to his Uncle Joe. Joe took his misfortunes with the ironic fatalism of old age. Charley was young, lean, dark-visaged, with imaginative eyes. He was a dreamer, ambitious, always full of plans. Yet he seemed heavily weighted with the worries and anxieties of the firm to which in a sense he had become heir. It was clear that for him Joe was the personification of the firm's misfortunes, as well as the unwitting agent of them. It was also clear that Joe, despite the gentleness of his manner, resented that fact that he, once senior partner, was virtually under Charley's orders.

Joe had two brothers, Harry and George, and one sister who had married a man in Bristol. The brothers were the active members of the firm when the crash came. But the principal creditors, because of the firm's old standing, and the circumstances of the crash, had come to an arrangement whereby the shipyard was allowed to carry on under the business managership of Charley (son of the sister) who in any case would have inherited a quarter share on his mother's death. Charley, born and bred in Bristol, had been trained in the marine motoring business. If shipbuilding was dead, there had been a hope that the firm might get on its feet again by building small pleasure craft, a hope that might have materialised but for the world slump which had set in.

Charley, indeed, had received Joe and me coldly at first. The recent letting of the hut had been done while he was absent on business, and without his "authority." Joe was apologetic, yet vaguely truculent in his explanation of the illegal "flit." Charley was politely sarcastic, and said it was just what he had expected: yet, as Joe had prophesied, his manner changed when I took out my pocket-book and offered to pay a quarter's rent in advance. I could have the hut. I could have a year's agreement. The firm would have the place cleaned, mend the roof and the fence, and I could do what repairs and alterations I liked. Workmen would be sent up the very next day.

I think the whole matter sank completely from his mind a minute after we parted. Four days later, when I took Dain to see the place, it was exactly as I had seen it first. We had called at the shipyard. Neither Charley nor Joe was there. Charley, we were informed, had gone away on business. Joe was over at St. Jude, and might not be back till dinner-time. We had hired a small rowing-boat, and landed at the cove.

Since writing to Dain, I had experienced some doubts as to the wisdom of what I had done. Looked at in cold blood it did seem daft, taking a derelict army hut, and proposing to set up housekeeping on a capital of less than twenty pounds, and with no certain prospect of earning more. But wisdom, I had long since discovered, was not an infallible guide to conduct. No matter how logically you planned your life things never happened quite as you expected, and on the whole it was well to trust to your instincts, if your instincts and reason clashed. We were in love. Instinct and reason urged that we should live to-

gether. We were poor, but not so poor as many thousands
of couples who had to live and keep their families on the
dole, for we had hope and confidence, we were healthy and
pretty tough, and if Dain was young, and I had been
hitherto a financial failure, we both had wits enough to save
us from starvation, if starvation ever threatened. I had not
minimised the risks and disadvantages of the proposition
in my letter. Dain's answer had been a laconic telegram
giving the time of the arrival of her train: and if I'd had any
doubts as to whether she would approve of the place itself
they were dispelled long before we had completed the first
quick survey.

We walked through the big room, and looked into the
little ones: and out through the other door, and down to
the spring, and up to the front door again, and all the time
Dain kept squeezing my arm and saying in an almost
breathless voice:

"It's thrilling—it's thrilling!"

We climbed the front door steps and looked down at the
cove.

It was a lovely day. The sun had risen above the morning
mist, and it was quite warm. There was no wind. The tide
was full. The creek was like a sheet of glass, pale bottle-
green in the fairway, dull red close in to the brackeny
opposite shore. From where we stood we could see no sign
of human habitation. A few herring gulls floated on the
creek. From higher up we could hear the plaintive cry of an
invisible curlew, and there was no other sound except the
soft chuckling of the little stream that ran by the hut,
which despite the tin cans and bottles, and other debris that
half-choked its course, was clear as the water from the spring
itself. We walked into the big room again. The filth was
appalling, and although we had already opened all the

windows, the stale "pub" smell persisted. I felt a wave of resentment against the firm of Hoskins.

"Damn it," I said. "I think they might at least have had the place cleaned. They promised faithfully they'd send some workmen up at once."

But Dain gripped my arm.

"Oh, what does it matter? Why bother about having any workmen? It would be twice as exciting if we did everything ourselves. If only the hut wasn't here at all—only a pile of planks, so that we could start at the *very* beginning!"

My resentment faded, but instinctively I felt the need to put at least a gentle curb on our enthusiasm.

"Dain," I said. "Let's be practical. But for the roof and the walls, we *are* starting at the beginning, and I'm not so sure we've got the roof to our credit. We'll see when it rains. The point is can we make it liveable in? It's got to be cleaned, it's got to be made weather-tight. Legally *they're* supposed to do that, but it looks as though we may have to wait ages, and we certainly can't expect too much from a bankrupt landlord, for a rent of three bob a week. We've got to have warmth, and some sort of comfort. We've got to have furniture. Actually, we're not much, better off than a couple of shipwrecked mariners, or the Swiss Family Robinson."

Dain's eyes sparkled.

"Who wants to be? Let's *be* a Swiss Family Robinson. Let's imagine we *have* been shipwrecked."

"Yes," I said grimly. "But the Family had their ship wrecked close to home, and it was pretty well stocked too. Before we can do a thing we've got to have tools. We need a hammer and nails and a saw."

"And we want some carbolic, and soap and brushes, and buckets. We want a fire and boiling water."

"We want a *devil* of a lot of things. And we want a lot more money."

"Oh, never mind the money. We could furnish it ever so cheaply to start with. We only want a table and something to sit on. Boxes or packing-cases would do. We could have camp-beds or hammocks to sleep on. We'd only need a few Woolworth pots and pans. What we ought to do is to make a list of things that we can't do without. We've certainly got to be practical. How much money have we really got?"

I knew that by now I had considerably less than twenty pounds, but I did not count it, for while I was still alive to the dangers of over-enthusiasm, it seemed equally important that we should not depress ourselves with a too realistic view of the financial situation. And Dain did not press the point.

"Look here," she said quickly. "If we clean the place ourselves and mend the roof then the least the landlords can do is to lend us tools and things, and give us the material. They've got plenty of wood, anyway. If that old ship we saw belongs to them, and they can't even afford the labour to break it up, they might let us take what we want. We could make all our furniture then. Wouldn't it be thrilling? We should scarcely need to buy a thing. Come on, let's go back and see if the old man's in yet. No. Let's look at every room first, and see what we've got to do. And then let's climb the hill, so that we can see the whole place and the garden. The stream can be made heavenly. We can clear it out, and put rocks in it and make pools and little waterfalls, and little bridges, and have flowers everywhere. If only we could start right at the very beginning and build every bit of the place ourselves."

The closer we examined the hut itself the more I was

inclined to agree in theory with this. The standard army hut, as I knew from experience, was designed primarily as a dormitory, not a dwelling house: and this *was* standard, except that the roof, originally corrugated iron, had been replaced with felted boards. And the conversion had been done apparently with the sole object of obtaining a maximum number of rooms with a minimum of material. Each room in the converted part was small and with only a single window. The room containing the stove measured nine feet by ten. It was in a fouler state than any of the others. Yet the stove, in spite of the grease and muck on it, appeared to be in good order, and Dain gave an excited shout when she discovered that a rail round the hot plate was brass. It was clearly a galley stove from some sailing-ship that Hoskins had dismantled.

"It will look thrilling when it's cleaned and polished," she said. "This has got to be our living-room. But it ought to be bigger, and we want more light. What a pity it doesn't reach across the whole width of the hut, instead of there being that other silly room. What about the partition?"

I pressed my hands against the partition that divided the room from the corridor. It was merely match-boarding secured to a light frame. I stepped through the corridor, and found that the partition of the opposite room was similarly constructed. I scraped off some of the wallpaper; the boarding itself was clean.

"We're in luck," I said. "They agreed I could do what alterations I liked. We can take down both partitions, and turn the two rooms into one. And if we do it carefully, we've got all the wood to use for something else."

"We can make cupboards with it. We can make the whole place lovely. We want *all* the wallpaper off, and the walls distempering, and the ceiling doing with whitewash. We needn't have anything on the floor at first. Just have it scrubbed; but later, when we *do* get some money, we want some plain linoleum on it, and we can make some sailor mats and rugs. Oh, come on. Let's get back to Porthkerris and get the things. I'm dying to begin. We'll just have a quick look into the other rooms and see what we've got to do. We'd best not *think* about the garden yet."

We resisted the temptation to climb the hill for the more comprehensive aspect of our new home, but it was hard for us to walk down the path to the cove by the gurgling stream, and not start planning what we should do with it. A few yards from the cove itself there was a bare outcrop of slaty rock, several slabs of which were detached and lying on the ground.

"Paving stones!" cried Dain. "We can pave the whole path with them. We can make real steps down to the cove. When we've got the stream cleared, we can have little crazy paths running everywhere. We've actually got a *quarry*. If we start excavating we'll have a cave there just like the one at Bramblewick where we made our fire, and talked about what we were going to do!"

"Yes. And we ought to get quite good fishing here too. We can set lines. We can rig up a net. When we get a boat of our own we can have lobster pots. We've got nearly all the thrills of life in Bramblewick, with none of the snags. Not a soul who knows us here, who cares a damn what we do. No one to stare at us, or spy, or sneer. No debts or other things to worry about. We're as far from Bramblewick as if we *had* been wrecked on a South Sea island!"

We walked down to the boat and pushed it off, and with a dozen strokes of the oars we had moved round the bluff of the cove and were completely out of sight of the hut, and as it were, in another world, for we could see St. Jude, and Porthkerris, and the fairway to the sea, up which a large cargo steamer piloted by two tugs was moving slowly. We hugged the eastern shore, passing the hulk of the *Amelia Hoskins*. Before we had reached the shipyard the steamer had been turned by the tugs, and was being moved slowly in alongside the three laid-up ships I had seen on my first day in St. Jude. Joe Hoskins was standing on the ship-yard wall watching the operation. He greeted us with a smile, made fast our painter for us, and as we climbed up the steps he said, pointing to the steamer:

"Be another ship come in to roost! Three more be coming this week, and there be talk of others too. Ah, things be gettin' worse and worse. Charley have gone off looking for business. Have heard of a Brixham trawler that someone wants converting into a pleasure yacht, but I told 'e before 'e went bain't no use. A job like that ain't likely to come our way. This be your missus?"

Joe beamed at Dain.

"How do you like living up the Pill? You've got a lovely little place, all to yourselves and no one to bother you. Damned if I wouldn't have liked to have lived there myself, and grown flowers for a living. Better than being here, waiting for jobs that never come, and never likely to neither. You'm settled down yet?"

One could not feel angry with such a benign and charming man as Joe, whose mind apparently was com-pletely detached from realities, but I saw that a discreet firmness was essential.

I went for him, reminding him of the promises he and Charley had made. He appeared to be genuinely regretful, but the blame, he said, was Charley's.

"Be just like 'e, to promise a thing, and forget all about

it. That's what Charley do call business, and 'e had the nerve to go for me about they other tenants, and after me bringing you along, and you puttin' the rent down, handsome. Well, I'll tell Charley soon as 'e gets back."

"Yes. But in the meantime we're paying rent for a place we can't live in. Look here, suppose we do the job ourselves: will you give us the gear and the material?"

"Why, yes," Joe said agreeably, "I reckons we can do that. Depends what you want, though."

"We want some buckets, and brushes, and soap, and some carbolic," said Dain.

"We want some felt to patch the roof, and some tar, and tacks and nails and a few tools."

"We've got plenty of tools," Joe answered with his familiar ironic smile. "This spot be full of 'em, and nothin' to make or mend. So you'm goin' to make the little bungalow shipshape yourselves? What you want is a few tins of paint, and varnish, and some whitewash. You can make the whole place handsome. I'd have liked to come and give you a hand, but I've got to stay about the yard while Charley be away, in case a job turns up, like someone wanting a sixty-ton yacht building, or someone wanting a bit of rope for a clothes-line, or half a gallon of paraffin. We'm shopkeepers as well as shipbuilders. Come on, I'll take 'e into our shop."

We followed Joe through the tangle of gear that covered the yard to a barnlike warehouse, the door of which he unlocked. A strong smell of tar greeted us. The place was huge but it was almost filled with an amazing variety of things. There was a sort of gangway leading from one end of it to the other. On each side of this, country-market fashion, were stalls: planks laden with nails, screws, bolts, coils of wire, shackles, chains, metal pipes, pots and pans;

some new-looking, but most of them second-hand.   Under
the planks were kegs, bags, tins of paint, rolls of canvas,
heavier coils of wire and rope, boat anchors, grapples, bits of
machinery, galvanised tanks, a bath and lavatory basin,
evidently from a yacht.   There were more coils of wire
hanging on the walls, and hundreds of rigging blocks and
shackles, and on a long shelf were scores of ship's lanterns
made of copper and brass.   We looked about us with an
excited bewilderment, and Dain whispered:

"What a place! What a *smell*!"

The smell of tar was mixed with that indescribable
spicy smell that a foreign-going ship exudes.

"This be our shop," said Joe.   "Do look more like a rag
and bone store at present, but then it's such a long time
since we did any trade.   Before the War we'd keep almost
everything a ship would need for a voyage round the world.
We'd have barrels of salt pork, and ship's biscuits, and lime-
water, and tons of sailcloth and ropes, and blocks and wire,
and pitch for caulking, and copper for sheathing.   Most of
this be junk from the ships we break up.   Most of they lamps
came from *Amelia*.   That bath came from a yacht that was
wrecked a mile or two from St. Jude, along the coast."

He pointed to a huge pile of old canvas in one corner of
the "shop."

"There be the old *Amelia's* sails.   Every inch be made in
our sail-loft.   Cost gettin' on for three hundred quid, and
now be lying there rottin' to pieces.   She be a lovely ship
that.   You ought to have seen her the day she sailed on her
maiden voyage.   Oh, she looked handsome.   Sun be shining
bright, and she'd got a nice nor'westerly breeze, and she
looked like a lovely bird skimming out to sea.   We didn't
think then that she be the last ship Hoskins would build, and
that one day we'd have she to chop up for firewood.   Now

what be you wantin' for the bungalow? I can give 'e some nice white paint. You'll want some brushes too. Would one of they ship's lamps be any use to 'e? We didn't think of having electricity put in when we made a bungalow of the place."

"It would look thrilling," cried Dain. "Think what it will look like when it's polished."

Joe laughed.

"Why—if you like polishing, there's a copper kettle somewhere abouts, belonging *Amelia*."

He searched under one of the stalls and produced a large flattish, hand-made kettle, thick with dust and verdigris.

"It's a *real* ship's kettle!" Dain cried excitedly.

"Yes. Be made by a Porthkerris man specially for *Amelia*. You couldn't buy a kettle like she in any shop. T'will look handsome cleaned and polished."

"How much do you want for it?" I said.

"Why—I ain't going to charge you for that, nor the lamp, if they be any use to you. Be no use to we. I give 'em as a present to the missus. Maybe one day she'll ask me to have tea at the bungalow. When be all your furniture coming?"

I saw no reason why I should be anything but frank with the amazingly generous Mr. Hoskins. I told him that we hadn't got any furniture yet. That we were going to buy it locally or make it. He beamed at Dain.

"Ah—you'm on your honeymoon, so to speak. You'm just starting housekeeping. No wonder you're excited, and wantin' to have everything look nice. But ain't you got anythin' at all? No tables or chairs, or carpets, or saucepans? Ain't you got a bed?"

"We haven't got a bedroom yet," I put in. "Least not one that we can count on being weather-tight, and clean enough to sleep in. You don't happen to have any second-hand furniture, do you, or know of a place where we can get some?"

Mr. Hoskins was thoughtful for a moment. Then he said:

"No. We ain't got any proper furniture, but I can let 'e have plenty of saucepans, and things like that, and crockery. Ain't fancy stuff. All be from ships. And we've got some mattresses too, belong that yacht. They be fancy, soft as eiderdown, only too narrow for a proper bed. But if you had two of 'em fastened together they might do all right. I've got they up in the loft. We'll go and have a look."

There was a step-ladder at the far end of the ware-house, and as Joe led the way towards it Dain whispered excitedly:

"It's our treasure ship. He's got *everything* we want. *Do* ask him about the bath. If he'd let us have it we could fix it in one of the little rooms, and have a real bathroom. Ask him about the old sails. They'd do fine for covering the walls. And don't forget about the wood."

We followed him up into the loft. It contained an immense amount of gear, but it was clear that most of this belonged to the pleasure boats laid up on the Pill Creek foreshore, for everything was very neatly stowed. Joe removed some sacking, heaved a packing-case to one side, and then pulled out a couple of cabin mattresses, badly-stained with sea water, but otherwise in good condition. He punched one of them with his fist.

"Ah, they be real fancy, as fancy as you'd find on a king's yacht. If they'd been a bit bigger I'd have had 'em myself. They be softer than a feather bed. Pity all the bunks were smashed up, or you'd have had everything complete. Be they any use to you? You could fasten 'em together, then you wouldn't notice 'em being narrow, not on a cold night. Can let 'e have some blankets too."

Conscience made me say again:

"How much do you want for them?"

Joe grinned.

"Why, that be for Charley to say, but I reckons he won't want more than five bob a piece. You take 'em, anyway, if they be any use. But how are you going to take everything back? Where did you get that boat from?"

"Hired it," I said.

"Bah—you don't want to be hiring a boat. Will cost you a fortune before you'm done. You ought to have a boat of your own. I've got a little skiff I can sell 'e cheap. I'll show it to 'e. We'll take the mattresses down below, and put everything together. She be old, that skiff, and maybe a bit the worse for wear, but she'm better than hiring."

A fleeting suspicion crossed my mind that Joe's generosity might after all be merely good salesmanship. We needed a boat, but in the present circumstances it seemed a dispensable luxury, and I hardened myself against temptation.

"We've got to go carefully," I whispered to Dain as we followed Joe out of the warehouse.

"Of course we have. But we've done jolly well so far, haven't we? Those mattresses are marvellous. We can make bunks for them, and until we do we can simply put them on the floor. Look, if he'll let us have all the things for cleaning, we can get at least part of the place done this afternoon. I can go and buy some food, and we can sleep there to-night. That would save us money. But don't let's buy the boat unless it's really cheap. We *have* got to be careful."

The boat was lying outside in the weather, keel up. She

was, as Joe had said, old, and the worse for wear. Her bottom was tarred, and patched in several places. Bits of her gunwale were rotten. But she was a useful size, roomy, yet small enough to haul on to our beach, and when Joe said we could have her for a pound, complete with oars, I felt ashamed of my suspicions. We made the deal. He would get someone to give us a hand, and we could have the boat moved from the quay into the water soon as we liked. But first of all we'd best get back to the shop and select all the things we wanted.

An hour later we were on our way back to the creek in our own boat, laden almost to the gunwales with the things we had bought, borrowed, or had presented to us by our landlord. We had a tin of crude carbolic, scrubbing brushes, buckets, some tar, a roll of roofing felt, a piece of sailcloth, an assortment of nails. Joe had loaned me a box of tools. In addition to the kettle he had given us some saucepans, some mugs, and a box full of odd dishes and plates. We had bought a bundle of blankets from him. They had belonged to the wrecked yacht, and had suffered from immersion in the sea, but they were clean. He had given us several tins of paint. We had a drum of paraffin for the lamp; and in the village we had bought a bag of coal, bread and milk, bacon and eggs, and enough dry groceries to keep us going. We were wildly happy, revelling in our almost incredible good fortune.

"Dain, it's marvellous!" I said. "It seems to me we've already got the place half-furnished, and for next to nothing. Those mattresses would cost something like five pounds each if you bought them new!"

"And that kettle would cost at least a pound, only, of course, you couldn't buy one like it if you wanted. Isn't Joe a darling? I think he'd have given us the whole shop if we'd asked for it. What shall we do first. I propose we clean the stove, then light it and get some hot water, and then scrub the galley floor. Then we might have a go at the partition. Then we ought to decide where we're going to sleep, and do that room. Isn't it *all* exciting? A home of our own, and a boat of our own!"

"Yes," I said fervently. "And it's scarcely a week that we were in Bramblewick, and a winter gale was blowing. It's as though we'd come not three hundred, but three thousand miles. It's a new country. It's a new life."

Bramblewick, and my own life there, indeed seemed immeasurably remote at that moment. We were pulling along the east shore (an oar apiece), and already most of the waterfront of St. Jude was hidden by the hill that enclosed our creek on the west. We had lost sight of the steamers. Although the sun was still shining, a haze hung over the south end of the town, blurring the shapes of the villas and the hotels, so that across the smooth surface of the harbour they looked foreign and romantic. And even the harbour, and the few small boats that made up its traffic, narrowed from our sight as we pulled farther into the creek towards the bluff that hid our cove, so that it was like a curtain being slowly drawn against the outside world. And we had almost reached the bluff before we became aware that a large rowing-boat was moored close in to it, and that three men were ashore on a narrow ledge of rock on the bluff itself. There was nothing immediately significant or alarming in what we saw. The bluff marked the southern boundary of the "estate," and was actually within it, but Joe had made it clear that the firm reserved the foreshore, with the exception of the cove, and the ledge where the men stood was below high-water mark. With them on the ledge were tools, a bag of cement, a coil of wire, and several thick steel posts, of all which they had evidently just landed from the boat. They were idle now, staring at us, yet in a kindly way, and it struck me that we and our laden boat must have presented to them an unusual spectacle. I said good-morning to them. They grinned, and one of them answered:

"'Morning, sir. Be a lovely day. You've got a big load in your boat."

I did not resent their curiosity, and anyway they must have already guessed who we were, for the same man added:

"You'm the new tenants of Joe Hoskin's bungalow?"

We stopped rowing.

"Yes," I answered.

"Be a nice place in summer," one of them remarked. "But desperate lonely in winter."

"Last man didn't stay long," the first speaker said. "Heard 'e did a moonlight flit, before he'd paid Hoskins a ha'penny rent."

"Ah," said the other, "'e was on the dole, and spent every penny of it on booze. 'Nother chap who had that bungalow drank worse than 'e, and his wife was worse still. She was a terror. Threw an axe at him one day and nearly split his head open. Joe's had gettin' on a dozen different tenants since 'e started lettin' that place as a bungalow. One kept hens, and another kept goats, and one started it as a tea place for summer visitors, but the police came after him for something or other. Hoskins put that hut there when they got a big ship to repair, just after the War. That be the start of all his bad luck."

By a look in the man's eyes I knew that we were to be given still another version of the Hoskins crash if I did not stop it in time.

"What are you going to do?" I said.

"We've got they posts to fasten," the first man answered. "Be a steamer coming to lay up here before long. These be for its stern ropes. Maybe you won't be so lonely up here this winter."

Dain and I exchanged uneasy glances, but no suspicion of the incredibly ironic significance of the man's remark was in my mind when I said:

"It'll be a small ship, won't it, to lay up here?"

"No. There be plenty of water for an 8000-ton ship to creep in here at high-water springs, with her ballast tanks dry. That barque that lost Joe Hoskins all his money was 2000 tons, and she was laid up high and dry in Joe's little cove. But you won't get any steamers laying up farther up the creek than here."

We moved on round the bluff into our cove, and out of sight of the men, yet not out of hearing distance, for the creek with its high surrounding hills, with the tide up and the air still, possessed the acoustic properties of a megaphone. We heard the men laughing, and one of them say:

"She have foreign blood in her, I tell 'e. She be dark as an Indian."

"'E be a queerish sort of chap," said another. "Joe said he thought 'e be some sort of an artist but seemed to have plenty of money. 'E came to Joe on Christmas day, told Joe 'e was looking for a quiet place to live in. Didn't say anything at first about his wife."

"Maybe they'm just married. Want a quiet place for their honeymoon. She do look too young to have been married long."

"Ah—maybe they haven't thought of getting married yet. They artists be a queerish lot. Remember that chap who lived in that bungalow near Porthkerris castle two winters ago? Damned if 'e didn't have three women livin' with him, one time or another. 'E went away sudden too, and forgot to pay any of his bills."

Their conversation and laughter was drowned by the sound of hammering, as at last they set to work. We were not deeply perturbed by what we had overheard. I had not tried to impose a pact of secrecy on Joe. It was inevitable that we should cause a certain amount of interest and gossip in a community which, including even St. Jude, was not much bigger than the one we had left. But no one could know anything that we didn't tell them. Curiosity, guessing, gossip could do us no harm. We were unknown, and we could remain unknown. Not even the wildest guessing could possibly establish a link between ourselves and that remote village in Yorkshire where my past was buried. As for the men themselves, they were out of sight, and in effect out of hearing, and we were too excited to think of them or of what they were doing. We pulled our boat into the cove, and began the job of off-loading our cargo.

3

THE STOVE was thick with evil-smelling grease combined with soot, and under this was a foundation of black-lead of extraordinary tenacity. But we swilled it with paraffin, and scraped and scrubbed it until at last we got down to the original metal. We cleaned out the flues, and I cemented the crack in the smoke pipe which apparently had caused the sooting of the roof and walls, and to our relief, the kindling roared away the moment we put a match to it, and greedily took hold of the coal. Dain, having polished the brass rail of the stove, resisted the temptation to start on the kettle. We filled it at the spring, and while we waited for it to boil we brushed the sooty cobwebs from the roof and walls, and swept the floor. We found spiders and earwigs, wood-lice, and a few cockroaches: but there were no bugs, or other human vermin. We took no chances, however. We swabbed the floor with a strong solution of carbolic, then scrubbed it hard with soap and hot water.

We worked at fever heat. While the floor dried, we set to on the partition between the galley and the corridor. Our chief difficulty was to restrain our desire to see the effect of "joining" the galley to the opposite room, to discipline ourselves to the job of prising off the planks and removing the nails before we stacked them. They were cleaner than I had thought, and the framework was all new wood of a standard two and a half by two and a half inch dimension. By the time we had demolished the first partition it seemed we had enough material for a dozen cupboards, and a door that would make an admirable table. But we did not stop.

We started on the second partition, and not until the last
bit of frame was down, and the last nail out, did we dare to
put our tools down, and take stock of the whole room.
Aesthetically the gain was nil. We had a room that
measured ten feet by twenty-four with a window at each
opposite end, and doors at each opposite side. The ceiling
slanted to an apex in the middle. The walls of the original
kitchen had been decorated most recently with a dark green
paper with a pattern of roses on it, while what paper
remained in the other room was imitation Dutch tiles.

We had a moment of discouragement.

"It looks frightful," I said.

"It was too small before, and now it's too big," said
Dain. "And it doesn't seem to be a bit lighter for having
the other window. Or is that because it's getting dark?"

It *was* getting dark. We discovered with a shock that it
was nearly four o'clock, and realised that we were both
ravenously hungry, for we'd forgotten about lunch. The
kettle was boiling. We made tea, and boiled eggs. I fixed
the door we had salved across two boxes, made a bench out
of a couple of planks, and we sat down to our first meal.
And before we were half-way through it our spirits rose
again.

"It won't look half so bad when we get the wallpaper
off, and the ceiling whitewashed," said Dain.

"It won't look so big when we get our cupboards and the
furniture made."

"We ought to make the cupboards at the far end, right
across the wall, so that the room won't look so long. And
the table can be at this end by the stove. Can't we have that
end for a scullery? Couldn't we fit the yacht lavatory basin
there for a sink, and have a draining board, and make a
dresser? Then it will be all labour saving."

"Yes. We can dig a deep pit just outside the window and run a pipe into it from the sink: cover it all in and we've got a septic tank. We can connect the bath to it, if we have a bathroom that side of the shack. If we had a pump, and a tank, we might even lay water on from the spring!"

Our enthusiasm was completely restored. We didn't wait to wash-up, but set to on the offensive wallpaper. Some of it came away easily enough, but there were patches that seemed to have been stuck on with pure glue, and we had to mop and soak them with hot water, and then scrape them inch by inch.

Slowly we began to see a reward for our work, however. The two rooms began to grow together as the contrasting papers disappeared: the bare wood was pleasing to the eye, and when we'd finished one wall, I knocked up a rough framework for the "scullery" cupboard across the far narrow wall. While Dain carried on with the remaining wallpaper I replaced the second of the dismantled doors to close off the corridor, and then made another rough framework at the stove end of the room, to carry the redundant door we were using as a table, fitting it close in to the window, so that it was like a quick lunch bar. We had another shock when we discovered that it was ten o'clock. We cooked bacon and eggs. We were tired, but our enthusiasm remained, and we had got the last bit of paper off, and fitted shelves into the scullery cupboard, and made the framework of the "dresser" before we decided firmly to cry off, and it was then midnight. We made more tea, and sat down on the table and surveyed the result of our labours. We were pleased. The walls were now visually continuous. The table at the stove end and the cupboard and dresser at the other had improved the proportions of the room. It did not look so long for its width. In spite of our resolution to do no more work, we could not stop ourselves screwing a few hooks into the shelves of the dresser, and hanging up some of the mugs Joe had given us and putting some of the plates behind them, just to see the effect, and I could not resist fetching the yacht bowl and fixing it temporarily under the window, between the dresser and the cupboard, in order to see if I'd planned the framework right. But when Dain suggested that we might start and whitewash just a little of the ceiling, I said resolutely:

"No, by Jove. We're going to bed."

We had worked so hard, and the time had flown so quickly, we had not even looked into the other rooms, yet alone prepared one of them for sleeping in. But the floor we had scrubbed was now dry, so we put our mattresses down on it, as close to the stove as we dared, and touching each other. We had no sheets, but the blankets seemed to have been well aired. We were warm and comfortable and happy, and too tired to talk. The night was very still, and we could hear no sound except the chuckling of the stream, and we must have sunk into a deep sleep almost instantly so complete was the contrast of my first waking sensation. There was a roar, a banging, a flapping sound, like that of loose sails, and the sound of dripping water. I felt water on my face, and a chilly draught. Then I heard Dain say, sleepily:

"What's the matter?"

I got up and lit the lamp, and by that time Dain was as wide awake as I was myself, and had leapt up from the floor out of the way of the water that was pouring, as though from a tap, from the roof on to our bed. The roar was the wind, blowing at least with the force of a gale: the banging I judged to be one of the hut doors; the flapping sound evidently was made by loose felt on the roof; and the dripping needed no explanation, for in addition to the stream that had wet us, water was pouring in from at least a dozen places in the roof, and the floor, except for one section immediately under the apex of the roof, was practically awash. Automatically we bundled the mattresses and the bedding on to this relative island, and we stood there for a while, listening to the roar and the racket which seemed to grow louder every minute. It was alarming. The whole fabric of the hut seemed to be loose and shaking. Save that the floor was level, we might have been aboard a storm-tossed ship.

We dressed. I lit the storm lantern. I opened the door into the big room, and a violent gust of wind slammed it behind us. At once we saw the reason for that internal blast. The front door, which faced the creek, had been burst open. The gale was actually blowing from the creek. The door was leaning inwards from the jambs. Its top hinge had been wrenched adrift, and as I tried to shift it the bottom hinge gave way too, and the whole thing crashed to the floor, missing our lantern by a hairbreadth. We got it up again, but it took me all my strength to hold it against the gale while Dain rushed back for the hammer and nails and a length of the partition framing, with which eventually we shored and battened it. The internal blast moderated, but outside the noise of the storm was loud as ever, and in the big room there was not a patch of dry floor. We went back to the kitchen. Our island was tolerably dry but it did not look like remaining so for long, for there were deepening pools at the stove and the scullery end of the floor, and the roof dripped like that of a subterranean cavern. We looked into the other rooms. They were worse. Suddenly I felt angry, angry with Joe and his Cornish

promises, angrier with myself for not having tackled the
roof before everything.

We had gone to bed with an agreeable sense of security.
Now all sense of security was gone. It was worse than if
we'd had no roof at all above us. Yet Dain did not seem
bothered, even when a particularly violent gust of wind
seemed to shake every plank of the hut, and the flapping of
the felt and the spattering of rain became deafening. We
went back to the kitchen and surveyed the dripping roof
again. Would it be possible to patch just enough of it to
keep our island dry, so that we could make our bed and
sleep till daybreak? We had the roll of felt, and the piece
of sail. I had my doubts, but Dain was all for the adventure
of trying, and we decided to make a reconnaissance. We
were already wearing oilskins and gum-boots. We opened
the end door, which faced up the valley away from the
creek, and stepped out. If anything I had under-estimated
the force of the wind. It seemed to be blowing from the
south-west, from the sea, and across the harbour, but the
hills enclosing the harbour and creek were baffling and
diverting it, so that even here, in what ought to have been
the lee of the hut, we could scarcely stand upright. It was
pitch dark. The rain was torrential. The little stream,
invisible from where we stood, itself was in a roaring
spate. We moved round the garden corner of the hut,
and we literally had to fight our way along the side
to the window of our room, whose light gave an exasperating illusion of cheerfulness and security. One
glance up at the roof convinced me of the utter im-
possibility of doing anything while the storm lasted.
Most of the felt had been torn off. Some of it was
hanging and flapping over the eaves. We had no ladder,
and even if it had been possible to climb up on it without,

we could not have handled so unwieldy a thing as a roll of felt or the ship sail.

And suddenly I was seized by a new anxiety. There was a roaring sound that was neither the wind nor the rain, but that of waves, and it came from the creek.

"My God," I shouted. "We've forgotten the boat, and the tide must be flowing."

We moved along the garden side of the hut, and reached what had been the path to the cove—path no longer, for the stream had overflowed its course, and we had to wade through at least a foot of rushing water, which made a cataract over the low cliff into the cove. We had to jump over this to reach the beach.

We had left the boat where we had landed with our things, and, as the creek had been so smooth, and the tide ebbing, I had merely secured her painter to a rock under the cliff. She was safe. The tide had reached her but the wind and waves, although they had thrown her broadside on, had simply washed her farther up the beach, and had done no apparent damage. We swung her round and hauled her up to the foot of the cliff; and it was not until we had finished the job of making her secure that we consciously noticed what the storm and the flood tide had brought into the cove. The main force of the wind evidently was blowing straight up the creek from the harbour and the sea. Here in the cove both wind and waves came at an oblique angle to the main storm, and the cove was a sort of whirlpool, in which had collected a mass of debris, much of it already washed on to the beach. Most conspicuous at first (for they looked like shrouded corpses) were several water-logged mattresses, one of them stranded, the others floating among masses of weed. We examined the one that was ashore. It was the kind used by sailors and ship firemen, stuffed with straw and known as a "donkey's breakfast," and of no value. But close to it, just washing, in was a large plank, and a useful-looking box: and as we rushed to salve them, we noticed a metal drum the size of a beer cask near the farther end of the cove. From that moment we became oblivious to the anxieties and discomforts of the weather. There were more boxes and planks, and half of a ship's hatch, and hundreds of bamboos, mixed up among the floating weed. There were bottles and empty paint tins, a damaged life-buoy, and the remains of a Madeira chair, and a very tattered oilskin coat.

"Has there been a wreck?" Dain asked.

At first I had thought it likely; but when we looked at the lifebelt, and found that it bore the name of the steamer we had seen coming in to lay up, the origin of most of the flotsam became clear. The mattresses had belonged to her paid-off crew, heaved overboard as valueless. The planks and the bamboos were dunnage, the boxes and other objects were the rubbish cleared from the ship during the necessary cleaning following the crew's departure, heaved overboard on the ebb-tide, in the belief that the sea would scavenge it, brought into our cove by the unexpected storm. The planks were rough, and of various sizes, but we saw in them the material for at least some of the furniture of our home. We collected all that had washed ashore and piled them at the cliff-foot. We waded in as far as we dared, and with the help of a long bamboo brought others ashore. We collected the bamboos, and we salved all the boxes and odd scraps of wood, knowing that they would make firewood if nothing else. The storm and the rain continued. We were wet to the skin, but too excited to care. The big metal drum was our hardest task, for the waves that came into the cove, although not dangerous, were short and steep and had a very powerful backwash, and we could not get an easy grip on the thing. But we won it, and rolled it up to the cliff. It was an engine-oil container, very strongly made, and furnished with two screw-in bungs.

"It's just the very thing we want for the washing-bowl water supply," I shouted as we examined it. "We can fix it outside, just clear of the window, and close up to the eaves, and run a pipe down to a tap above the bowl. Even if we can't feed it from the spring, we can use rain water from the hut gutter. It doesn't look as though we'll suffer from a shortage of that!" I added, thinking suddenly of the leaking roof.

We were still excited, but it seemed that we had now salved everything of value, and that it was time to get back and face that very urgent problem of the roof. But as we turned up the beach towards the path Dain, who was carrying the lantern, gave a sudden yell.

"Look!"

She was looking across the stream (where it coursed down the beach) to the farther foot of the cliff, and I felt a shiver down my spine as I saw two glowing points of light in the darkness there. Dain clutched my arm.

"Look. What *is* it? *It's something alive.*"

I felt distinctly nervous as I took the lantern and advanced to the stream, Dain following close. We waded through the stream. The "lights" grew bigger and glowed like opals. We stopped and I held the lantern high. Then Dain cried:

"It's a cat!"

We moved more easy of mind towards it. It was a cat, or rather a three-quarters grown kitten. It was crouched, trembling, against the rock, its back arched, its mouth opened, but making no sound; its fur wet and completely bedraggled.

We paused and then moved more cautiously towards it for it was obviously in a state of terror and exhaustion. Dain knelt down and tried to coax it towards her. It tried to snarl at her, but still it made no sound; then it tried to raise a forepaw, as though in defence, but instead it drooped forward and put its head almost on to the ground. Then we saw for the first time a length of thin rope looped round its neck. We did not hesitate any longer. Very gently Dain picked it up, and held it in her arms while I started to ease off the rope.

"My God!" I said. "Someone's tried to drown it. Perhaps from that ship. Chucked it overboard with a weight on the rope, the weight must have come loose. Perhaps it got on to one of the mattresses and floated here. It's just about dead."

It did not struggle, it made no sound while I got the knot undone, but its eyes were still open and moving.

"We've got to save it. We've simply *got* to," Dain cried. "Let's hurry back, get the fire on, and give it some hot milk."

She opened her oilskin coat, and clutched the kitten to her breast, and we moved as fast as we could back to the hut. Water was dripping on to the stove, but fortunately not so that it interfered with the grate, and there was enough dry wood for me to get the fire going. The storm continued as bad as ever, but we had got the measure of its sounds, and apart from the actual discomfort of the dripping rainwater, it did not bother us. We put on some milk. Dain sat down on a box in front of the fire, between two leaks, the kitten on her lap, and she gently rubbed its body with a towel. When the milk was warm she held its head while I opened its mouth, and put a few drops in with a spoon. It made no

attempt to swallow at first, but we persevered, and suddenly
it made a decided licking movement with its tongue.

"Keep at it," Dain cried excitedly. "It's getting warmer.
I can feel its heart beating."

She continued to rub its back gently with the towel. It
licked again, and then actually swallowed, and Dain gave an
excited shout:

"It's purring—it's *purring*! Can't you hear it?"

It was purring, very weakly, it was true, but enough to
convince us that we had brought it round, and gradually its
swallowing became stronger.

"It's all right," cried Dain. "I'm certain it's going to
live. Isn't it thrilling? After all its adventures and what it
must have suffered. Do you really think it got on to that
mattress? It must have been half-drowned first."

It would not have been wise to let our imaginations
rove too far on the adventures and sufferings of our little
castaway, or the human brutality that had caused them.
Enough that its sufferings were over. It was soon purring
quite strongly, and was beginning to lap the milk from the
spoon. It did not seem to be hurt in any way. Its fur was
nearly dry, and after it had lapped at least a dozen spoonfuls
of milk it sensuously arched its back under Dain's caress,
and started licking its paws, purring loudly.

All this time the storm had given no signs of abating.
The wind roared, the loose felt slapped the roof, and water
dripped on to the floor around us, and hissed on to the stove.
It was half-past four, three hours to daybreak. We were wet
and cold, but although I saw Dain shiver and stifle a yawn,
all her concern was still for the kitten.

"It's got to be kept dry and warm," she said. "Can't we
make a little bed for it in a box near the fire, and put something over it to keep the rain off?"

I got a box, put one of my guernseys in it, and laid it in front of the fire, then arranged a couple of planks over it to form a roof. It looked extremely comfortable, and the kitten must have thought so too, for it snuggled into it, purring loudly, and promptly went to sleep. One could not help but feel a little envious; but suddenly, and it might have been the sight of the kitten that suggested it, I had an idea.

The "island" where we had piled our bedding had, as I had feared, become wet, and there was a leak in the actual apex of the roof, but the piece of sail had kept the bedding itself dry. It was a good piece, almost square, and with no holes. I took a length of the partition frame wood, nailed another to it at right angles, and nailed the free end to one of the walls. We had plenty of rope. We stayed the apparatus laterally, then pulled the piece of sail over, braced it from its corners with more rope, and made a tent. It was the quickest and simplest, and most efficient job we had done since we had started on the hut. It occurred to me that we might have done it when the storm had woke us up; but then probably we wouldn't have ventured out, we might have lost our boat, missed the treasures we had salved, and the kitten undoubtedly would have died. We mopped the floor underneath it, spread some of the roofing felt to protect us from the damp, and once more made our bed. I put more coal on the fire. We took a last look at the sleeping kitten. Then we undressed, I put out the lamp, and we lay down.

The storm continued; the gale roared and howled, the rain beat on the leaking roof, but the leaks dripped harmlessly on the tent that had once been a sail of Hoskins's last-built ship: and soon Dain was fast asleep. But I could not sleep myself, and I had no wish to. I was thinking of Bramblewick; of Henry and John, and Marney Lunn, the men whose lives I had shared until the time when my invention of a collapsible lobster pot, and my grandiose plans for a new and vigorous inshore fishing industry had failed. It might have been the sound of the storm that roused my imagination, but it was as though I were back in Bramblewick, reliving that life of feverish excitements, which was in its essence a gamble against the sea. It was as though in the storm I could hear the thunder of the surf on the bar of Bramblewick Landing, that treacherous sunken reef which formed a fortified gateway to the bay, ordering all our activities. I could picture the scene on Bramblewick slipway, in the pale light of a winter's dawn, the Lunns and the two grim Fosdyck brothers, Luke and Tindal, staring at the seaward horizon, stifling the age-old hostility that existed between the two families, while they measured the intentions of the common foe. I could see us hauling lobster pots in the tide rip that boiled round Low Batts, or us running before a sudden north-east gale for the landing. I could see us in Henry's warehouse at night, baiting lines or mending salmon nets; I could see the living-room of Marney's cottage, with Amy knitting a guernsey or a garment for the bairn, and Marney making a mat or sewing a sail while he yarned or bantered good-naturedly with his wife.

In my mind I was back, but I had no yearning for reality. I felt instead a fiercely reawakened desire to write; to make a record, not of my own life with these men, but of the men themselves. They stood for something in this cynical, capitalistic, mechanised age. They had their faults; their stupidities, their spites and prejudices: but they had courage and skill and audacity: they were loyal and kind-hearted: and above all they had a zest for living. They were so deeply immersed physically and mentally in their struggle against the sea, they had no time to be self-conscious, to bemoan their hardships and misfortunes.

In the past few months at Bramblewick I had made several attempts to write; but, although I had been less actively engaged with the Lunns, I had been too close to my subject, too raw about my failure, too bothered about my personal affairs to succeed. The record had to be an impersonal one. I had to invoke the figures in it, as they lived among themselves. So long as I was near to them, and Bramblewick, my subject was fluid and confusing. I was receiving new impressions, most of them because of the changed circumstances, conflicting with those I wished to record.

But now, although I could recall every detail of the Bramblewick scene, smell the tar and the bait in Henry Lunn's warehouse, hear the voices of Marney and Amy Lunn as if I had been with them in their cottage, it was with a new sense of personal detachment. My view had become objective, and suddenly my pictures, my vividly-remembered impressions, began to form together into a single plan. I saw the shape of my book. It did not need a plot. The theme would be the antagonism and rivalry between the Fosdycks and the Lunns, between the old and the new generation of fishers, and how both families had a common antagonist in the sea. I saw the beginning of it in that scene on Bramblewick slipway at a winter's dawn, with a gale threatening: the Lunns (with their mobile motor coble) eager to take a chance and shoot their lines, the Fosdycks (dependent on oars and sail) against it, yet unwilling to stay ashore and see their rivals return with a catch. I saw how that double thread could be woven into and unite the various adventures and activities of a year's fishing seasons: cod, lobster, and salmon—salmon leading to cod again at the end of summer: the Fosdycks against the Lunns, Lunns against the Fosdycks, both families against the sea. The Lunns, because of their physical and mental youth, must win over the Fosdycks but the victory would be a material one. In spirit the old brothers would be unconquered to the end; and that end, the end and climax of the book would be, I saw in a flash, the joining of both families in common issue against the sea. The Lunns caught at last in an unpredictable storm, the Fosdycks going to their rescue. I had been witness and had participated in such an incident. Eliminate myself, and all that I need do was to write a straightforward account of what I had seen. I was suddenly possessed by a wild exultance. The framework of my book was complete. I could write it now. With all the characters fixed in my mind, with no complicated plot to bother me, with the incidents wanting little modification from those of my own experience, I could do it quickly too.

I had found in this Cornish cove a perfect sanctuary, completely remote from all the elements which at Bramblewick had made work impossible. It would be an easy matter to make the roof watertight when the storm was over. We could have the whole place tolerably shipshape in less than a week. I'd work like hell. When I wasn't writing we could go on working at the hut, making our furniture, doing the garden, or fishing, or exploring in our boat. Like the men I was going to write about, we'd be so busy we'd have no time for self-consciousness. In a sense we'd be living the same sort of life as theirs. But the book must be the main thing, if for no other reason that we must have money to satisfy those creditors who had helped unconsciously to drive me from Bramblewick. I did not imagine that I would be able to keep my whereabouts unknown to them for ever.

Besides I had no wish to bilk them, for I had a Yorkshire-man's conscience, and a hatred of being in debt. So long as none of them bothered me until the book was finished, I'd pay all of them in full, provided, of course, that it was a success.

Would it be that? Its theme was unusual: the lack of plot and love interest might tell against it from a publisher's and the public point of view, but with a book one never knew. It might be the very lack of these would give it special interest, cause it to be a great financial success, a best-seller. We *might* make a fortune out of it!

Thus, I might have recalled, I had thought and dreamt about my patent lobster pot, when I had made my first model out of an old bedstead, and a broken baby-carriage I had salved from Bramblewick midden, and proved that its collapsing device would work. I'd seen a fortune in it, which my friends would share. But I did not recall that ironic episode now. My new-found confidence remained exultant and complete. In the glow of the fire I looked at Dain, and for a moment I was tempted to wake her and tell her what had happened, to share my wild joy. I resisted the temptation, however, got up and lit the lamp, and, dodging the leaks, rummaged among my things for writing material. I took a peep at the kitten. It was purring softly in its sleep. I got into bed again, arranged the lamp so that it was shaded from Dain's face, and while the storm went on began the first chapter of my book.

4

ONE OF Dain's ancestors was a freelance sea-captain and
trader, who in the course of an adventurous career had
mixed himself up in the political affairs of a small, mari-
time, tropical state, famed for its primitive culture, for the
fierce independence and warlike ardour of its men, and for
the grace and beauty of its women. He had become the
personal friend and adviser of the ruler of this state, had
helped to organise its fighting forces, and had himself
fought valiantly in a revolution headed by a jealous,
treacherous relative prince.

The revolution had succeeded. To save his life the
ruler had been obliged to make a desperate flight to a
neighbouring country, taking with him his family, his
personal belongings, and the state treasure. The captain
went with him, and indeed was largely responsible for the
safe termination of the flight. Some time later, after an
abortive attempt to foster a counter-revolution, the ex-ruler
died. The captain had already married one of his daughters,
a very beautiful and accomplished woman, who now
inherited a considerable portion of what had been the state
treasure. With this the two of them purchased a schooner,
and after a period of very profitable trading acquired a
large tract of land on a fertile island in the Caribbean Sea,
turned it into plantations, built a house, and settled down
to the production of what eventually became a large family
of sons and daughters. The plantations for a long time
prospered, but in his later years the captain, who had always
been of a convivial disposition, took to gambling and

drink, and secretly borrowing on the security of the estate which, when he died, was found to be so heavily mortgaged that the grown members of the family had to scatter and fend for themselves. The widow was allowed to retain the house and a small plantation which she worked chiefly with her own hands, and by scraping and saving she was able to rear the younger children and see them all fledged or married before she died. The youngest of them all was Dain's great-grandmother, who married one of the wealthiest planters on the island and herself had a very large family, but left them no wealth, for a terrible hurricane swept the island before she died and her husband was ruined.

To her distant female ancestor Dain undoubtedly owed the darkness of her hair and skin, and much that was primitive in her nature; her love of the sea and boats and open-air life, her passion for making things with her hands. Her coming to Bramblewick had been fortuitous. Her parents were not well off, and she wished to earn her own living. The farm where she had stayed, run by comparative newcomers to the district, specialised in intensive poultry production, and offered tuition in return for work. But apart from the open-air life, she had found little that was congenial in that occupation of coaxing high-bred fowls to produce unnatural quantities of eggs at unnatural seasons of the year, and from the first her main interests had been on the shore, and the village of Bramblewick and its fishers. While I had been away in London pursuing that vain quest for capital to finance my invention she had established a warm friendship with the open-hearted Lunns, so that she could walk into Henry's or Marney's living-room as easily as I could myself. From Mrs. Lunn she had learnt to knit the guernseys whose complicated pattern had been handed down from generations. She had learnt to braid nets and lobster pots, and bait lines, and listening to the gossip of the women and the yarning of the men, she had been drawn deeply into the fascinating atmosphere of their lives.

We were awakened soon after dawn by the kitten, rubbing itself against our heads and mewing for milk. The storm was over. The sun was shining, there was neither wind nor rain. As soon as we had eaten breakfast I read to Dain what I had written, and explained the plan of the book. To me, while I read and talked, neither had the virtues they'd seemed to possess before I'd finally gone to sleep: but Dain's excitement and enthusiasm were obviously sincere, and soon my confidence was in some measure restored.

"It's wonderful—wonderful," Dain kept saying. "It's going to be a marvellous book. It's so *real*. It's just as though you were there on the slipway. I can just see them all, and hear the sound the sea makes when it's rolling on to the scaurs in the early morning when the air's still. It doesn't matter a scrap about it having no love interest. There's plenty of feminine interest in it, anyway, with Amy and Mrs. Lunn. It ought to be a terrific success. Do get on with it quickly. We ought to start straight away making a working-room. You ought to have a little stove in it, and a nice easy-chair. Which room will you have?"

A room to write in certainly seemed a necessity, but the first and most urgent job was the roof; for inspiring though the storm had been, I had no wish for another night like our first one. We went out. The kitten followed us to the back door, but hesitated there, bewildered and frightened by the earthy smells. Probably it had been born on board ship, and until it crawled from the stranded mattress on to the shore of our cove, had never touched the land. It followed us round the corner of the hut, however, lifting its paws high in the wet grass and sniffing everything suspiciously, but with slowly growing confidence, and we had no doubt that soon it would find that for a cat it was much nicer to have earth to walk on and smell than the steel decks of a ship.

We examined the roof. The gale had practically stripped it bare of felt. The roll Joe had given us would cover only a small part, even of the section above our living quarters. But there was no sign of damage to the actual structure, and we were not disheartened. We had the whole day in front of us. And what a day it was, the sun shining brightly, the air mild, yet with none of the mugginess of the past few days in it. It felt like spring!

We had actually climbed on to the roof, which had a very low pitch. We had a new and fascinating view of the immediate surroundings of the hut: the vegetable garden, sodden and choked with weeds, but exciting in its possibilities, the little stream, now back to its normal flow and with its bed washed almost clear of refuse, even more exciting in what it suggested to our itching hands.

"We ought to start clearing the garden as soon as possible," Dain remarked. "You can't begin too early getting things ready."

Dain, fortunately, had some experience of amateur gardening, although it was confined chiefly to flowers. I had none, for the Bramblewick cottage where I had spent my childhood had no garden, and was so closely shut in by other cottages and got so little sun that even my half-hearted attempts to grow nasturtiums in a window-box had been a failure. But now I felt the onslaught of a real gardening fever, and the infection may have been more deadly because my blood was virgin.

"Yes," I said, "we must start as soon as we can. This is

Cornwall, remember. Joe told me it was a wonderful garden. We can grow early potatoes. I wonder how early? And peas and beans, and the Lord knows what. Can't we grow strawberries and rasps and gooseberries? Why shouldn't we have an orchard, and have apples and pears and plums?"

"We *can*. We can have all the vegetables and fruit we want. And think of the flowers we can grow down the side of the stream—tulips and daffodils and irises. It'll look heavenly in spring and summer, and right into autumn if we have chrysanthemums, wallflowers and sweet williams; we want masses of them everywhere, and hollyhocks, and red-hot pokers, and poppies. I do wish we could start *now*."

I wished so too; but the roof was urgent, and anyway we had no gardening tools. We needed more felt. We'd best get down straight away to Porthkerris, see Joe, and do our general shopping too. The thought of shopping gave me a momentary pang of uneasiness. We needed bread, butter, milk, meat; and we'd go on needing them, and these were things that didn't wash up like drift-wood, but had to be paid for in cash. Soon that thinning wad of notes I carried would vanish altogether. How would we do our shopping then? Well, I thought, sufficient unto the day is the evil thereof. I'd been broke plenty of times before, and I'd never really starved, or allowed any one I was responsible for to starve. Something would turn up. We'd find some way of earning a living until the book was finished, and then everything would be simple; and I said nothing of what was in my mind to Dain, who as we climbed down from the roof remarked:

"If we're going by boat we ought to try and get a fish. There's bound to be fish in the harbour."

We had no fishing gear, but we could get some in

Porthkerris. We gave the kitten the rest of our milk, and
leaving her the run of the hut we went down to the cove.
But for the evidence of the wood and the other things we
had salved and piled at the cliff-foot, and the pile of weed and
muck on the shore, it would have been hard to believe that
last night's adventures had happened. The tide was down.
The creek had narrowed to a ribbon of glassy water winding
among the level mudflats which reached beyond the clean
shingle of the half-tide shore. Wading at the water's
edge, in extended formation, was a flock of curlews, and
nearer to us, so near that we could see every detail of its
plumage, a heron walked sedately over the mud, stopping
occasionally to peck at some morsel it had found.

It was the first time we had really seen the creek at low
water. Again we momentarily forgot the urgency of the
roof. We walked down to the edge of the mud. There were
no rocks, but here and there huge baulks of timber
(evidently the remains of the "slip" Hoskins had built for
the beaching of their unlucky barque) projected from the
shingle and mud. They were grown with weed, and as we
moved to one of them, a bird flew up from it; there was a
flash of bright emerald in the air, and we saw that it was a
kingfisher. We were fascinated, and as excited as two
children on the seashore for the first time, and we scarcely
knew what to look at next. There were shells everywhere;
razor shells, oysters, mussels, cockles, small cowries, empty
of course, but I scratched into the shingle, and soon found
a live cockle; and when we came to look closely at the
timber we found masses of mussels under the weed. Our
excitement began to take a more practical turn. Bait, I
thought, and food too, for we were far enough away from
the harbour for there to be no risk of contamination.
Cockles and mussels! Not a diet, but a pleasant and a useful

variation, and, translated as bait into terms of fish, likely
to subtract a good lump from that budget of inevitable
daily expenses that had been bothering me.

And as we continued our exploration a new idea came
to me, and took definite shape when on one of the pieces
of timber I noticed a small marine animal and recognised
it as a comparatively rare species of sea-anemone. I
recalled a period in my life at Bramblewick, before the
War, when I had been fascinated by the study of marine
zoology, and with the aid of such text-books as I could
get hold of had acquired at least a good smattering of
the subject. I had discovered, incidentally, that certain
marine animals had a definite cash value. Marine
zoology is an important side line to the general zoology
taught in all universities. There was a constant demand
for living specimens, supplied chiefly by a firm of
naturalists who, however, could not afford to employ
whole-time collectors for marine animals only. I had made
a "connection" with this firm. The "market" varied. Things
like sea-urchins, starfishes, anemones were required for the
general student's course; but somebody, perhaps a fully-
fledged biologist, might be doing a research on one particular
animal, as for example a tiny crustacean that was a parasite
of a certain species of sea-slug. This parasite, whose name
was Splanknotrophus, after a period of free-swimming life
in the sea, entered the body of its host, and settled down on
the latter's reproductory organs, feeding on them and
rendering them sterile, yet with no other apparent effect on
the slug, which continued to live a normal happy life. But
the parasite itself was fertile. When mature it produced a
little sac of eggs, and this sac was forced up through the
soft body of the slug and exposed, so that when the eggs were
hatched the larvae could swim free, and eventually infest

other slugs. To work out the details of a life history such as this, a biologist would require thousands of living specimens. It was an interesting job collecting them. It helped me with my own studies (although these had led me nowhere), and if there had not been a living in it, I'd often made as much as twenty shillings in a week. Here, evidently, was a richer "collecting" ground than Bramblewick. I decided I'd write to the firm asking if the market was still open.

The temptation to go on exploring was strong. Apart from the animal life there were other things to fascinate us. Higher up the creek where the schooner and the laid-up pleasure boats were moored, were the bare ribs of several old sailing ships, and here the shingle was strewn with long iron bolts, chains, pipes and other metal scrap. We turned our faces resolutely from this tempting field for pottering. We got some mussels, and by digging into the mud with our hands a few worms. We dragged and pushed our boat down over the shingle and across the mud to the creek, and set off for Porthkerris. We observed as we passed the bluff that the workmen had completed the setting of the iron posts, but our interest was soon attracted to a ship anchored in the middle of the harbour off Porthkerris. She was a steel barque, obviously foreign, and we saw at once that she had been in serious trouble, for her mainmast was broken and some of her canvas was hanging over her side. We kept on our course to Porthkerris. As we drew near we observed signs of unusual activity in Hoskins's yard. There was a sound of hammering and chopping, and having made fast our boat at the steps we climbed up and found the whole yard in a turmoil of industry. A space had been cleared among the things that had littered it when I had first met Joe. Here, supported by trestles, was an immensely long piece of timber on which at least a dozen men, including Joe himself, were working, shaping it from the square to the round with adzes. And among them were women and children, collecting the chips in aprons and baskets. There was a powerful smell of pitch-pine in the air.

Joe, in his shirt sleeves, and his brow dripping with sweat, at once stopped work and came towards us beaming.

"Ah," he said. "We've got a job at last. We'm making a new mast for that foreign barque anchored off there. 'Tis an ill wind that blows nobody good. She came in early this mornin' just after daybreak. Had a terrible time in the gale. Mainmast carried away, and one man washed overboard and the mate with an arm and his ribs broken. They've taken 'e to St. Jude hospital. We've got a job at last. Lucky we had a big enough piece of pitch-pine in the yard, or she'd have gone off to Chardmouth for repairs. How did you get on last night? You'd scarcely know there was a gale blowin' up there in the Pill. I reckon you'd sleep through it all."

We gave Joe a brief account of our night's experience, but it was evident that he was preserving his own romantic conception of the place: that he could not believe the storm had disturbed its Eden-like tranquillity.

"Ah, yes," he said. "But down here it be blowin' like a hurricane. You wouldn't get much wind in that little valley, with the hills all round 'e. Of course, you'd be bound to get a drop of water in through the roof. If only Charley had been back we'd have been up and mended that. Charley only got back this mornin'. He be fairly full of himself. Thinks he's got that job he went to see about, convertin' a Brixham trawler into a yacht. Ah, but he ain't signed no contract yet. I reckons that as soon as we get this mast finished we'll all be on the dole again. A few bob in our

pockets, and everybody in Porthkerris lighting their fires
with pitch-pine chippings for a week—that be all."

There was no object in trying to convince Joe that the
storm had given us an anxious night. He readily agreed to
give us all the felt we wanted, and led the way to the warehouse. But we hadn't reached it before we encountered
Charley, and Joe, without another word, left us and went
back to his job. Charley gave what was clearly an angry look
at his uncle's retreating figure. My first impression, that
there was a constraint between the present and the one-time
manager of the firm, was strengthened: so was my impression that Charley was a much harder man to do business
with, for when I stated the object of our call he at once
launched on a history of the hut and its several tenants.
How much the firm had spent on it from time to time, how
little of this had come back in the way of rent. Felt was
expensive stuff. The firm had put nearly three pounds worth
of it on the roof for one tenant, and like the last he hadn't
paid any rent at all. Couldn't we patch it for the time
being at any rate?

I saw his point of view. Harder though he was we liked
him, and he had won our sympathy. He had got his troubles
and anxieties, and we both felt a reluctance to add to these
in any way; yet the roof was a matter of great urgency.
Our case was strong; we had paid our rent in advance, we
had made a legal agreement, and Charley at last must have
been convinced of our honesty, for he led on to the warehouse.

"You've had a bit of luck this morning, anyway," I
remarked conversationally as we stepped inside that
fascinating place. "That mast should be a useful job."

His face darkened.

"Luck!" he muttered. "It might have been luck, if I'd

got back an hour before I did, and Uncle Joe hadn't done the
deal. That's just the sort of thing that happens here. I go
away on business. Joe's left in charge. The skipper of that
barque comes in. A Finn, but he speaks good English. Got
a perishable cargo, overdue as it is, and his owners must
have wirelessed him to have his repairs done as quick as
possible and never mind the expense. What does Joe do?
Quotes a price that just about covers the cost of the wood,
takes on a dozen of our old workmen who haven't been off
the dole for three years, full wages of course, and let's all
Porthkerris know there's free pitch-pine kindling to be had
for the picking up. That's the sort of thing I've got to put
up with. Uncle Joe can never get it into his head that
we're a bankrupt firm carrying on by the grace of our own
creditors. We sell paraffin. What happens when one of these
unemployed comes in and tells Joe his missus can't cook the
kid's dinner because she's got neither coal nor oil, and no
money to pay for either? Joe let's him have a gallon. Tells
him he can pay when he gets a job!"

Thinking of what had happened yesterday in the warehouse, and of Joe's generosity, Dain and I exchanged uncomfortable glances, but evidently Charley was pleased to
have someone on whom to unburden his complaints, and he
pulled out four rolls of felt without any suggestion of
resentment at our demands.

"It's all right being tenderhearted when you've got the
money," he went on. "We'd all like to be that. But you
can't run a business like that, particularly one like ours.
Joe would give his trousers to any one who got round him
the right way. That's no use in business!"

"What about the job you went to see about?" I asked as
I helped Charley to move the rolls outside. He actually
smiled.

"You mean that trawler? Yes, that will be a bit of luck, if it comes off. I shan't know for a week or two. The chap who owns it has got pots of money, retired banker or something. Wants her stripping and converting into a pleasure yacht, new canvas, and a Diesel engine putting in. A real swank outfit. Yachts—that's how this firm could get on its feet again if it had a chance. I'll say that for Uncle Joe, he's the best designer and craftsman on this coast, bar none. But when it comes to money and business, he's the biggest fool. Have you got a boat? I'll give you a lift down with these. What about nails, and tar?"

In the circumstances I thought it would be wise not to let Charley see the boat, in case he asked us the price Joe had named: but he embarrassed us further by inviting us to look round the warehouse to see if there was anything we needed. Anything for the hut itself, like paint or nails, we could have at cost price. Other things he'd sell cheaper than we'd get them in any of the local shops, and, of course, we could pay at our own convenience. We were obliged to tell him that we had already done some "shopping" with Joe, that we had bought the mattresses and various other things. I strongly emphasised the word "bought." Charley grinned ironically, but his manner did not become less cordial, and when we left him at last it was with the modified impression that if he was a harder man than Joe, he was just as kindhearted and generous under the skin.

We went into the village to do our shopping. It was a desolate place. Although St. Jude on the opposite side of the harbour was bathed in the winter sun, the lower part of Porthkerris was in shadow, its narrow streets were wet and its cottages looked poor and miserable. I remembered that Joe had told us that more than a hundred Porthkerris men, normally employed on the china-clay jetties of St. Jude were on the dole, and the rest of them only working half-time. We wondered where they were, for apart from the dozen or so men working on the mast and a group of loafers outside the village pub, and a few miserable-looking children, the place was deserted. Later we learned that they had to report every morning to the Employment Exchange at St. Jude, where they would hang about in the vain hope that something would turn up.

We caused no surprise in the village grocer's by asking the price of everything and doing a canny shopping. Nor was the butcher surprised when we asked him for the cheapest joint of meat, and when that seemed too dear, buying a sheep's head, which from experience I knew to be an extremely economic and yet agreeable form of nourishment. Clearly the blight of poverty lay heavily on the place. I went to the post office which was also a general store, and having bought a couple of fishing lines, I wrote a letter to the firm of naturalists: then we made our way back to the shipyard. We were not feeling so ecstatically happy as we had done when we had set off from our cove, and Dain expressed my own thoughts when she said:

"Isn't it awful. Everybody here so poor and depressed. Why should men have to be unemployed? It isn't as though they're lazy and don't want to work. Why should someone have the power to ruin a firm like Hoskins? Why should there be a man with pots of money, like the man Charley was telling us about, and others starving, and what's worse, letting children starve?"

"Yes. But it's the man with pots of money who can buy the yachts that Charley wants to build and that could put the firm on its feet again, and take at least some of these poor devils off the dole. It's all wrong. Look at my lobster-pot! If I'd found someone to put up the money to start a factory for it, it would have been like a blood transfusion to the dying fishing industry on our coast. It would have meant new life to places like Bramblewick. It would have given employment to thousands of people, apart from fishermen. And all that I wanted was the price of a Rolls-Royce car! I met one man who had three Rolls-Royces, one for town, one a sports car, and another for touring. And the Lunns have a twenty-year-old, crazy, six-horse Kelvin in their coble to get them through Bramblewick Landing mouth in a north-east gale. But there you are! It's the man with the Rolls-Royce who eats the lobsters that give the Lunns any sort of a living. What's wrong with us, of course, is that we're *not* rich. Then we could do all the things we expect the rich to do for us!"

"Well, we *might* be, some day. Suppose the book was a terrific success! Wouldn't it be thrilling to come to Joe and Charley, and tell them we wanted a huge yacht building, as big as one of the ships they used to build. Think of the excitement. The shipyard going again full steam, everybody in the place employed and happy. If we were rich we could help the Lunns too. We could buy them a new boat! It is possible, isn't it? Authors do make fortunes!"

Yes, it was possible, but remembering the absolute faith I'd had in the commercial success of my invention, an infinitely more practical thing than any book, I checked my imagination, and deliberately made myself think of the sheep's head I carried under my arm, and the sixpennyworth of carrots and turnips we'd bought to go with it in a stew. I could not help smiling ironically, however, at the thought of buying the Lunns a new boat. You could undoubtedly impress and help an easy-going man like Joe with your wealth. But the Lunns were different. You could do them a small kindness, and although there'd be no resentment in their attitude, you'd know at once that you had created an instinctive obligation: that what you had done must be paid back. To offer them a boat would be a challenge to their strongest instinct, their unassailable independence. They'd call it charity, and hate you for it. . . .

We had reached the shipyard. Charley was not in sight, but as we loaded the felt into the boat Joe left his work on the mast to speak to us confidentially and rather nervously.

"You didn't tell Charley I gave 'e that paint, and the copper kettle?"

"No. We only told him about the things we bought."

"Ah—that be all right then. Charley be in a very funny mood this mornin', ready to find fault with anything. You'm going back to the bungalow now? Wish I was coming with 'e. Did I tell 'e you'm likely to have company up in Pill Creek to-day? Be another steamer due in on the flood. Going to lay up there just below our land. Don't you ever let on to Charley about that paint."

We pushed off. Curiously, the information Joe had given us about the steamer made little impression on our minds. From the workmen we had already learnt that there was no possibility of any steamship being laid up higher than where they had fixed the stern mooring posts. There was no reason why we should fear any interference with our privacy. Besides, we were now both excited at the prospect of fishing. We pulled out towards the fairway, passing close to the disabled barque. As a ship she was not particularly interesting. Steel seemed an incongruous material for the hull of a sailing vessel. Her fallen sail had been cleared and her crew evidently were below. We pulled up-harbour until we were almost opposite to Pill Creek, then dropped anchor and started to fish.

To the angler there is a peculiar fascination in fishing for the first time in unfamiliar waters. In a sea that he knows he has a pretty shrewd idea when he feels a bite what species of fish it is, and from the moment it is hooked, of its size. Here we were far enough from Bramblewick, where at this season the only fish to be caught were cod, for us to anticipate something quite unfamiliar, and Dain gave an excited shout when she got her first bite, and started hauling up. I had hooked something myself before she had got hers to the surface. There was small justification for the excitement, however. Dain's first capture was a whiting about four inches long. I lost mine, but lowering again I at once felt another bite, and shortly brought a couple of the same sized fish on board.

Whiting! We fished for half an hour, and by then were forced to the conclusion that the bed of St. Jude harbour was a solid mass of these tiny fish: that if there were any other species, the whiting were so hungry and quick they would not let them see, let alone take our bait. We could have filled the boat if we'd cared to go on, for they were just as ready to devour cut-up portions of themselves as mussel and worm. As food they were not to be despised; there was our kitten to be catered for too. But it was poor sport, and we were not tempted to continue at it any longer, so we hauled up the anchor and set off up the creek for home. But we had a few worms left and I thought I'd try an experiment. I took the sinker off my hand-line, put a single hook at the end, baited it with a worm and let it go over. The tide was flowing up the creek. I gave the line to Dain, took the oars and kept just enough way on the boat to trail the boat over what soon became the shallow mudflats of Pill Creek. Nothing happened. We drew near to the bluff. Our cove and the hut opened out. I aimed in for the beach, and Dain started to wind the line in, for the bait was touching the bottom. Then she gave a sudden shout.

"Stop! The hook's fouled something. Must be weed or a rock!" And then, before I'd stopped the way of the boat, "No, it's a fish. A *terrific* one!"

There wasn't more than a couple of feet of water close astern of us; ahead, we were only a boat's length from the dry shore. Standing up, I could see over Dain's shoulder the swirl of the struggling fish, and I yelled to her:

"Don't try to haul it in. The line will break. Slacken it if you can."

The line was a cheap one. We had no gaff or net, and I saw that we'd never get the fish into the boat direct.

With one of the oars I poled the boat into the shore, then swung her broadside on so her stern was aground. I took the line while Dain got out, then handed it back to her and got out myself. Then holding the oar as a club, I told Dain to haul in, gently as she could, and slacken if the fish made a sudden rush outwards. It was a breathless minute. But the fish itself helped us. It did make a violent rush, but shorewards, and as it came within range I half-clubbed, half-scooped it out of the water, and Dain pulled it clean ashore. It was a bass, weighing at least eight pounds. We danced about it like a couple of savages wild with excitement. Dain was almost incoherent.

"Isn't it a *beauty*! I've never caught anything so big as that. I thought it was going to pull me overboard one moment. What *is* a bass? Is it good to eat? Isn't it exciting? Isn't *everything* exciting? Look—we're in our own cove— and we've caught a monster fish—and we'll cook some of it for dinner if it *is* good to eat. And we've got the hut to get on with, and the garden, and all the things that washed up last night, and the kitten. Won't it be excited when it sees the little whiting. Come on. Let's get up to the hut. I'll carry the fish. Everything's so wonderful, it's like a dream."

It was. We were completely shut out from the world again. We had forgotten Hoskins, and the poverty-stricken village we had seen. We were aware only of ourselves and our happiness. But I had enough sense of reality this time to moor the boat properly, with a line running up to the cliff, so that we could haul it closer in when the tide flowed. And I made a powerful resolve that no job, no matter how agreeable and exciting it might be, should take precedence over the mending of the roof.

The kitten was glad to see us and the fish. The markings of her fur were very primitive, closely resembling those of a wild cat, and seeing that she was going to have a fairly primitive existence we named her Choo-i, which is the word the natives of East Africa (where I'd served during the War) give all small members of the cat family. The fish (she ate two of the whitings in as many minutes) seemed to give her courage, for she followed us into the garden without hesitation, and started smelling among the grass for mice while we made our preparations for doing the roof.

It was a big job: for we had to remove all the nails that had held the original felt: and we confined ourselves to that part of the roof which covered the living quarters. But there was an extraordinary satisfaction in laying the new felt on, in nailing it fast: in the thought that every yard of it laid increased our security against the weather, against a repetition of last night's discomfort. We broke off for a meal. We half-boiled some potatoes, then chipped and fried them. We cut steaks off the bass and fried these too, and we found that in flavour the bass is even superior to the haddock. For a sweet, Dain made pancakes. It was a thrilling, completely satisfying meal. When we'd done we

made a calculation of what it had cost. Reckoning everything, the cooking eggs we'd used for the pancake, flour,
butter, potatoes, even pepper and salt, and the coal we'd
used, it came to eightpence. We felt justified in spending
another twopence on a pot of tea. Eightpence for dinner.
With breakfast of tea and toast costing at the outside sixpence, another sixpence for tea and another eightpence for
supper, that brought our daily bill for food to two shillings
and twopence: fifteen shillings and twopence a week. That,
of course, made no allowance for meat, but it looked as
though we could get fish whenever we liked, and meat
shouldn't cost us more than another half-crown. We
could live on a pound a week; on less than this when the
garden was cropping!

Except that we had dismantled the "tent," our living-
room was in the same state as when we had stopped work
last night, but we could now appreciate the advantage of the
increased space and the extra window. We itched to get on
with it, to finish the cupboards, to whitewash the ceiling,
but we resolutely went back to our job on the roof. We'd be
able to carry on with the interior work after dark. Yet, if
the laying of the felt completely occupied us physically, it
did not stop us glancing down at the garden and the stream,
and planning what we should do. And all the time deeper
in my mind I was thinking about the people in my book,
and particularly Marney Lunn. What had drawn me to
Marney more than anything, I thought, was his enthusiasm
for doing things. Not only fishing. He'd be just as enthusiastic if he was whitewashing the ceilings of his little
cottage, or fitting a new shaft into a broom, or making a
model boat, as making a lobster-pot, or trying a new
fishing ground, or persuading his father to put to sea in
bad weather when the Fosdycks said no. The only thing that

could ever make Marney unhappy was inactivity, as once
when he had poisoned his right hand with the spine of a
"stale" gurnard, and he could not even use a sewing-needle.
Amy, his wife, although she had a deeper sense of responsibility since her baby came, and worried over their
poverty, had just the same zest for life. The thing was
infectious. You couldn't go into that cottage and not feel it
and respond to its rhythm. They were happy: happy
because they were in love and physically well-mated,
because they had jobs to do and liked doing them. And
I suddenly yelled at Dain who was fitting a piece of felt
round the base of the chimney pipe:

"My God—I'm happy. Aren't you?"

She answered gleefully:

"Yes. But I wish I had two pairs of hands, and at least
one extra brain, so that I could do two jobs at once, or that
the days were twice as long. I want to be sewing curtains,
and making our room look lovely, and doing the other
rooms, and digging the garden, and laying paving stones
down to the cove, and fishing, and exploring the shore, but
I want to be doing this job just as much. How shall we
find time to do everything we want to do? When shall we
start making our furniture? And the book must come before
everything. We really ought to start on your working-room
the moment we've finished this."

It was a problem, this matter of time. The sun had
lowered, more than half the afternoon had gone before we
had completed the laying of the felt, and we still had to tar
it. But it was only the problem of the child at a Christmas
party, with too many nice things to eat and do. The tarring
itself was a pleasant occupation. It gave us a very satisfying
sense of the completion of one extremely important job.
We were hungry again. We began to think of tea, and a

half-hour's spell of rest during which we'd discuss and plan the next job to be done. But just as we'd finished and were preparing to get down from the roof, we heard the loud blowing of a steamer's horn from the harbour, and I remembered what Joe had told us about the ship coming to lay up. Looking down at the cove I saw that the tide was nearly high again.

"Come on," I said. "Let's see who our neighbours are going to be. It ought to be quite exciting watching a ship come close in and make fast to our own shore."

"Do you think they'll throw any more things overboard? We can do with all the wood we can get, can't we? But I hope they'll keep their wretched mattresses and other rubbish, and not try to drown any more kittens. It *is* exciting."

We rushed up the hill to the point above the bluff which gave us a view of the harbour. At once we saw the steamer. She was standing just at the mouth of the creek, with a tug at each side of her. They had evidently just completed the tricky job of turning her about, and were preparing to move her in stern first. She was an ordinary tramp, of about six thousand tons. There was a name on her stern, but it wasn't until she had moved right into the creek that we could read this as *Heather Wyke*; and although that name had a homely sound it was unfamiliar to me as the name of a ship, and had no unusual significance.

The tugs moved her very slowly. A pilot launch came ahead of them, and, rowing close to the shore, I saw the old man who had ferried me over to Porthkerris on Christmas Day, on the look-out for a job when the ship was moored. From our high vantage point we soon had a clear view on to her decks. We could distinguish the figure of the captain on the bridge, and on the forecastle deck an officer, evidently the mate, and several seamen standing by the winches. There was a shout from the bridge. An anchor was dropped, and the inward movement of the three vessels continued to the rattle of the winch and chain, as the latter was paid out. Presently the stern of the ship was not more than a hundred yards distant from the bluff where the posts had been secured. The pilot launch steamed in and landed a man, then returned to the ship, and we heard the man in charge of her shout:

"All right."

The tugs put their engines astern. The rattle of the chain ceased, as the steamer was brought to. There was a group of seamen standing by on her poop. The officer who had been forrard came hurrying along the deck and joined them, and the pilot boat moved to take one end of the mooring cable which the men had lowered over. For the first time then I heard the voice of the ship's officer shouting to the men to lower away. My heart suddenly seemed to stop still. Not only was the accent of that voice "Yorkshire," it was a voice I knew.

I stared at the man, completely oblivious now to what else was happening. He was leaning against the rails looking down at the launch. The light was failing, and a hundred yards is a long distance at which to identify even a very familiar person, that alone someone one has not seen since boyhood; but I knew at once that I had made no mistake.

I grasped Dain's arm, and hurried her back to a gorse bush which screened us from the ship. She was astonished, and frightened too, for it was impossible for me to disguise the fact that I was badly frightened myself.

"What's the matter—what's happened? Why have we got to hide?"

I stared at the ship, at the figure of the mate, and I must have startled Dain further by laughing aloud, for the whole thing suddenly struck me as being supremely ironically funny.

"My God!" I cried. "My God! Can you guess who that officer is, the one at the stern watching the rope being paid out to moor that ship on to *our* land? Don't you recognise at least his Yorkshire accent? That man comes from Bramblewick. That's ' Grab ' Fosdyck, once prize bully of Bramblewick Wesleyan School, chief of the gang that made my life hell when I was a kid, until I learnt how to box, and knocked the stuffing out of him one day. I haven't set eyes on him since those days. He went to sea when he left school, but I know his home's still at Bramblewick. He'll be married to a Bramblewick woman, and I expect he'll have a house on Bramblewick ' Bank-top.' Bramblewick! We thought we'd got as far away as if we'd gone to the South Seas. And here's Bramblewick within speaking range!"

My appreciation of the ironic humour of the situation was growing stronger, but so was my sense of calamity, and it was this I must have communicated more strongly to Dain.

She clutched my arm.

"Are you *sure* you recognise him? What does it *mean* if he sees us?"

"I don't know. But Grab always hated me like poison. In those days there was nothing we wouldn't have done to spite each other short of killing. I can't imagine he's forgotten our last fight. I'm not afraid of him physically. But if he sees me here, then depend upon it Bramblewick will know about it. We don't know, of course, whether he'll be staying with the ship, but he's the mate, and mates often do when a ship's laid up, in which case he may be here for months, it depends how long the slump lasts. He'll be writing home to his wife. You know what Bramblewick is. The news will spread like wildfire. There's the people I owe money to. There's the county court bailiff, with God knows how many writs he's got waiting for me by now. They'll be on our trail in no time, and every one here too will know about it."

Dain clutched at my arm.

"It doesn't mean we'll have to go, does it? To leave the hut, and everything?"

I looked down into the valley which we had imagined was so remote from the outer world, and for one ghastly moment considered the full implications of Dain's remark. But I fought my thoughts back, and I said to Dain:

"I don't know. He may not stay. He may leave the ship to-morrow. They rarely have more than one officer in charge. If he does, then he's simply not got to recognise me. He won't know you anyway. We'll have to dodge him. If only the ship wasn't so close. If only it hadn't happened till the book was finished. Come on, let's get back and have tea, and think things out."

I did not look at the ship again. We crept stealthily to another clump of gorse, then over the ridge into the privacy of our valley, and then ran down to our home.

5

My SLENDER hope that the mate of the *Heather Wyke* would leave the ship, along with the paid-off crew, was not realised. Early next morning I went up to the gorse bush to which I had hurried Dain in the first moment of alarm. The tide had ebbed and the forepart of the ship was high and dry on the mud. The crew had already gone. Her decks were deserted. Her furnaces had been drawn. But there was smoke from her galley, and it wasn't long before I saw the figure of the mate emerge from the galley door and walk out on to the after-deck. I could not see his face clearly even when it was turned in my direction. But I knew by the very way he walked that I'd made no mistake. It was Grab, my boyhood enemy; and evidently he was left in sole charge of that steamer, literally moored to our own land.

We had discussed and rejected as quite unfeasible an immediate flight. For one thing we had nowhere to go to, and if we had known of a place we had no money to get to it. I had dared at last to reckon up my capital, and found that it was now less than five pounds. Besides, it wasn't likely that Grab would recognise me without my being aware of it, and if he did write home, and consciously or unconsciously put my creditors on my trail, we'd probably get some warning. But it seemed to me that I could not over-estimate the seriousness of what had happened, the danger we were in. We'd have to stay where we were for the time being at any rate, but we must take Grab's personal animosity for granted. We must assume that he had only to discover my identity for him to pass the news on. At all

costs we must elude him. If, after all these years, I had
identified him by his voice and the shape of his figure at such
a distance and in a failing light, it was not likely that he
would fail to recognise me if he saw me close. We must
maintain a constant watch on the ship. We must acquaint
ourselves with his habits. He would have to go ashore
occasionally either to Porthkerris or St. Jude. We must
be careful not to be in those places then, and to plan our boat
journeys accordingly. The ship lay very close to our side
of the creek, out of the fairway. When we passed her, as we
must to reach the harbour, we must hug the farther shore,
and keep our faces averted until we were well out of the
danger zone. I had stopped shaving. A beard and moustache
should be a valuable disguise, if by accident Grab and I did
meet face to face.

A shadow had fallen on us. Yet, in our valley completely out of sight of the ship, we found it possible to put
the fear of her out of our minds by a frenzy of labour. We
made ourselves ignore the possibility that all our labour
might be for nothing: that we might eventually have to
make a flight more ignominious than that of any of the
hut's previous tenants. We whitewashed the ceiling of the
living-room. We distempered the walls dove-grey. We
finished the cupboards and the dresser, leaving the wood
bare, sandpapering and then polishing it with a compound
of wax and turpentine. The water supply, we decided, must
wait. We fixed the lavatory bowl, and with a piece of old
lead piping carried its outfall through the side of the hut
to a temporary pit. We knocked down the partition between
two of the other rooms and made a bedroom. We built a
wardrobe in it, and a large "bunk" to take our two mattresses,
and little cupboards on each side. Everything we "built-in."
That, I thought grimly, would be extremely disconcerting

for the agents of the law if ever they came to distrain our goods. Everything, except our pots and pans and personal luggage, would be "landlord's fixtures," and they should certainly form an agreeable farewell gift from us to the firm of Hoskins in case we hurriedly went; certainly better than the beer bottles and tin cans of their last tenant.

For the time being we abandoned the idea of a "working-room." I found that I could write in the living-room, in odd snatches during the day and at night when Dain went to bed. I wrote at fever heat, and with little conscious effort, for having set the scene, and got my people moving in it, the thing seemed to grow by its own force. The Fosdycks of the book, protagonists of the Lunns, were related to Grab. The Lunns were comparative newcomers to Bramblewick, having emigrated to it from a village farther up the coast shortly before my own father, a struggling landscape painter of Irish descent, had been lured by its red roofs into settling in the place. The Fosdycks were the oldest and biggest of the Bramblewick families. Originally they were all fisherfolk, but in the eighteenth and nineteenth century when the development of the north-eastern coal industry brought into being a large fleet of cargo sailing-ships, many of them became sailors. It was natural that their sons should follow in what was now becoming a far more lucrative profession than fishing, and that when "sail" gave place to "steam" the tradition should be carried on. They were indeed fine seamen, and there were few among the family who did not rise quickly to officer's rank and to the command of ships. But whether like Grab's branch of the family they were sailors, or like Luke's, fishermen, the Fosdycks were united in their hatred of "foreigners." In my boyhood I had suffered as much from this hatred as had the Lunns. For Henry Lunn it had been personified in the shape of Luke Fosdyck, who regarded him as a trespasser on the fishing grounds of Bramblewick Bay. For me it was Grab, two years my senior, nearly half again as tall, tough and wiry as a cat, fearless, like all the Fosdycks, and a ruthless torturer and bully.

While I was writing, even about the Fosdyck brothers, my mind was completely oblivious to the ironic circumstances of the present; and so long as we were working inside the hut it was easy for us to maintain an illusion of security. But we'd no sooner step outside than I'd wonder what was happening on the ship, and the path up to the spy-place became worn with our feet. By the end of the week we had formed a good idea of Grab's habits, however. As we had anticipated he made a daily excursion to St. Jude. For this he used the ship's jolly-boat, which he kept at the foot of a rope ladder falling from the fore-deck on the shoreward side, and thus within our sight. She was a heavy boat, and he sculled her with a single oar. In our small boat it would be an easy matter for us to avoid him if we chanced to be afloat at the same time; but as he never ventured towards Porthkerris, we could do our own shopping there while he was at St. Jude, and get back and actually observe his own return from our hill.

We saw Joe. The mast was finished. There was no more news about the trawler job. The workmen were back on the dole, Charley was away on another business trip, which Joe referred to with a customary irony. Things had turned out just as he'd said they would. Charley was out of his mind to think that that job or any other job was going to come off at present. Trade had never been so bad. Still more ships were coming to lay-up shortly. He'd heard that a Cardiff company had booked berths for a whole fleet of twelve colliers up the Pol, above the clay jetties. The dredger was working up there now moving a sand-bar. Joe had commented on my growing beard and moustache and he'd asked us if we'd seen anything of the officer on board the *Heather Wyke* yet. It had been on the tip of my tongue to ask Joe if he met the mate himself, to say nothing to him about us and the hut, but I repressed myself. Our safest outward attitude, so far as Joe was concerned, was one of complete indifference to the ship and her solitary occupant. I'd given up shaving because we were working so hard putting the place straight, and had no time, I said, and he had asked no further embarrassing questions.

In the general store at Porthkerris, I had bought a pair of cheap, tinted "sun" spectacles, and I carried these handy, ready to slip them on at a moment's notice. With my beard soon a respectable length I began to nurse a hope that after all we might be able to keep our existence unknown to Grab indefinitely. We began to breathe more easily when we moved outside the hut, and as the weather continued to be dry and mild, we began our first onslaught on the vegetable garden. We had bought a spade and a fork, and a sixpenny handbook that gave detailed instructions for the cultivation of every type of vegetable from potatoes to Jerusalem artichokes, with chapters on the preparation of the soil, on manures, pests, and diseases. I had been surprised, on first reading this book, to find that gardening really is a very complex business. I had imagined that it consisted merely of breaking up and manuring the soil, sowing seeds, watering the plants in dry weather, weeding, and finally harvesting the crop. I had not guessed that digging itself was a very technical process, that soil was a subtle compound which if deficient in, or overcharged with, certain chemicals, would grow nothing but weeds. I knew that slugs and caterpillars fed on lettuces and cabbages, and I had heard of such things as wart disease, and Colorado beetle, and aphis, but I had not imagined, because the subject had never been of direct interest to me, that every garden vegetable or fruit is subject to the attacks of not one but innumerable diseases and pests; bacteria that destroyed your seed even before it germinated, or produced cancerous growths on roots, or wilted leaves, or turned fruits rotten. Insects which, with the same diabolical cunning as the little crustacean parasite of the sea-slug, laid eggs on roots, or stems or buds, which hatched into destructive grubs. When you sowed peas or beans, said the book, you must soak them in a mixture of paraffin and red lead or mice would eat them. When the plants came up you must protect them from birds. Later you must watch out for things called saw-flies, which ate the leaves, for another pest which ate the flowers, for still another which established itself in the forming pods.

Yet, in the garden at present, there was no sign of this vast, variegated horde of pests and parasites, for there was nothing growing in it except weeds, and weeds it seemed, by an ironic dispensation of Providence, were largely immune from their attacks. I had read the chapter on "soil preparation" several times, and we decided to follow the writer's instructions to the letter. In a new garden, or one that had been badly cultivated, the first process advised was that known as deep trenching, and there was a diagram to show exactly how this was to be done. First you marked out your plot into strips two feet wide. You dug out the spit of soil from the first of these strips, and carried it to the farther end of the plot and made a heap of it, marking this heap A. Then in the first trench you dug out another spit, but this time only a foot wide, and this you carried to the farther end of the plot and marked it B. This, theoretically, left you with a trench with two steps in it. You didn't dig out the lowest part of this, marked C, but you forked it over and loosened it, and put in some manure, then you dug out the adjoining spit and laid it on top of the manure, and you covered this again with a spit of top soil from the next *strip*, so that again you had a sort of "stepped" trench with the deep part of it to fork over and cover with manure. So you went on until you came to the end of the plot, and a final "stepped trench" which you filled in from the heaps of soil marked A and B, making sure that they went in in the right order. The advantage of this process was that you were loosening and aerating the soil to a very great depth, creating a new underlayer of humous, and yet maintaining the original relationship of top-soil to sub-soil, which apparently was very important.

The diagram and the instructions were easy to understand, and the job might have been comparatively easy but for one important factor. The diagram showed each "spit" of earth as an even cube, the bottom of each trench dead flat, the walls vertical. If you were working in clay it might have been so, but our soil, we soon discovered, was a crumbly loam which disintegrated when you lifted it. Our spade left not a clean wall but an uneven sloping one with a V-bottomed trench instead of a flat one, and when we started to dig out the second spit the adjoining walls simply crumbled into it, mixing top-soil and sub-soil together, so that it was quite hopeless trying to get at the third stratum below. Our task was further complicated by the fact that the top-soil was thickly matted with the tough, stringlike roots of nettles, that there were dock roots, which, like giant white carrots, reached down through the sub-soil and appeared to be anchored in a bed of cement; that, running horizontally in every direction, twisting among nettles and docks, were the tube roots of bracken, tough as rope, which

when you pulled at them simply lifted the soil and caused
further crumbling of the trench walls. Clearly "deep
trenching," however important it might be, was not for us,
and we soon abandoned it for a process the book called
"bastard trenching" by which you left the third stratum
alone, and merely dug and shifted the other two. But even
this defeated us before we had got to the end of the first
strip, when we decided that the only thing to do was to
dig our trenches deep as we could, remove the weed roots,
put in manure and bury it with the soil from the next
trench, hoping that the manure would counterbalance the
evil effects of mixing top-soil and sub-soil together. It
had already occurred to us that we might use sea-weed for
manure. The book recommended it. Used liberally, it said,
it made an admirable general manure. We carried it up in
sackloads from the cove, from the pile that had been left
there the night of the gale, and as some of the straw from the
mattresses had got mixed with it we fetched these too, split
them open, and buried weed and straw together.

It was hard work but immensely exciting. In spite that
we had not carried out the instructions of the book, the
slowly-growing patch of clean weedless earth *looked* good
and fertile, and our only regret was that even in Cornwall
it was still too early in the year for sowing. Out of sight
of the ship, we could for long periods forget the menace of
her existence, and yield ourselves completely to the enjoy-
ment of the present; the beauty of our little valley, and the
cove and the creek, the winter sunshine, the flavour of spring
(however false it might have been) that was in the mild air.
The only sounds we could hear were the cries of the gulls and
curlews in the creek. A cock robin had appeared from
nowhere a few minutes after we had dug out the first spit of
soil. It infuriated Choo-i (now thoroughly at home in the

garden) by hopping along the trenches and picking up the worms almost under our very spades, and then unconcernedly flying up out of harm's way when Choo-i sprang.

Joe had been right. There was something Eden-like about the place, and we felt it most strongly when we worked outside: digging, tearing out the nettle and dock and bracken roots; forking in the weed, the rich ozone of it making more exciting still the exciting smell of the soil. Once while we took a spell of rest Dain remarked thoughtfully:

"Would it cost a lot of money to have a baby?"

It was a subject which like gardening I had only the vaguest notions about.

"I don't know," I answered. "I expect it would. You've got to have a doctor and a midwife, and a lot of things like napkins and binders and safety-pins and perambulators, and feeding-bottles."

"Don't be silly. Those things wouldn't cost much. We wouldn't need a perambulator here, anyway. There wouldn't be anywhere to push it. And you don't need feeding-bottles if you feed it yourself. It couldn't have cost Amy and Marney Lunn much to have had theirs, could it?"

"Good God, you don't say that you want to have one, do you?"

"Well, not now, of course. With everything in such a muddle with the ship, and feeling that we may have to fly at a moment's notice. But supposing we haven't to, that that man doesn't find out about you, and no one comes to bother us. And supposing the book is a terrific success, and you can pay off all your debts, and still have plenty. . . . It would be wonderful, wouldn't it, having a baby of our own. It couldn't help but be a boy, you know. What a place for him to be born in and grow up in. Can't you just picture him, here in the garden, or running down to the cove, barefooted, finding treasures on the shore? Can't you imagine teaching him to swim, and row the boat, and how to fish. . . . It would be wicked to live in a place like this and keep it all to ourselves."

So far as I could remember I had never experienced a conscious desire for children. Few men do, I believe; for unless a man is definitely philoprogenetic, liking children for what they are, or he has large possessions or a distinguished name or title to pass on, or sufficient vanity to believe that his own physical or mental virtues are worth perpetuating, he can only (if he thinks selfishly and cold-bloodedly about it) regard reproduction as a process full of peril to the woman he loves, and children as an added source of responsibility, anxiety and inconvenience. It seemed that one of the main feminine functions of physical love was to overcome this instinctive reluctance of the male to take on the fuller responsibilities of life, to lull his fears, to induce in him a self-importance, a sort of reckless gallantry. Not that this was a conscious artifice. When you were in love it seemed that you were both in the grip of forces about as involuntary as those which made your eyes blink, or your heart pump: the vital difference being that between the rousing of the creative impulse, and the fateful all reason-obliterating contact there was a space where cold reason might have some say.

We did not look at each other. We started digging again, but for a moment I did imagine myself a father, and felt very pleased with the idea. Then, as though an icebag had been laid on my head, I thought of our fix; our diminished capital, the fact that I'd had no answer yet to my letter about the animals: that within less than a fortnight at the out-

side, unless something turned up, we'd have no money at all.
And I said to Dain coolly:

"For heaven's sake don't start thinking about babies.
We've got to think about the book, and growing potatoes
and cabbages and peas; and how to make enough money to
keep ourselves; and how to keep on dodging Grab."

"Yes, I know. We can't possibly afford to have one yet.
But you can't always help your thoughts, can you? And it
would be thrilling."

For the first few days, we had made a habit of taking an
hourly observation of the ship: but with my confidence
growing we relaxed this, and merely took a peep at her before
starting any prolonged job outside. There was no reason for
us to fear that Grab would actually come ashore on our land.
His duties as sole officer in charge, even of a laid-up ship,
would keep him pretty busy. His daily trip to St. Jude never
took less than one hour. Besides, he was evidently cooking
his own meals, for the galley fire was always smoking round
about meal times, and he was never visible then. And if, by
any chance, he did take it into his head to come ashore, the
only place where he could land his heavy boat was the cove,
and then only when the tide was at least half-way up. Unless
we were inside, a boat could not land without our seeing it
first.

We had, indeed, taken an observation before starting
work in the garden the very next afternoon. The jolly-boat
was fast to the ladder. Grab was not visible. The galley was
smoking and we assumed that he was engaged with his
midday meal, and that as the tide was just starting to flow,
he would make his trip to St. Jude later. We had ourselves
been in to Porthkerris in the morning, and so far as we knew
he had not left the ship once during the day.

It was just about tea-time when we heard the unmistakable sound of a boat in the creek, close by the bluff.
The tide was about half-flown. There would, I realised, be
just enough water to float a ship's boat into the far corner
of the cove. I put my glasses on (there was a mist hiding
the sun, but tinted glasses were worn for other purposes
than sun-glare, so that was not important) and we hurried
to the top-end of the garden, which gave us a clearer view of
the cove. We were just in time to see the bow of the jolly-
boat moving round the bluff. In it, sculling with his back
towards us, was Grab. And on the midship thwart was a
woman, sitting half-turned and looking towards our shore.

I had a clearer sight of her face than, so far, I'd ever had
of Grab's: but for a moment I could scarcely believe the
evidence of my own eyes. Then Dain herself confirmed my
recognition.

"That woman," she whispered. "I've seen her dozens of
times. She comes from Bramblewick. Don't you recognise
her?"

"My God," I whispered back. "I should think I do.
Keep down. Keep out of sight."

We lay flat on the ground, with our heads just
sufficiently raised for us to keep the boat in sight. It had
cleared the bluff, but although the woman was still looking
towards the shore, Grab was still sculling slowly ahead, as
though his intention was to pass the cove and carry on up
the creek. I found small comfort, however, in the hope that
the boat would soon be out of sight. I was measuring the
full implications of our new discovery.

True that I did not know the woman very well. There
were two distinct communities in Bramblewick. Most of the
sea captains, active or retired, lived in the modern brick villa
part we called "up-bank," near the railway station and the

new parish church. During the last phase of my life in the place, I had made few contacts with the inhabitants of this community. My interests had been in the old village, close down by the sea. But I knew them all by sight, and they knew me. I did not know the Christian name of the woman in the boat, but I knew that she was one of the several daughters of a retired sea-captain, himself a member of one of the oldest families in the place. That he was a man who took a prominent part in local affairs; that he was a sidesman of the church, a member of the rural district council, a magistrate on the local bench; above all that he was a director and part-owner of the local gas-works whose "account" was one of the several I had been obliged to leave unsettled. She was good-looking, youngish, yet matronly. It was a safe guess that she was Grab's wife: that she had come down (and had arrived either last night or very early this morning) to live with him on board the ship.

My heart sank. A man is never so curious about other people's affairs as a woman. Provided that we did not meet him face to face, our chances of keeping our existence unknown to Grab had been fairly strong. For one thing, even if he had known the details of my later life in Bramble-wick he had not acquired them first-hand, for he certainly had not been home during that period. He could have no *fresh* curiosity to stimulate him. But his wife, if she was true to Bramblewick type, would have a nose like a blood-hound. She would be freshly familiar with all that had occurred. Doubtless she had already regaled her husband with the latest "Bramblewick" scandal, including that of my own departure. Was it pure chance that had brought the two of them in sight of our hut now? Was it just casual interest that kept her looking towards the shore?

The boat was half-way across the mouth of the cove

when we heard her speak to Grab, and then actually point up to the hut. Grab stopped sculling and looked too. And then he swung the boat round, and began to scull again straight in for the shore.

"Come on," I whispered urgently. "Let's get inside the hut."

We were about twenty yards away from the back door, and fortunately there was a slight hollow in the garden, which gave us cover from the cove. We ran, keeping our heads down, and scarcely breathed again until we were inside, and had the door bolted behind us. Then we hurried to the other door, made certain it was fast, and then huddled down on the floor in the corner nearest to the cove.

"Do you think they're coming up?" Dain whispered. "Do you think they've found out?"

"God knows," I whispered back. "Do you think she'd recognise you if she saw you?"

It was a foolish question. If Dain had seen that woman in Bramblewick many times, and remembered it, then we could be assured the woman had seen her, and would remember even better: for if Up-Bank Bramblewick was in many ways cut off from the old town, any sort of scandal would make a bond of common interest between the two communities. We had no chance to discuss the matter further, however. We heard footsteps approaching up the path from the cove. Breathlessly we listened until at last they stopped only a few yards away from the end of the hut. Then we heard the woman's voice, speaking with a slow, all-too-familiar "Bramblewick" accent.

"That must be the door. Go up and knock."

"And what shall I say?" answered the even more-familiar voice of Grab.

"Why—just ask. That's all."

"I'd rather you did than me."

The woman laughed mockingly.

"I will, if you're afraid to. Go on. You've only got to ask."

There was a moment's horrible silence, then a more horrible sound of heavy footsteps slowly ascending the wooden steps to the front door; another silence; and then a loud rapping. I felt Dain clutching my arm. We both looked at the door, at the battens I'd shored it up with the night of the storm, and it seemed to me the whole door shook, when after a long-seeming period of silence the rapping was repeated. But we didn't move, except to breathe, and this we did as quietly as we could. Another silence. Another prolonged rapping, then a definite shaking of the door as Grab apparently tried the latch.

"Door's locked," he said then. "There's nobody in or they'd have come by now."

"Aye, that's true," the woman answered. "Oh, look, Will, there's a kitten. *Puss, puss, puss, puss.* Look, it's quite tame."

In our eagerness to reach sanctuary we had forgotten about Choo-i, who had been in the garden with us at the first moment of alarm. Judging by the sounds outside, the woman had picked her up, and was stroking her.

"What a pretty kitten! I wish we'd got a cat on board, Will. We'll have to get summat to kill all those rats. What a ramshackle-looking spot it is. Fancy anybody living in such a spot. But, of course, if they wanted to keep quiet it's all right. Did you say he'd got a beard?"

"Aye. But I've only seen him once, with my glasses. They never come nigh-hand the ship. It was a chap in the harbour office told me about 'em, but he didn't know much

himself, and he didn't know their name. We'd best give it
up, anyway, and get back to the boat."

"I'd like to have a look inside," the woman remarked.
"Is there a keyhole? Perhaps we could look through one
of those windows farther up."

To our intense relief, we heard Grab moving down the
steps again, and say firmly:

"We'd better not! We'd look daft, wouldn't we, if they
came back sudden and caught us spying. Let's get back. We
can come again when we're sure they're in. It's not *that*
important."

There was another period of silence, during which
presumably they were both standing by the hut, separated
from us only by a distance of several feet, and that thin
wall of weather-boarding. Then we heard their footsteps on
the path and shortly the woman shouting, "Go back, pussy,
go back, there's a good pussy," and the footsteps became
indistinct, in the direction of the cove. But it wasn't until
we heard the sound of the boat, the creaking of the scull,
that we dared to get up and peer through a chink in the
front door. And it wasn't until we had watched the boat
move out of sight round the bluff that we breathed freely
again: and then we were both seized by an almost hysterical
fit of laughing.

It did not last long, however. The situation had been
funny. It was funny enough just to think of the presumed
wife of Grab Fosdyck (and the undoubted daughter of the
part-owner of Bramblewick gas-works) holding our kitten
in her arms and getting goofy over it, and of Grab himself
shaking that door, which if it had given way would have
revealed the two of us practically hiding behind it. But it
wasn't so funny to imagine what would have happened
then; to recall their conversation. Why had they called?

What was it they wished "just to ask?" It wasn't funny to think that it was their intention to call again. Did they know anything? Did they at least suspect? Would they come again, if so could we dodge them so successfully?

We could laugh; but we knew that the shadow that lay over us had grown deeper; and we gave up gardening for that afternoon. We called Choo-i inside, and we bolted the back door, and lit the fire and put the kettle on for tea, for which we'd collected that morning a pan full of cockles. The cockles were delicious, and Choo-i had her share. But it was an unusually silent meal. We'd had a very bad fright, but it wasn't until Dain had gone to bed, and I'd started work on the book, that I dispelled it.

6

Dain woke me next morning with a startled whisper.

"There's someone outside the hut moving about. It must be them!"

Before I had time to collect my wits and realise who Dain meant by "them," there was a loud rapping at the front door.

"It's *them*. It must be," Dain whispered. "What shall we do? What if they look through the window?"

I had worked very late at the book, and I had a hard job to keep my eyes open. But a second, and a louder rapping helped me. Dain was sitting up in bed. I could feel her shivering. I sat up too, and at once realised why she *was* shivering. A drastic change had happened to the weather. Even inside the hut it was freezing hard.

Nothing is worse for destroying the courage of the average man than cold, and at no time is he more susceptible to the effect of cold than in his first waking moments. I was now almost conscious. I knew that it must be Grab or his wife knocking at the door. But my first reaction was cowardice.

"Lie down," I whispered. "Both doors are fast. They can't get in. Let's keep the blankets over our heads. It won't matter if they do look through the window. They'll go away soon, anyway."

We lay down, still shivering, but appreciably warmer.

"I wish we'd made curtains for the windows," Dain whispered. "I just hate the idea of any one peering in. What do they want? Why can't they leave us alone?"

I didn't answer. There was no more knocking at the front door, but now we heard footsteps outside, walking up the length of the hut and pausing actually under our bedroom window. The window, I knew, was just low enough for a tallish man to peep inside. We pulled the blankets over our heads. But the steps continued up the hut and round the end, and halted this time at the back door. There was another violent knocking. A short silence. And then it seemed that our caller had picked up a stone and was belabouring the door with it in a supreme effort to attract attention. There was something peculiarly imperative and insolent in that final noise. Something that suddenly roused all the violent passionate hatred I'd had for Grab Fosdyck as a boy. It was as though I could hear his mocking laugh, as he'd pounce out at me from some dark Bramblewick alleyway and start twisting my arm, or pinching me, the mild prelude to the punch in the face that would finally send me flying on to the hard cobble stones, in those unhappy days before a heaven-sent visitor boy had taught me the art of fighting. It was as though in those blows on the door I could feel the impact of Grab's fists on my own body, and I was possessed by a fighting rage. I leapt out of bed.

"Where are you going—what are you going to do?" Dain whispered anxiously.

"Hell," I said, "I've had enough. I'm going to see him."

Dain leapt out of bed too. She clutched my arm.

"Don't be silly. Put a coat on anyway. You'll freeze. Where are your glasses. Do have a bit of sense."

But I was beyond sense, beyond caution. Clad only in pyjamas, barefooted, I strode into the corridor: and, as though the continued battering on the door was not enough to infuriate me, I put one foot down hard on a roofing tack, so hard that its flat head was almost flush with the skin of my heel. I pulled it out, and took another furious stride towards the door. I grasped the bolt and felt the vibration of the hammering.

"All *right*," I shouted. "For God's sake stop that bloody noise."

The hammering ceased. I unshot the bolt, unlatched the door, and swung it open, prepared to see Grab Fosdyck face to face, and not caring whether he recognised me or not. But I did not see Grab Fosdyck, only a slight, pale-faced, middle-aged man in postman's uniform, standing with a stone still in his hand, well back from the door he had been belabouring; who at once said in a nervous, very apologetic voice:

"Beg pardon, sir, if I knocked a bit too hard. I knew somebody must be inside, but I thought you must be fast asleep and couldn't hear. I've got a letter for 'e. Joe Hoskins say you be livin' 'ere. Be a cold mornin', ain't it."

The ground and the whole of the valley within sight was white with frost. The postman's fingers were blue, and his hand trembled as he took a letter from his bag and held it out to me. My own hand was trembling too: my teeth were chattering.

"Be a long time since I had to come out this way with a letter," he remarked conversationally. "Last people who were here never had no letters, but one chap who was here before had plenty, only they were all bills and summonses. Be a lonely place in winter-time, but all right in summer."

The man evidently had the local habit of loquacity. Also he seemed anxious to remove the bad impression he had made on me by his hammering. With a little encourage-ment, I had no doubt that he would have given me more intimate details about the various ex-tenants of the hut, and probably another version of the Hoskins crash. But although my rage had gone, I was in no humour for gossip. I thanked him and shut and bolted the door, and limped back to the bedroom and got into bed. There was no need for me to explain what had happened. Through the window we watched the postman climbing up the hill in the direction of Porthkerris, and not until he was out of sight did I open the letter. It was, I had already guessed, from the firm of naturalists, replying to my own. The delay was due to their address having changed since I had last done business with them. They were pleased to hear from me. They regretted that at present there was not a special demand for any marine animals, but they would be glad to have a list of those I could offer, and in the meantime could I supply them immediately with any of the animals mentioned on the enclosed list, especially the earthworms and spiders?

The list was a long and varied one. I read it out to Dain. It included frogs, 4d. to 6d. each according to size. Half-grown tame rabbits, the price two shillings. Dog-fish, a shilling each. Centipedes and millipedes, twopence each: dung-beetles, cockroaches, honey-bees, honey-bee and wasp grubs, all at twopence. There was a demand for freshly killed but undamaged grey squirrels at one shilling: brown rats and moles at sixpence, certain species of field-mice at threepence. Twopence was offered for large star-fish. Threepence for male shore-crabs, and sums varying from one penny to fourpence for certain marine animals which had no popular name, only a Latin one. But two items in the list were marked with red ink: earthworms, large, at threehalfpence each, house-spiders, large, at the same price. One hundred of each were wanted per week for at least three weeks.

I felt an intense relief. Here at any rate was the solution to our major problem, the payment of our weekly food bill.

One hundred worms and one hundred spiders a week at threeha'pence each, worked out at twenty-five shillings. We could actually save out of it, and this without reckoning the other things on the list. It was warm in bed, and I had completely recovered from the shock of my awakening. Somehow or other the fact that I had braced myself to meet Grab had lessened that fear of him which yesterday's experience had increased. I felt jubilant, but Dain did not seem so pleased when I had finished reading the list.

"What on earth do they want all those animals for?" she said. "Tame rabbits, and squirrels, fresh-killed—it just sounds horrible. Fancy keeping rabbits, and getting fond of them, and then killing them in cold blood. Fancy killing a squirrel just for a shilling?"

I had never been a university student myself, neither had Dain, but I'd seen a university zoological laboratory, and I could picture a long bench covered with bottles and microscopes and dishes and bunsen burners, and a number of very serious and intelligent-looking young men and women sitting on stools, with sharp little knives or scissors or probes in their hands cutting or poking into the carcases of the rabbits or frogs or worms that were fixed on slabs on the bench before them. The animals were dead, and it was the task of the student to dissect and trace out the anatomical structure, the ramifications of the digestive, reproductory and nervous, and lymphatic and blood circulation systems, and find out how they all worked. I could imagine that many people would find this a rather repulsive occupation, and I think I would have jibbed at dissecting a tame rabbit if I'd bred it myself and grown fond of it; or even selling one for such a purpose. And I didn't fancy the idea of dealing in grey squirrels. But such animals obviously were not in our line, and I said to Dain:

"Good Lord, we're not going to breed rabbits, and we'd certainly not earn much out of squirrels in a place like this. I doubt if there's one within miles of us. We may get rats and mice and moles. We'd want to kill them anyway. But it's the worms and little things we're going to make cash out of. If only we'd known that earthworms were worth three ha'pence each. Think how much we could have earned the last few days. That robin must have eaten at least ten bob's worth!"

"Yes," Dain answered more cheerfully. "And how many spiders and cockroaches have we killed inside the hut? I shan't mind getting things like those, and rats and mice. What a pity we're not friendly with the Fosdycks. Did you hear what she said about the rats on the ship?"

Temporarily our acute fears about the Fosdycks had been allayed again, but they were at the back of our minds. As soon as we had dressed and got the fire on, I walked up to the spy-place. There was still no wind, but the grey overcast sky looked really wintry, the ground was hard as metal underfoot. Even the ship had a mantle of frost. There was no one in sight. The boat was at the ladder. The galley chimney was smoking. Grab and his wife were evidently busy with breakfast. But for how long would we be safe, I wondered? How long would it be before they landed at the cove again and we had a repetition of yesterday's embarrassing experience. What on earth was it that woman wished to ask?

I found myself wishing that it had been Grab instead of the postman who had called. We should have known the worst, anyway. But as I turned to go down to the hut I had a sudden idea. From the first Joe had insisted that the cove and the foreshore was his. Except for the shore where the boats were laid-up all his rights had passed to me by the terms of my tenancy. Couldn't I stop any one landing in the cove, or at least coming up the path? Over breakfast I elaborated my idea to Dain.

"Why the hell should we allow any one to come prying about the place? The cove is ours so long as we pay our rent. No one's got any right to land there, that alone come up the path. Why shouldn't we put up a notice saying ' Private Cove, No Landing '?"

"It's a *fine* idea. And we could have another one near the path, saying ' Private, Trespassers will be Prosecuted.' We *could* prosecute any one who trespassed, couldn't we?" Dain added not quite so confidently, "Even them."

The idea of prosecuting Grab Fosdyck and the daughter of the part-owner of the Bramblewick Gas-works for trespassing on our land struck me as being very funny. In fact when I looked at it one way the whole idea of my trying to stop people from trespassing was funny, for I could never remember an occasion when a notice-board forbidding trespass or threatening prosecution had done anything but lure me on. From what I remembered of Grab, I was not very hopeful that such a notice would frighten him away either. Yet we must do something. It was bad enough having to dodge him outside. Life would be intolerable if we were to feel that even inside we were not safe. We had plenty of boards, and posts and paint. One of the boards that had washed up was already painted white. I sketched out on it in large letters,

PRIVATE BEACH   NO LANDING

and we began to paint it at once.

It was one of those jobs that looked easy, and soon proved otherwise. Half the morning had gone before we had finished it, and a smaller board bearing the legend, PRIVATE. TRESPASSERS WILL BE PROSECUTED, and, although we had done them as neatly as we could, they did not give us much satisfaction, such as we'd got out of doing something for the hut, or the garden. Looking at them they only made me feel angrier with Grab and the fate that had brought him so close to us. I took another observation of the ship and made certain the coast was clear before we carried them out to put them up. Even this was a harder job than we'd guessed, for the soil was frozen almost to the consistency of rock, and we required deep holes for the posts.

Choo-i, after a few sniffs of the morning air, had decided she'd stay by the fire; but we'd no sooner started digging than the robin appeared, and he'd smartly collared a good-sized worm before I remembered that worms now had their price. We got a tin, and we shooed him away as I broke each spit of soil, but we didn't find any more worms. We fixed the PRIVATE BEACH board on the edge of the cliff so that any one coming round the bluff in a boat would see it at once. The other one was half-way up the path: so that any one who did try to call on us would certainly *know* they weren't wanted. But again neither of us felt too happy about it when the job was done, and we did not, as we might have done with anything else, stand back and admire our work.

I was already feeling slightly perturbed by the fact that we had found no more worms. Perhaps this was because we had dug the holes for the posts in uncultivated soil. We hurried to the garden, the robin following hopefully. But here the top-soil was frozen even harder, and when we did break through it, and dug down into that illusive soil C of the gardening book, there was no sign of the enormous worms which had been as common as bracken roots the day before. I remembered that worms always rise to the surface after rain, particularly in warm weather. We fetched the kettle, and sprinkled boiling water on the ground, but although we and the robin waited hopefully for a long time the worms apparently were not deluded into thinking that an April shower was falling, and none came up.

"Well, there's still the spiders," said Dain. "The cold can't affect them like it does the worms. I mean they can't bury themselves deep in the soil, can they? There must be millions inside the hut, especially in the part we haven't cleaned, and cockroaches too. And it will be warmer for us there too."

Despite our intense labours we were both very cold. The frost, if anything, was growing keener. The sky had become more heavily overcast. There was more than a suspicion of impending snow, and the idea of a warmer hunting-ground was good. Dain consoled the robin by throwing a handful of bread crumbs outside the back door. We went into the big room, which, except that we had swept the floor and removed the old mattress, was still as the flitting tenants had left it. It wasn't long before we put up a good-sized cockroach from one of its dusty corners. I had never tried to catch a cockroach alive, and I was amazed at the speed with which it scampered across the floor.

Choo-i joined in the chase. Unfortunately Choo-i won, and had given the creature a damaging jab with her paw before I could retrieve it. We locked her up in the kitchen after that, and, with Dain doing the driving and me the stopping, we bagged about a dozen good specimens which I dropped into a jar. But there weren't any more, and we began an intense hunt for spiders. There were plenty of spider webs. Indeed there was not a corner or crevice in the

room which was not festooned with them. There were
plenty of spiders too, but most of them were very small, and
the big ones were almost as active and elusive as the cockroaches. They took sanctuary behind the strips of damp and
decayed plywood which covered part of the walls, and when
we tore these down crept into the crevices between the
weather-boards. Our bag, when we stopped for lunch, was
no more than a score, which with the cockroaches brought
up our morning's earnings to four shillings and sixpence.
Still, that would do more than pay for our meal of sheep's
head stew (the same had done for yesterday's lunch and
would make soup for another) and rice pudding; and
looking at the list I noticed the item "male shore-crabs" at
threepence each. The tide was ebbing. We ought to be able
to collect at least a score of these, and perhaps a few of the
other listed animals, before it was time for us to leave for
Porthkerris to catch the post. It would be a mixed bag we
would have to send off, and it was unfortunate about the
worms, but it would at least convince the people I was keen
on doing business!

Hunting shore-crabs was certainly more in our line than
cockroaches and spiders. We were luckier too, for the cold
did not seem to bother them, and we found plenty by
searching among the masses of wrack which covered the
rock at the cliff-foot "up-creek" from the cove. You can
tell a male from a female crab by the rudimentary "tail"
which folds on to the underpart of the body. In the female
this is broad, and in the breeding season enfolds the mass of
eggs or "berries." In the male it is narrow. We found more
males than females, and they were all fine specimens.
Luckier still, I found one that was "infested" with a parasite
called Sacculina, a crustacean which has the habit of
attaching itself to the abdomen of its "host" and feeding on

it by a system of fine roots which penetrate even into the tips of the claws and legs. Sacculina was one of the type examples used in the study of parasitology, an important branch of biology, and although it was not specially listed I had no doubt that the firm would pay a bigger price for crabs that were infested.

In spite of the cold the beach was as fascinating as ever. We could not see the ship because of the bluff, but we had a clear view "down-creek," and a boat could not have approached without our having good warning. There were so many things to interest us, apart from the shore-crab hunt, for every foot of rock or shingle or mud seemed to have on it an animal of some sort. There were limpets on the rock under the weed, and stuck on to the shells of quite a number of these were dog-whelks, which drill a tiny hole through the limpet's shell, and then suck out the soft body. There were dog-whelk shells with hermit crabs living in them instead of them instead of whelks, with an active little worm harmlessly sharing the abode, and a sea-anemone stuck on the "roof" also, living in harmony with the tenant-in-chief, which showed that life in the sea was not always a matter of "if I don't kill you, you'll kill me." But in contrast to this we found a starfish which, with its five arms furnished with thousands of tiny suckers, had completely engulfed a hermit crab (presumably sub-tenants too): and a gorgeous anemone that was just spewing out the fleshless and disjointed shell of a crab. We found another anemone on which a large sea-slug was steadily browsing. We "bagged" specimens of most of the things we found. We got some worms too, in case we should find time to go fishing after we'd been to Porthkerris, and we got some limpets for Choo-i in case we didn't and there was no fish for her to eat.

We had to pack all our specimens; and when we'd finished we decided to walk to Porthkerris, instead of going by boat, by the same route the postman had apparently taken on his outward journey.

It was a rough, meandering path: but from the top boundary of our land, it more or less followed along the ridge of the hill which sheltered the Porthkerris side of the harbour, and it gave us an extensive panoramic view. We could look down, clearer than from our spy-place, on to the decks of the *Heather Wyke*. Mrs. Fosdyck evidently had been having a wash day, for a line hung with clothes reached across the after deck. The boat was not at the ladder. Soon we distinguished it nearly half-way across the harbour, with Grab sculling and his wife amidships, clearly bound for St. Jude. Two "new" steamers, "light," were moored at the entrance to the Pol near the other laid-up ships: and as we walked along we saw a smaller steamer, laden, and with her decks and top-sides white with china-clay dust emerge from the Pol, heading down-harbour for the sea. She was out of sight behind the seaward headland before our path brought us to the first cottages of Porthkerris, and a better-conditioned path which led down into the village itself.

With its roofs frosted, and the few people we met looking half-perished with the cold, Porthkerris seemed more desolate than ever. We posted the parcels and did our shopping, and then, remembering we had run short of nails, we went to the shipyard. Outside in the yard and on the quay there was no sign of life. The boats, the gear, the debris, the crane, wore an undisturbed mantle of frost; but a door into one of the sheds was open and we went in, and I gave a shout up a staircase that led to a room above. At once Charley May appeared at the top of the stairs and genially asked us to come up. The room was really a work-shop, with a joiner's bench running down one side of it. There were no shavings or sawdust on the floor, however, and what tools were visible were neatly placed in racks and (I perceived with a newly-revived zoological interest) were thickly spun with spider webs. But at one end the room was partitioned off, and here was an office, where Charley evidently had been at work when we shouted. He led us inside and shut the door, and at once we were nearly suffocated by the fumes of an oil stove, whose wick was turned too high.

We had already guessed that Charley was in a state of repressed excitement. His inquiry as to our business was only a polite formality. Yes. We could have all the nails we wanted. But were we in a great hurry? Were we interested in boats? Did we know anything about Diesel engines? There was a large table in the room, most of it littered with documents and catalogues, and copies of yachting and marine motor journals: but there was also a drawing-board and on it an architect's plan of a largish sailing vessel, to which Charley pointed dramatically.

"That's the Brixham trawler I was telling you about—that conversion job. That's how she stands at present. And here"—he unrolled another plan and spread it on the board—"and here's what's got to be done to her. She's going to be made into a first-class cruiser. Everything posh. See? Everything inside her stripped. A big saloon. Posh cabins. Lavatories, two baths, electric light, electric cooker. A 200 h.p. Diesel. New canvas too, but practically the same rig. A real swank job. And we've got it too," he added with a sudden note of triumph. "The first really big job the firm's had since the smash. *And* in face of competition. More than a dozen other firms put tenders in."

For the time being we were oblivious to the suffocating atmosphere. We were as excited as though a colossal stroke of good fortune had happened to ourselves. We congratulated Charley. Enthusiastically he explained the details of the plan, how the existing fish-hold and crew's living-quarters would be stripped, and refloored and partitioned off. How the engine would be installed. The modifications to the steering gear. We were thrilled, but more by the thought of what the job meant to the firm and Porthkerris than by the thing itself.

"By Jove," I said. "It's a stroke of good luck. When do you start? It'll mean work for months, won't it? The whole yard working at full steam?"

"Why it won't mean that exactly. We'd want half a dozen jobs like this going at the same time before we'd be working to capacity. It isn't as though we were building the whole boat. And even then that would be a small job for Hoskins, compared with what they did once. Still it's a start. There's no reason why we shouldn't actually build yachts when the slump's over. She's lying at Chardmouth at present. She'll be sailing down some time this week. Uncle Joe's gone off to see her this morning to check up dimensions, and then go to Salmouth and select some special timber. I've got to go up to Glasgow this week to see the engine people."

"What's Joe think of it?" asked Dain. "Isn't he pleased?"

Charley's enthusiasm momentarily seemed to cool.

"Yes. He's pleased. You ought to have seen him dressed up in his best clothes this morning. Like a kid going off on a holiday trip. It's a good job I've got the contract signed and sealed, or I wouldn't have trusted him on his own like that. He'd be good enough to tell the owner to knock fifty quid off the price, or to agree to some extra that's not specified at all. When I told him we'd got the job, it took me all my time to stop him going round Porthkerris, and telling all our old workmen they were engaged. It is a bit of good luck this, but we've got to go carefully, I can tell you. It's a very close price we're working on. We wouldn't have got it else. The devil is that Joe's got more experience than any of us. He can tell, almost without looking, what you can do with a piece of timber, how to get over any problem of boat design or construction. I'm no good at that sort of thing. My job's engines, and looking ahead, and smelling business. I sometimes feel that Uncle Joe is like a bit of lead ballast tied round my neck, and yet the firm can't do without him."

We had spent more time in Porthkerris than we'd bargained for, and I was feeling a bit anxious about the Fosdycks. We hurried up the village lane, and we'd no sooner reached the path than we saw the boat, already half-way back to the ship and ahead of us, and keeping close in to the Porthkerris shore. A bitter south-easterly wind had sprung up while we had been in the village, increasing the discomfort of the frost; but although the path ran fairly high above the shore, we daren't hurry now, or we should overtake the boat at a point where our courses converged, close to the ship itself.

We were cold; too cold to talk about Charley's exciting news, but we were not unduly alarmed. Grab and his wife, once they reached the ship, were not likely to loiter on the deck in this temperature. Like us they'd be thinking about their fire and tea, and once they'd disappeared into the galley we could run the remaining distance into the lee of our valley. But to our astonishment Grab, instead of sculling in to the ladder side of the ship, steered out into the creek fairway, under her bows, disappeared, and shortly appeared again, still sculling direct for the bluff of our cove.

"My God!" I shouted, "they're going to call again. Blast the man. What *does* he want?"

We continued to walk slowly until the boat was out of sight round our bluff. Then we ran: turned off from the path on to our own land, and continued down the hill more warily until we came in sight of the cove and saw the boat again half-way into the cove. We crouched down into the gorse. Grab had been sculling very slowly, but now he stopped and we saw them both staring hard shorewards. They were too far away for us to see the expression on their faces, or to hear what they were saying: but it was evident that they had seen at least the big notice-board, PRIVATE BEACH. NO LANDING, and that they were discussing it.

My heart sank. I wished we hadn't put it up. The more I thought of it, the more foolish it seemed. To a man of Grab's spirit, unless he had changed vastly since the old days, that bald command, "no landing," could only read as an impertinent affront. It was worse than slamming a door in his face. If only I'd put "*please*, no landing," or thought of some more politer phrase! It was too late now. We could not stop them landing. We could not stop them coming up the path, for if the first board did not work it wasn't likely the second and more impertinent one would. If they did, we'd just have to wait here in the cold until they went away again, and even then we'd be no better off. There'd be no justification in that for hoping it would be their last attempt. To make things worse it had started to snow.

Suddenly Grab started sculling again. He swung the boat round until she was heading in for the shore. But instead of coming in, he went on turning, until she was heading down-creek towards the bluff and the ship.

"They're going," I whispered excitedly. "They're going.

It's the notice. I didn't think it would work, but it *has*. What luck!"

The boat moved out of sight behind the bluff. We took our chance and ran, and in a minute were safe inside the hut with the door bolted behind us. We had banked the fire up, and it was gorgeously warm in the living-room. Choo-i purred an affectionate greeting, smelling our shopping parcels to see if we had brought her anything to eat. We put the kettle on, and we squatted down in front of the fire to thaw the cold out of us. Dusk was beginning to fall. It was now snowing quite heavily, and the felt on the part of the roof we had not yet repaired was beginning to flap with the rising wind. But above us we knew that everything was secure and weather-tight. Suddenly we were happy again, forgetting Grab, and all that belonged to the world outside our little valley. We sat very close to each other, with Choo-i purring and rubbing herself against our knees. We were warming up. Soon the kettle would boil and we'd have tea. We'd light the lamp, and I'd read what I'd written last night: and then we'd get on with one of the many "inside" jobs that were waiting to be done; have supper and keep on working till bed-time. And it wouldn't matter how cold and stormy it was outside. We'd be warm and secure.

7

THROUGHOUT THAT spring, and into early summer, we lived (financially) on earthworms, spiders, cockroaches and other insects: on starfish, and sea-slugs and shore-crabs, the parasite infested crabs fetching a premium price of nine-pence apiece. We were paid promptly by postal order, to which the firm generously added the cost of carriage, and we averaged a clear twenty-two shillings a week.

It may have been the climate (there was no more snow after that January storm, and very few frosts) or our sheltered position, or some inherent richness in the soil, or the abundance of seaweed we dug into it, but the garden proved a miracle of fertility. Everything we sowed or planted grew and prospered; early potatoes, greens, cos lettuce, peas, french beans, rhubarb, gooseberries, currants, rasps, logans. There was a nursery garden near St. Jude, and we had bought our plants and fruit bushes there very cheaply, and although the book said that fruit trees should be planted in the autumn, we took a chance with a couple of self-fertilising apples, and a Victoria plum, and as they had blossomed profusely, and the fruits were forming, it seemed we could break the rules and still succeed.

And we were just as successful with our flowers. We had cleared the stream for the whole length of the hut, dammed it in several places with rocks, so that we had a series of little pools and waterfalls, with beds on each side. We formed a bank on the far side, where the two stunted willows stood, and we planted this with masses of primroses and foxgloves which we had found growing up the valley. In the other

beds we sowed annuals; nasturtiums, cornflowers, marigolds, godetia, tobacco-plant, love-in-the-mist, and a packet
of mixed seeds which yielded many flowers that Dain could
not name. We had a clump of giant sunflowers growing
close under our bedroom window, and promising to reach
above it before they blossomed. At the back-end of the hut,
which was more sheltered and got more sun than the front,
we made a tiny lawn which we mowed with a pair of
scissors, and in surrounding beds we sowed more annuals and
the seeds from a medicinal opium poppy head I'd seen in a
chemist's shop in St. Jude, which had grown to an enormous
size and produced numbers of large white blooms that
exuded an almost overpowering drowsy smell.

Green-fingers! Undoubtedly we had our share of
beginner's luck, but it hadn't been all plain sailing. No
sooner had the first tender shoots of our peas broken the
soil than myriads of tiny grey slugs appeared from nowhere
and began to devour them. The book said sprinkle the shoots
with soot and lime, trap the slugs with bran or pieces of
orange peel, or pick them off by hand. We tried all three
methods, but the last was the only really effective one.
Every night before bed-time we made a flash-light tour,
picking off the slugs and dropping them into a jar of water.
The pity was that the firm did not want specimens, even at
the special price I quoted of sixpence a hundred.

We had to spray the first leaves, which opened like the
wings of a delicate butterfly from the shoots, to kill the
weevils that attacked them after dark, and later when the
flowers came we had to fight thrips and pea beetles. The
slugs and other pests were just as active among the lettuces
and cabbage and cauliflower plants, and in the flower
garden too. Many of our greens started to wilt before
they were half-grown. Pulling one up we discovered a

curious swelling on the root like a small potato, and from the book identified it as club-root, against which there was no present remedy. You had to lime and fumigate the soil in the autumn, and be careful to examine all roots when planting out. In early spring we had experienced a six weeks' drought. We had religiously watered the entire garden every evening during the last fortnight of that period, and except in really rainy weather we had never omitted giving the peas and runner beans an evening drink of sun-warmed water from the buckets we had standing near the rows. Our potatoes gave us the least trouble. By carefully scratching away the soil under the most advanced plants, and selecting one or two of the biggest tubers from each, we had our first "boiling" before the end of May. And now, in June, a single haulm would give us more than a day's supply. We had an abundance of delicious green peas such as you'd never buy in a shop, flavoured with fresh mint of our own growing. We had dwarf french beans as tender as the peas, and we could throw away half of the outer leaves of our cos lettuces, and have more in the white, closely-packed heart of a single one than we could conveniently eat at one meal.

With the garden keeping us so busy, it was a wonder we found time for other activities, but we did. We cleared the room next to the kitchen, and opposite to our bedroom, and installed the yacht's bath, connecting its waste-pipe to the pit. We built up a stage of timber against the hut wall outside, and fixed the big steel oil-drum on it, just below the gutter, and ran pipes down from it to the bath and the kitchen sink. We toyed with the idea of building an exterior fireplace under the drum, so that we could burn wood and garden refuse in it, and thereby heat the bath water, but decided it might be too dangerous. So long as it rained

fairly frequently, we had plenty of cold soft water for the
sink and bath, and as the bath was small a couple of kettles
of boiling water from the fire would bring it to a reasonable
temperature.

We had refelted the rest of the roof over the big room,
the interior of which looked barren, but less dilapidated
since we had torn away all the old plywood in our search for
spiders. One day we'd had a bright idea. The windows of
this room were in the side walls, and there was only the door
in the end wall, which faced the creek. The door was very
big and heavy. We hadn't used it since the night it had been
torn from its hinges and we had shored it up. By careful
measurement, we discovered that if we removed it entirely,
frame too, boarded in the lower half of the "hole," and
removed the boards to right and left of it for a distance of a
foot, we'd have a horizontal rectangle which would exactly
take two of the windows, joined together. That if we
removed one of the windows from the wall which faced the
stream from the end nearest the creek, we could replace the
door here, make a short step, and fit the steps to the original
door to this. It had been a big job, but we were well re-
warded for our labours. The double window gave us a
magnificent view down to the cove and across the creek.
The new position of the door vastly improved the plan of
the room. We saw it now *as* a room, instead of a general
dumping ground for our spare wood and unwanted gear.
With the walls relined, and some sort of a fireplace, it could
be made really thrilling. What *couldn't* we do when we got
some money?

We fished. Bass weren't so common as our first capture
had led us to suppose. We rarely caught more than a couple
in one fishing trip, and usually we got none. But we could
get baby whiting whenever we liked; we could catch

flounders by the same method we had used for the bass; trailing a line slowly over the mud on the flood-tide; and when the weather permitted, we had made more ambitious and exciting trips out of the harbour and along the coast.

And all this time Grab Fosdyck and his wife were still living on board that ship, moored not more than two hundred yards in a direct line from our hut, and still evidently unaware of our identity. For it was inconceivable that they should have found out, and not told some of the people they met ashore, the harbour officials for example. Equally inconceivable that if the news had got about, Joe would not have heard it, and shown by his manner that he had. We had never relaxed our precautions. At least four times a day, and always before we set out in the boat, we'd take an observation from the spy-place; and if we were at work in the garden, and the tide was more than half-way up, the sound of oars or voices from the creek would be an instant signal for us to crouch down out of sight, until we were sure that it was not the Fosdycks, or if it was that they were not coming ashore.

But the notice-boards which had caused us such mis-givings, and still twinged my conscience whenever I thought of them, seemed as effective as the red flags that warn the pub-lic from straying on to a rifle range. Not only did they keep the Fosdycks off, but all other potential disturbers of our privacy. We discovered when the finer weather came, that the Pill was a favourite week-end boating haunt for the people of St. Jude and Porthkerris, and later still for "visitors," particularly if the sea outside the harbour happened to be rough. On Saturday and Sunday afternoons, if the tide suited, dozens of rowing-boats and sometimes motor-launches would move past the cove, but although the occupants were obviously bent on picnics, and the cove

must have looked ideal, none ventured to land. Yet, thanks
to the extraordinary acoustic properties of the creek, we
heard many comments upon the place and ourselves,
suggesting that we had become a topic of at least mild
interest, in both St. Jude and Porthkerris. Most of the boats
would slow down as soon as they came in sight of the cove
and the hut, and often stop for quite a long time, while
every one in them gazed ashore. Some of the remarks we
overheard were complimentary. They referred to the
garden, the brilliant show of flowers, the rows of peas and
potatoes; or to the alterations we'd done to the hut, or to
the paved paths we'd made. We heard such comments as:

"Yes. He must be a handy man. That garden weren't
no better than a wilderness!" or "Maybe they'm growing
flowers and vegetables for a living," or "They're making a
handsome little place of that old hut."

We gathered that there was much speculation as to how
we did get a living. We heard one man remark authori-
tatively to what was evidently his wife and family (they
were all dressed up in their Sunday best), that I was an "out
of work carpenter, too proud to go on the dole." We heard a
professional boatman inform his party of visitors that we
were artists. And another, a Porthkerris man who evidently
was familiar with our regular visits to the post office, that
I was some sort of scientist, doing experiments on animals
and things, or inventing something. Without any justification (for although we were accustomed to the sight of
our own naked bodies, we had never appeared outside the
hut clad in less than shirts and shorts) we were described as
"nudists." And there seemed to be a general opinion among
those who paused to observe and talk (probably without
knowing that on a still day even a whisper travelled over the
creek as through a megaphone) that there was something

mysterious and immoral about us. Many times we caught
the word "sin," and we observed that whenever a boat had
children in it, or very respectable-looking ladies, the males
in charge kept farther out from the cove and did not pause
at all, although they stared hard enough, and perhaps were
disappointed at what they saw.

Yet so long as we were not identified, so long as nothing
happened to connect me in the public mind with Bramblewick, so long as we could keep the Fosdycks at bay, it did
not trouble us what the local people thought or said. We
had no doubt that Joe and Charley shared the opinion that
Dain and I were "living in sin." We had no doubt that Joe
at least discussed us in the local pub, for he was an inveterate,
if unspiteful gossiper, and his close contacts with us would
make him quite an authority on the subject. But if we had
tried to convince Joe that his, and the general assumptions
were wrong, taken him deeper into our confidence, we'd
have gained little: and that at the expense of making a
definite breach in the wall of reserve we'd built between
ourselves and the outer world.

Anyway, neither Joe nor Charley showed much curiosity
about us. They had their own continued problems and
anxieties. The trawler had come and gone. In our almost
daily visits to Porthkerris we had watched the stripping of
her internal structure, the scraping and recaulking and
painting of her hull, the laying of new floors, the building
of the saloon and cabins, the installing of the engine.

The relations between uncle and nephew had not grown
smoother during the job. A date for delivery had been
specified in the contract. There had been delays, owing to
the non-arrival of material and certain fittings, for which
no member of the firm could be blamed. But according to
Charley, Joe behaved as though he was completely indifferent

to the importance of the job being finished to time: that the only thing that mattered was it being done well. Joe was first and last a craftsman. For him a cabin door, for example, was not just a convenient structure to be hinged into a frame. It was a part of the ship, requiring as much thought and skill in its construction and erection as the mast or any other gear. That door would have to be sand-papered to fit its frame like a glove before Joe would pass it, and he expected and insisted on the same meticulous attention to detail from the other workmen. Charley, just as anxious to see the thing done well, was harassed all the time by the mounting wage bill, by the extras in the shape of "rejected" timber and fittings, which Joe considered not good enough for a first-class job: all of which were narrowing the very close margin of profit that had enabled him to submit the winning tender. That profit, Charley confided in us disconsolately when the "conversion," three weeks behind schedule, was complete, was practically nothing. His one consolation was that the owner, despite the delay, was highly satisfied, and that the craft, cruising round the coast in summer, would be a fine advertisement for the firm. Against this was the fact that the general trade slump was growing worse and worse. There was no immediate prospect of another job. Three more steamers, in addition to the fleet of colliers, had come to be laid-up in the Pol estuary. The slump had hit the china-clay trade very badly. The local roll of unemployed, to which was added again the men who had worked for the firm, had reached a record figure. Who was going to have yachts built in times like these?

But there was no indication that the slump was affecting the worm and spider and shore-crab trade. There was no appreciable increase in the price of those commodities like milk, and bread, meat and butter, we had to pay for in cash, and the garden was giving us more than return for the capital we had put into it. We had saved nothing in cash out of our weekly postal order, but we had paid something off our account with Hoskins, and another quarter's rent. My fear of the Fosdycks had relaxed. It seemed that, bar accidents, the ship might be laid-up there indefinitely, without them finding us out. True, there were a thousand things we needed for the hut and ourselves. We wanted linoleum for the floors, plywood for the big room, more paint, cement and material for the proposed fireplace. Most of these things we could have got on credit from Hoskins, but we resolutely refrained from taking further advantage of their generosity. Our wardrobe was getting threadbare. Appearances didn't matter much, but there was a limit to which worn-out flannel bags and shirts could be darned or patched, and I'd had the uncomfortable experience one day, when we'd made a necessary call at St. Jude, of splitting my best bags across the seat while I was making the painter fast, and this in sight of a party of very smartly-clad people landing in a launch from a motor-yacht that had just arrived in the harbour.

We had stolen out past the Fosdycks' ship that evening to fish, and had anchored close to the yacht. She was a huge vessel, painted white, lined with gold. We had been told in St. Jude that she belonged to a stockbroker, and was on a month's cruise of the coast before leaving on another cruise in the Mediterranean. We did not identify the stockbroker, so that we couldn't guess whether he was enjoying his cruise or not, but the party on board, numbering at least thirty, did not seem to be worried about the trade depression. They were all in very high spirits. Most of them were young, and there was about an equal number of girls and men. Some of them were in bathing dresses. They chased each other round the decks, then they dived overboard, and frolicked in the water, and then swam back to the companion ladder where two smart stewards waited with brightly-coloured bathing wraps: then, later they all appeared on deck again, the young men in "tails" and the girls in beautiful gowns, and they stood in groups laughing very loudly, while more stewards moved among them with trays of cocktails. We were near enough for us to catch the whiff of cooking that came from the after part of the yacht, and it was easy for us to imagine the meal that awaited the guests when the dinner gong sounded and they had finished their drinks. We would not have been human if we had not felt at least a spasm of envy as we sat there in our little boat, mechanically hauling up baby whitings, which, seeing that we'd had bacon and eggs for lunch, and our larder happened to be empty, would have to serve for our evening meal.

We agreed that for once it would have been very pleasant to wallow in luxury. I should have liked to have shaved off that blasted beard of mine, which was hot and sometimes tickled, and after a real bath in a real bathroom got into a laundered shirt and "tails." I should liked to have seen Dain in a smart frock, with silk stockings and elegant shoes, and her hair "done" by a good hairdresser, and us both standing on the deck of that luxury yacht drinking cocktails, feeling good and important, and slightly hilarious, waiting for the dinner gong to sound.

We tried to console ourselves with the reflection that the stockbroker who owned the yacht, and could afford to entertain so lavishly, was probably at this moment far more worried about money than we or Charley, or the unemployed of Porthkerris, had ever been: that the appetites of the young people on board were probably so jaded that they'd get far less kick out of their cocktails and their food than we could out of tea and fried whiting; that the grapes were *very* sour. We'd have liked to have tasted them just the same, and for once given all our fish to Choo-i. The truth was that there was no merit in being poor, in wearing shabby clothes, in buying cheap meat, in "doing without" many of the necessities, and nearly all the luxuries of civilised life. There was less merit in being colossally rich (unless you used your wealth to help the needy, in which case you couldn't stay rich anyway): but somewhere between the two states, there should be one where you could have all the necessities, and a fair share of the luxuries, according to your tastes, and without depriving any one else of what they wanted.

"I think we'd be bored stiff after a couple of days on a boat like that," I said. "There'd be nothing to do but eat and drink and play bridge and flirt. No gardening, no *real* fishing, no making things or doing things for yourself. No privacy. A steward waiting even to drape a towel over you when you'd had a dip."

"I'd hate it," Dain said loyally. "It would be worse than living in a hotel. You'd have to have your hands manicured, and you wouldn't dare to touch a rope, let alone put a worm on a hook or take a fish off."

"Stewards to wait on you. Sailors to weigh the anchor. Engineers to start the engines. Paid officers to do the navigation. Horrible."

"Yes. But it would be different if we had a small boat of our own, wouldn't it. Something just big enough for us to live in and cruise in. We'd still be able to do everything for ourselves, only it would be jolly nice when we got into a port like this, to tidy up and change and go ashore, or perhaps invite someone to have a meal with us, and have a little party, with drinks and things. I *do* think we ought to get Hoskins to build us a yacht when we have a lot of money. It shouldn't cost such a lot anyway. After all, it would only have to hold the two of us, or perhaps three, if we did have a baby, and he wouldn't need much space at first, would he?"

It was a pleasant fantasy to set up against the disturbing influence of the stockbroker's yacht, and although I knew that even a small cruising yacht would cost several hundred pounds to build, and that the idea of having one was as impractical as having a baby in the present circumstances, we allowed it to possess us from that time on. After all, we might be so rich one day that we could afford to own a craft as big as the stockbroker's. No one could confidently prophesy how many copies a book would sell, especially if it was by an unknown author. There were books which, although they were far from being works of genius, had sold as many as half a million, and on top of the royalties from these, the author had been given a colossal sum for the film rights. Then, with his name a household word, magazines and newspapers would give him high prices for short stories or articles; lecture societies, literary and luncheon clubs would pay him to give talks about himself and his work, and if he was really out to make money he could pick up some big fees by writing testimonials for patent medicines or for somebody's cigarettes, or correspondence colleges, or systems for improving your memory or your personal magnetism. Success was a snowball!

It was a night soon after this that I wrote the last chapter of the book. We had supper early, and I started work as soon as Dain had gone to bed. At once I was "back" in Bramblewick, living through the exciting moments of that summer storm, which in reality had come near to costing Marney and his brother John their lives. It had broken, not without warning, at dusk of a very hot windless day, with the sea dead smooth. Both families then had been engaged in salmon fishing, a business that could only be carried on in calm weather, for the fish ran close in to the shore, and the nets were set at night across the scaur "ends," so that the fish were trapped when the tide ebbed. The closer in to the shore you shot your nets, the greater your chance of a good catch, but the greater your risk of losing nets and boat if the weather changed suddenly and the sea got up. The Fosdycks, noting a heavy bank of cloud lying to the west, into which the sun had prematurely sunk, had advised caution. That cloud-bank meant thunder, thunder meant wind, and likely enough that wind would be from the north-east. To venture far from the Landing mouth, to "shoot" anywhere where you couldn't haul quick and be under way for home at the first sign of a northerly blow, would be asking for trouble. But Marney, resentful that since the salmon season had started the Fosdycks had consistently done better at it (the motor coble was no advantage here because of its big draught and, like the Fosdycks, they were using a small rowing-boat) had scoffed at Luke's warning. And so Marney and his brother (for Henry happened to be laid up in bed with an infected hand), had set off at dusk, and with a deliberate defiance Marney had chosen to fish at the south end of the Bay, close under High Batts cliff, an excellent place for salmon, but notoriously dangerous in a northerly or easterly breeze.

The describing of that storm, which as Luke had pro-phesied, progressed from thunder and squally shifting winds, and a deluge of rain, to a swiftly-rising gale from the north-east, needed little invention and no elaboration. It was one of the worst and most disastrous the coast had ever known. At Burnharbour, six miles north of Bramblewick, seventeen out of the score of boats that happened to be fishing that night, lost all their gear. Three boats were capsized, and four men were drowned. To the ordinary peril of the wind and rough sea was added that of a driving rain and then a dense fog which made it impossible for us on shore (Henry, of course was "up") to see more than a few feet ahead of us as carrying lanterns we tramped along the scaurs at low-water mark, searching for what we expected to be the wreckage of the Lunns' boat, and the bodies of its occupants: for from the first it had been inconceivable that they could have survived. There was no need either for me to invent or elaborate in my description of the behaviour of the Fosdyck brothers (who had started hauling their nets as soon as the storm broke, and yet had got through the Landing mouth only in the nick of time) whose rancour throughout that night had been suppressed by a genuine concern and sympathy towards Henry. I wrote simply as I had seen and remembered, with no more modification of details than was necessary to fit and smooth them into the design of the whole book; and the return of the boat at daybreak (Marney and John had managed to pull out to deep water, and riding to a makeshift sea-anchor, and baling continuously, had safely weathered the gale), the reactions of the Fosdycks and Henry, the reawakening of the "feud" after that night of truce, *did* fit in as simply and inevitably as the last remaining units of a jigsaw puzzle.

8

WE HAD planned that we should celebrate the finishing of the book with a holiday. The weather was perfect next morning, windless and hot, and without a cloud in the sky. As soon as we'd had breakfast we went down to the cove, and got a big tin of rag-worms: then we packed food and cooking utensils and fishing gear into the boat, and leaving Choo-i the run of the hut and the garden (although she'd always be down on the beach to meet us from a fishing expedition, we could never persuade her to set foot in the boat) we took our usual observation of the ship, and slipped out past her to the harbour and down for the harbour mouth and the open sea.

Although we had made several trips along the coast, they'd all been necessarily short ones, because of the host of jobs to do ashore, and this was the first time we'd had a really calm summer sea. There was not even a suspicion of swell, and the water was so clear that we could row in perfect safety within a few feet of the shore. We turned east from the harbour mouth. For about a mile the cliff fell almost sheer into the sea, then the line of it was broken by a series of small beachless coves, and at last by a rugged headland which hid the coast beyond from our sight. The longest of our previous trips had stopped well short of this point, which was a good two miles from the harbour mouth. But to-day our minds were free of all anxiety about getting back. The headland lured us, with the promise of the unexplored, and we pulled on steadily towards it.

There were clouds in the sky now, but they were the

small, compact, high-flying clouds of fine weather, and there was not a breath of wind to ruffle the sea. Yet apart from one or two motor-yachts steaming well out from the land, and a large sailing-yacht that was becalmed off St. Jude harbour, we saw no boats, and the shore and cliffs were as deserted as though it was mid-winter and not mid-summer. Not that we yearned to-day for the sight or company of other people, or for the flesh-pots of the stock-broker's yacht! We cut across the tiny bay the headland formed, and then, close into the rocks again, pulled round it; and we saw that on its eastern side the headland receded again to form a cove which, unlike the others we had passed, seemed to have a definite beach. We pulled in for it, picking our way between the half-sunken rocks into a narrow channel which suddenly shallowed and ended on a patch of shingle. We grounded, and Dain, barefooted, jumped out and ran up the shingle, but she stopped when she reached the part that had not been wetted by the tide.

"Hoy!" she shouted excitedly. "The shingle's almost red-hot. You can hardly walk on it. Look, there's piles of drift-wood. There's some real sand. There's a sort of cave up there by the cliff. Isn't it *hot*! Do let's stay here. Let's make a fire and have lunch here, and bathe and fish and have tea, and go on bathing and fishing all day. It's simply perfect. Let's bathe at once."

The tide was ebbing. We off-loaded our things from the boat, pushed her off into the channel with a trip anchor, and then as excited as though we had never seen a Cornish cove before (we who had one on our doorstep) ran up the beach, shouting and laughing like a couple of schoolchildren. But there was a difference between this cove and our own. This was wilder, grander, more primitive, and although the sea was as tranquil as the water of our creek, one felt

that it was the *real* sea, and that the cove had a more direct
relation to it. There was no mud. The shingle, composed
of wave-rounded, polished pebbles was clean. The sand
glittered like particles of glass, and even the debris that was
piled along high-water mark looked cleaner, and in a peculiar
way more exciting than that which was left on our own
beach, and that despite that there was nothing among it
comparable in value or interest with the planks and other
things washed up by that memorable storm.

The beach extended well beyond high-water mark to
what was virtually dry land, although this would be awash
with a really rough sea. Here lay the sand. Above it the cliff
was not sheer. It was broken and fissured irregularly with
ragged ledges and overhanging terraces on which clumps
of heather and beds of sea-pink had found root hold, and the
lowermost of these terraces projected over a corner of the
beach towards a fallen rock to form a sort of cave big
enough to stand up in. Beyond this there was a definite
gully in the cliff-face where grass and fresh-water weeds
grew almost all the way down, and although we could not
see water, we knew by the vivid green of the vegetation it
was there.

The place was a sun-trap. Shingle, sand and rock were
almost baking hot to the touch. The sweat poured from us
as we moved about, searching among the high-tide debris
and among the crevices in the rocks for wood, and gathering
stones to build a fireplace with. We did not find the heat
disagreeable, however. We took the precaution of putting
our food, and a precious bottle of milk, in the shade and
comparative cool of the cave, then lit the fire, and scrambled
over the rocks to the gully, where we had no difficulty in
filling our kettle with clean water. We put the kettle on the
fire, then we stripped off our scanty clothes and picked our

way from rock to rock until we found one by the channel with deep water below it. The bottom was shingle and almost white, but from the rock-side fronds of brown oar-weed waved gently, and among them swam shoals of little fishes and prawns, and we could see scarlet anemones and sea-urchins on the rock itself. Dain dived in first. I watched her brown body swoop down through the crystal water, and flatten out over the shingle, then curve up again; then as her head emerged I dived myself, eyes open, so that I saw the bottom the whole way down. Then, turning on the ascent, saw Dain floating above me, her limbs elongated and contorted, and festooned with bubbles that were like strings of pearls. We swam together out to another rock, and dived again, then we swam back along the channel, past the boat, and ashore.

Although we were both well tanned, we had too much respect for the fierce sunshine to loll about the beach naked. We dressed again, and cooked our lunch. We had brought eggs and some cold, boiled, new potatoes, and lettuces. We made an omelette, and fried the potatoes until they were browned. An almost level slab of rock, half with-in the shade of the cave, served us for a table. Instead of a sweet, we finished up with tea and a plum cake Dain had made the day before. And then I fished out from among our gear the manuscript of the last chapter of the book, and while Dain lay stretched on the sand in front of me I read it aloud. I found myself gulping when I came to the last few words, and when I'd done I daren't look at Dain, for she said nothing, and I had an awful terror that her silence meant disappointment. But the next moment her arms were round my neck and she was half-sobbing.

"Oh, it's good, it's good, it's *good*. It's a splendid book. It's so real. It's Bramblewick and Marney, and Henry, and

Mrs. Lunn, all of them real, and all of them fine. *They're* the people! There's no humbug about them. They're brave and strong and kind, and you've *got* them just as they are!"

I had no direct sense of triumph or exultation or pride in what I had done, as I might have had in something I had just made with my hands. Even in that moment I could think of the book quite dispassionately. There was nothing startling in its theme or in the way I had written it. I hadn't propounded any new theory or philosophy of life, or made any "exposure," or tried to put over any propaganda. It was simply a story of fisherfolk absorbed in their daily struggle against the sea and present day economics, and its merit was, I thought, that I had kept myself out of it, that I had let the characters speak for themselves, and weave the tale of their lives. They, not I, had written the book.

And then suddenly I did think of it possessively, as a thing that I had created, that was mine, ours; as something that was valuable, not artistically but commercially, that could be sold, and make money.

"Do you really think it's so good, Dain?" I asked. "Does it *get* you, does it make you want more. Does it make you feel you want to shout out to everybody, ' Read it, buy it '? I mean if you didn't know who'd written it, and you didn't know Bramblewick and Marney and the Fosdycks, would it still get you? Do you think people will be interested in a book about the sea and fishermen?"

Dain's eyes were sparkling.

"Yes," she cried. "Yes. I'm certain of it. Everybody will want to read it. Everybody will want to buy it. How could people help not liking it? It's so real; there's nothing dull about it. It's got everything, adventure and excitement, and there *is* a love interest with Marney and Amy and their baby, even though they're married. And there's plenty of humour too, and every one likes books about the sea. It's a *grand* book!"

It was a grand lobster-pot I'd invented, I might have thought then. As a practical device it had been pretty well perfect. It fished better than an ordinary pot. It was as cheap to make. It was indestructible. Every lobster fisherman in the country, throughout the world, could not help but appreciate its value, could not afford *not* to use it. It ought to have sold by the million. It hadn't sold at all. But a book was a very different proposition to a lobster-pot, and for a moment my enthusiasm soared without restraint.

"God!" I cried. "You're right, it *ought* to go. It ought to sell in thousands."

I went on soaring.

"Have you thought what a marvellous film it would make? Imagine someone actually doing it at Bramblewick, getting the Lunns and the Fosdycks to take part in it. Can't you *see* it as a film? Imagine a shot of the Lunns hauling pots off Low Batts with a gale blowing and the coble standing up almost on end, and the seas washing over her, and both cobles racing for the Landing and coming through the surf. Think of the effects you could get in the old village and on the shore. The dock, the alleyways, the scaurs, the gulls. And it wouldn't be just an 'interest' film. It would have a story in it, like the book, but it would all be real!"

"It would be marvellous!" Dain cried breathlessly.

"It would make history, if it was done properly! It would be a terrific success. And apart from what the film company would pay us for the rights, people who saw the film would want to buy the book. We'd make pots of money. We'd be rich! We'd be able to do anything we wanted."

For a moment Dain looked thoughtfully out to sea, then she said:

"It would be nice, not being poor, but I don't think I'd like us to be very rich. I think it would spoil everything being able to buy just what you wanted. You wouldn't know what you did want then, there'd be so much to choose from. I shouldn't like a life much different to this. I couldn't imagine anything much more thrilling than what we're doing to-day; the boat and the sea and the sunshine, and having a meal like we've had, and bathing and fishing, and then going back to our own place, and Choo-i waiting for us. Only I do want a baby, and if we had more money I'd want more than one. I'd like three. I'd like six if I knew we could really afford to. How long will it be before we do get some money for the book?"

I shot back to earth.

"Good Lord, we mustn't *think* about a baby yet, let alone a family of them. It may be months before we get anything. It's got to be typed yet. Then we've got to decide on a publisher, and submit it, and he may keep us waiting weeks before he takes it. And he may not take it. We may have to try several. And when it is taken, I expect we'll get so much down as royalty in advance, but we'll be lucky if we get more than twenty-five pounds. Of course, as soon as it's published and it begins to sell we'll get some more, bound to."

"And how long will it be before it is published?"

"I don't know. That might be months too, but usually there's a clause in your contract that they do it within six months, provided there's no industrial strikes, or wars, or unforeseen calamities. But naturally a publisher brings out a book as soon as he can, for he's as anxious as the author to see if it's going to be a success. Call it six months anyway."

"Well," said Dain, "it takes longer than that to have a baby, and it doesn't cost anything until it's born. Good heavens, if we're to wait until the book's out before we decide to have one, that means nearly a year on top of that. What a waste of time!"

"Yes. But we've simply got to go carefully," I protested. "I've got all those debts to pay off. Before we start a family we want to see things reasonably straight ahead."

Again Dain was silent. Then she said:

"Oh, well, it's a silly thing to quarrel about. And anyway, it's stupid to work out having babies to plan, like putting things in a garden, deciding to have some cabbages to grow up there, and other vegetables somewhere else, so that everything will be ready just when you want it. Babies ought just to happen. It's a *grand* book. Everything's wonderful. Come on, let's fish. Have you forgotten we've got some bait?"

Leaving our things ashore we got into the boat, and pulling out to deeper water began to fish for pollack. We used the same technique that had given us the bass, a long cast with a light ledger, and keeping just enough way on the boat for the bait to clear the bottom. We had caught pollack before, but never bigger than a couple of pounds in weight, and we got very excited when Dain hooked the first fish, for it was very heavy. I stood by with a gaff, while she hauled it towards the boat. We soon caught sight of it through the clear water, and saw at once that it wasn't a pollack at all but a big wrasse, and in spite of its weight it swam so sluggishly that I got it over the gunwale without hurting it with the gaff. I knew by experience that wrasse was no good for food, but it was a thrilling thing to look at: its back purple and its belly silver-white, and its sides barred and mottled with shades of green and yellow and red, like the clouds of a spectacular sunset. We removed the hook very carefully from its mouth and let it go, watching it swim at first rather uncertainly, and then with assurance, down home, until it was just a grey dissolving shadow. We baited again and went on fishing.

But we did not pursue that occupation with the same serious zest as usual. We didn't much care whether we caught any fish or not. Quickly we were becoming intoxicated, with the sunshine, with the powerfully-ozonised air, with the colours of the sea and the cliffs and the sky, with the enchanting beauty that surrounded us. Although the water was deep we were still shorewards of the actual point of the headland, and the coast towards St. Jude and the west was hidden. But to the east stretched a line of rugged cliffs, topped with heath and pastures and cultivated fields which in the far distance all merged into a blue that was hardly distinguishable from that of the joining sea and sky. Far out, to the south, the sea in patches was now a darker blue verging on purple. The smoke from a steamer moving east along the horizon was moving with it instead of trailing out astern, indicating a following westerly wind. Yet the little puffy clouds seemed to hang static in the sky, and close in the water was still like glass.

That water, like the sight of wine to a half-tipsy man, was irresistible. After we had caught our first pollack (it was so small that we let it go), we stripped again and dived in from the boat, and abandoning her swam in to the nearest rock of the headland cliff, and hauled ourselves out into the sunshine again. We were drunk and quite hilarious.

We shouted and laughed, and pretended we were seals come out to bask, and we tried waddling over the weedy rock, using our hands as flippers, and we tumbled into the water again and had a race back to the boat. We went on fishing aimlessly and unsuccessfully, and not caring. The heat soon drove us into the water again. We dived and swam, and laughed so much that in the end we were too exhausted to climb back into the boat, so we each took a side, and paddling with our legs moved her slowly back to the beach. Then we threw ourselves down on the hot sand and went to sleep instantly, like drunkards.

We were awakened by the loud crying of gulls. We were astonished to find that the sun had sunk behind the headland. That the tide was nearly high, and our boat was riding quite a distance from its edge.

"Good Lord," I said, "we must have slept for hours. It must be nearly nine o'clock. We ought to be getting back."

"Must we?" Dain answered, still a little sleepily. "It's so lovely here. How stupid of us to have gone to sleep like that. What a waste of time! What are the gulls making such a fuss about?"

The gulls, there were hundreds of them, were circling low over the water about a hundred yards out beyond the boat but inside the headland. We jumped up.

"It must be a shoal of mackerel," I shouted.

"Mackerel? Can't we catch them? Come on, let's get into the boat and try."

It was an exciting spectacle, one well calculated to send us tipsy again, for mackerel are summer fish, and hitherto we had never encountered them. And there was no mistaking that it was mackerel. For the water over which the gulls were circling was suddenly stirred and broken as though a spout of torrential rain was falling, and we could hear the very hiss and spatter of it. But at the same time I observed something which instantly checked my own rising excitement. Although the sun was behind the headland it had not set, and was still shining on the sea clear of the point; and there out of the lee of the land the sea itself was no longer calm, but choppy and flecked with wind. It was not a storm. The sky was cloudless. It was the sort of wind you could expect on a summer's day, but it was from the west, directly against our course for home. Already it looked strong. It might freshen, it might back to the south-west, in which case we'd be on a lee-shore, in a boat, which, even if she'd been new and sound would have been little better than a canoe. And she was neither.

"Come on," I said very soberly. "Let's get packed up and be off for home. Look at the wind outside. We've got nearly three miles to pull against that."

"But can't we fish first?" Dain protested. "We can't pass a shoal of mackerel and not try. There can't be very much wind. There's not a breath here. It doesn't matter how late we are getting back. Just let's have a few minutes. Look at them. They're jumping right out of the water."

I tried not to think of the fish as we hurriedly packed up, hauled the boat ashore, and got in; yet, as the shoal lay just ahead of us, and the faster you pull for mackerel the better, I quickly changed the hook on the pollack line for a spinner, and Dain began to pay it out as soon as I got under way, pulling my hardest for the point. It really was hard to believe that the wind was waiting for us round the corner. Here there was not a breath, and the cliff exuded a heat that was almost as powerful as that of the clear sun. The gulls screaming loudly sheared off as we approached the shoal, but without looking ahead I could hear the mackerel breaking water (they were themselves pursuing a shoal of sardines or herring fry) and Dain who was sitting in the stern and looking ahead gave an excited shout.

"Pull your left oar a bit—nearer to the rocks. We're right into them. Look, you can see them in the water. Thousands of them."

I had seen shoals of mackerel many times before, but I was no less thrilled for all that by the sight of those fish moving past the boat in an almost solid mass, which broke and flashed like an explosion under the impact of my oars. The water was so clear that you could see the huge eyes and the gaping mouths of individual fish, their vibrating fins, the lovely markings of their bodies. Yet I was not so thrilled that I forgot wind, even when Dain almost screamed:

"I've got one. *I've got one.*"

I went on pulling. She had stood up, and was looking astern, hauling in, and I saw the line cutting through the water, zigzagging in the manner of mackerel.

"Careful of it. Careful. Swing it right inside."

I saw its silver belly flash in our wake. Then Dain gave a brokenhearted shout.

"Oh, it's gone. I've lost it. Oh, damn!"

"Never mind," I shouted. "Let your line go again. You'll soon have another."

She paid out the line and stood upright, watching it, ready to check it the moment another took hold. But there was no sign of another, and Dain suddenly turned and yelled at me in an exasperated voice:

"Need you go so fast. We're getting away from them. Look, they're all behind us now. Surely a minute or two won't make any difference. We may never get a chance like this again. Just let's have one turn back!"

I took a glance over my shoulder towards the point,

now not more than a hundred yards away, and saw a short steep wave break on an outlying rock and its spray sweep to leeward, and at the same time I felt the first eddying puff of wind. I hardened my heart.

"It's no good. We daren't risk it. Even as it is we're going to have a pretty tough fight. Look at that rock ahead. But keep on fishing. You may get one yet."

We were still within the lee of the land. The puffs of wind were only lightly marking the surface, but I could feel a deeper movement, a queer sort of eddying swell as we neared the actual point. The puffs became gusts, and suddenly it was as though we had stepped out of a heated room into the air of an autumnal night. We felt the real wind.

"It's no use," I said. "You'd better haul in now."

Dain at last had grasped the seriousness of the occasion, and without a word she hauled in and stowed the line. We had reached the point, but the outlying rocks gave us shelter for another twenty yards or so. And then, as I reached the last of them and turned, a wave seemed to swing out from behind it and pounce upon us, and with such force that if I hadn't got the boat's head to it we'd have filled for certain. As it was we got the spray only, and it did nothing but drench me to the skin. It was a steady wind that was blowing, nothing more; a cool west wind which people on shore would no doubt have found a pleasant relief to the day's sweltering heat, and yachtsmen probably would have thought not quite strong enough. The waves were not rollers. But they were steep and short, and their tops wind-broken, and I'd no sooner set my back to the job than I discovered that I was fighting not only them and the wind, but a powerful tidal current. We had only a single pair of oars. It would have been no help if we pulled one each, for

it would have been quite impossible to adjust our strength
to prevent the boat swinging, and everything depended on
keeping her head on. Yet I made some progress. We were
more than abreast of the point, the final rocks of it were
astern, and looking over my shoulder I could see the coast
to St. Jude, and I thought that once we were well clear of
the headland the tide at least would slacken, and the going
would be easier. And at the same time I saw quite a big
wave advancing on us.

"Look out," I yelled. "This one will wet us."

I took a quick stroke of the oars, to give the boat enough
way to ride it, and another more powerful one as we rose and
I felt its force. And it was that final stroke that was our
undoing. I heard a crack, felt the strain on my right arm
instantly relax. I shot backwards over the thwart, and before
I was up again the boat was lying almost broadside in the
wake of the wave with another following. What saved us
from swamping then was luck and nothing else. The blade
of my right oar had broken off like a carrot. I was still
holding the left oar, but I had no time to use it. The crest
of the wave merely splashed over our gunwale and swung
us completely round, so that we were stern on to the next
and travelling with it, and before the boat had time to swing
again Dain and I had changed places, and I had got the single
oar in the stern rowlock, and was sculling like mad back to
the point, with the wind and tide and the waves themselves
helping. In two minutes we were in the half lee of the
rocks, and in another minute well behind the point, with
the water smooth and the windless air warmer by contrast
with the seaward air, than it had been even when the sun
was at its zenith.

I stopped sculling. I'd had a scare. Not that we had
been in immediate serious danger. If the boat had filled

we could have swam to the nearest rocks with ease, or we could have swam round the point to where we were now. But it would have been a vastly different thing if that oar, which I might have guessed was rotten, had smashed farther on our journey when we would have had only precipitous cliffs to leeward of us. If the boat had swamped then our chances would have been very slender indeed.

"Dain," I said, "we're a pair of bloody fools. Fancy any one in their senses coming out on a trip like this with only one pair of oars, and those rotten. We ought to be ashamed of ourselves, or at least I ought. Think what might have happened."

I did feel ashamed of myself, but Dain was looking anything but ashamed or perturbed.

"Don't be silly," she said. "It's no use worrying about what might have happened. We're all right. Isn't it gorgeously warm again?" She was silent a moment, then, "What are we going to do? We can't get back home with only one oar, can we, so long as that wind is blowing?"

I looked at the shaft of the broken oar. I had no doubt that I could fix up some sort of a blade for it, out of the driftwood ashore, that would do for calm water. But even with two good oars I was convinced that it would be foolhardy trying to get back until the wind dropped, and there was no telling when that might be. The alternative? I guessed what was in Dain's mind.

"Damn it," I said, "I believe you're quite pleased about it."

She smiled.

"It was horribly cold in that wind. We'd have been frozen before we'd got home." She suddenly looked shorewards to where the gulls were still circling noisily over the water. "Look, the shoal's still there. Can we go fast enough for mackerel, just sculling?"

I know that as the older and more experienced and responsible one of us, I should have been thinking of that wind, and the possibility of it backing south and freshening, and that we might still be in a very awkward fix. But already the warmth, the calm beauty of the cove, was beginning to affect me as it had done before.

"We can try," I said. "Get the line over again, but keep it short."

I sculled in towards the cove, and we'd scarcely got a couple of lengths before Dain hooked a fish, and this time she got it in safely, a lovely mackerel. She had hooked another before she had paid out the line.

"Do have a turn," she shouted when she'd landed it. "I'll scull. We simply must take turns. God, isn't it exciting!"

It was. We might neither of us have caught a fish before, the way we shouted and laughed and tumbled over each other as when we changed places after each fish. The fish themselves seemed to have gone mad. As we got closer in to the channel of the cove, we saw that it was packed tightly with a mass of fry, among which the mackerel were shooting at terrific speed, forcing the little fish up, so that the surface of the water was like a mass of boiling silver. We gave up sculling. I rigged up a couple of lines with bare hooks, and baited them with strips of mackerel skin, and we merely had to throw these overboard for them to be seized; and with a few lulls during which the fish seemed to sulk we went on like this until dusk, when there came a lull long enough for us to realise that we were ravenously hungry. I looked seawards. The wind was still blowing, but although there was a gentle swell in the cove it was just as calm and warm as ever.

"Let's go ashore," said Dain. "Let's make a huge fire and fry some mackerel. Fresh mackerel! Think of it. And tea. What a good job we brought enough milk and bread and things."

"And then what?" I said, trying to be sober.

"Why, then we can catch some more fish, or if they're really gone we can have another bathe, and then we can just go to sleep. It would be no good trying to go home now even if the wind did go down. It will be dark. We can sleep in the cave. I know what. We can get lots of heather and put it in the cave, and lay our oilskins over it. It will be like a spring mattress."

I sculled in to the shore. After all, I thought, with a flash of real sanity, there was nothing else we could do but stay here until the wind had died, and if we hauled the boat up above high-water mark nothing short of a southerly gale would be likely to harm it or us. The tide had just started to ebb, so we hadn't far to haul. There was plenty of wood left in the heap we had gathered. I put on one side a piece of box-wood that would do to repair the oar. Then we got the fire going, and while I split and boned a couple of fish, Dain climbed to one of the cliff-ledges and gathered armfuls of ling. The light of the fire soon made the growing dusk seem like night, so that while we sat on our haunches, cooking the fish, we could see nothing beyond the cliff and the cave and the edge of the beach, on which the harmless swell threw little lines of foam.

The smell of the cooking fish (we grilled them as we had grilled the codling that wild winter's night in Bramblewick) made our mouths water. We dabbed butter on them, and we ate them ravenously and in silence. Then we made tea, and with the mugs in our hands sat closer to the fire again, looking into the flames. The shoal must have gone, for the gulls were silent. The only sounds were the cracking and spluttering of the fire, the breaking of the surf, and that queer breathing sound that a slow swell makes when it moves over weed and rocks. I watched Dain, with her elbows resting on her bare sunburnt knees, move her mug to her lips and drink. I saw the firelight gleaming on her wet black hair and in her eyes, and I said quietly:

"What are you thinking about?"

She laughed.

"I'm not thinking. Not really. I'm just feeling. I'm feeling that blazing sunshine, and the slap of the water on my face when we dived, and the kick of those mackerel at the end of the line. . . . And I'm feeling the boat swaying up and down when we got round the point. And I'm feeling the heat from the fire, and I'm feeling I've had just what I wanted to eat, and that there was nothing I wanted more than some tea, and I've got it. And I'm feeling gorgeously tired, but not a bit sleepy, and that I'd like to have another swim but not just yet. I'm feeling *good*. . . . Don't you feel good? Or are you still worrying about the wind and the oar. Or are you thinking about all the debts we've got to pay, or the Fosdycks, or your old lobster-pot, or the book? . . . Oh, it's a grand book—it's a grand book. You ought to feel good, to think it's finished, and that it's going to be a terrific success. What *are* you thinking about?"

I did not look at Dain at that moment. I reached my hand round for the shaft of the oar, and the piece of wood, and I laid them together to see whether I could make them fit, then still looking into the fire, I said:

"I'm not thinking either. I'm not worrying about the

wind or the oar, or the Fosdycks, or my past or future life. I'm not thinking about the book. I'm *not* thinking. I just know that I'm alive, that *we're* alive. That——"

I looked at Dain. Our eyes met. I threw away the oar and I said:

"Dain, I'm drunk—with too much sun, and too much sea, and too much joy. I'm past thinking, past caring!"

And she said.

"What *is* there to care about, except love?"

9

We got back all right, for the sea was dead smooth again next morning. The weather had settled into a fine hot spell. But there was no more holidaying for us. We borrowed a typewriter from Charley, bought a packet of paper and carbon paper, and set to on the terrible task of typing the book. The machine was a very old one. You had to thump the keys very hard to make a legible impression on the paper. In spite of the liberal oiling we gave it, it had a habit of sticking, and then slipping a dozen spaces or more. The paton was worn, so that as you got down to the bottom of a page, the spaces between the lines increased on one side like a fan. The only way to stop this was to hang on to the spacing device with one hand while you pressed the keys with the other. Neither of us was expert at the job. We did it in turns, a page each, which the other dictated, and we began first thing in the morning, and stuck at it until dusk, with breaks only for meals and swift shopping trips to Porthkerris, and to collect animals.

My opinion of the book suffered a gradual deterioration during this back-breaking and exasperating task of transcribing it into a legible script. Sentences that I had thought smooth and good became disjointed and almost meaningless. The design was no longer compact and balanced, and passages which, when I'd written them, and read them out aloud, had seemed so lively were slow and dull. Our tempers got frayed. Dain was a shocking speller, and she seemed completely ignorant of the art of punctuation. Sometimes when she was dictating, she would read a sentence in such a way that it completely altered its meaning, and this infuriated me, and I would accuse her of having been insincere in her praise when I'd first read that passage, as obviously she couldn't have been listening. Time after time (and we both erred in this respect) we'd come to the end of a page and discover that we'd put the carbon in the wrong way round, so that it all had to be done again; and on an occasion when I found I had done exactly the same thing with the "repeat," I nearly flung the typewriter out of the window. But we stuck at it, and at last, in a session which continued through an entire night to broad daylight, the job was done.

We had bought a copy of one of the two famous Sunday newspapers which specialise on book reviewing and carry the advertisements of publishers, and I had decided that the best firm to send the book to was that of Mr. Kaufman. True, there were several other publishers who, judging by their statements, seemed very successful. All were advertising books that were "best sellers." One of them, Mr. Parker, had a very large list of titles. Every one had gone into four or five "printings," and was described either as "an established success" or an "immediate success" or "in very great demand." But most of them were detective or adventure stories, and although it looked as though Mr. Parker could *sell* books, and would be a very good man to do business with, I didn't strongly fancy him for ours. He was "lowbrow." I was far more tempted by the advertisements of Mr. Mackenzie. One of them (there were two) contained books by two very distinguished writers whose work I admired, and although there was no indication as to how they were selling, the other advertisement was devoted to a single novel which had been "chosen" by a book society, and it had sold more than 50,000 copies. Both these advertisements were artistically drawn up, and modestly phrased. Mr. Mackenzie was definitely "high-brow." But Mr. Kaufman seemed to run a middle course between "high" and "low." His advertisement was large and bold without being vulgar, and it announced the titles of three books under the convincing top caption of THE THREE OUTSTANDING SUCCESSES OF THE SEASON, and under the lowest title the plain statement NOW IN ITS HUNDREDTH THOUSAND. Apart from this I knew that Mr. Kaufman was supposed to have a genius for spotting new authors, and establishing them at once. This "hundredth thousand" book for example was a hitherto unknown author's first.

Although my original confidence in the book was not restored I felt better when we'd sorted out the top copy pages and pinned them together into a neat little jacket Dain had made. I wrote a letter to Mr. Kaufman which I thought was businesslike and to the point. It would have been bad policy to tell him that I was very hard up, and that my whole future depended upon this book. Publishers had no time for sentiment, and experience had taught me, too, that you are far more likely to do a good deal with a business man if he thinks you're independent than if he thinks you're poor. But I did express a hope that he would be able to give me an early decision. We made a parcel of it, sealed all the knots, and sent it off by registered post from Porthkerris, at the same time as we posted a packet of a hundred wood-lice the firm had specially requested.

"How long do you think it *will* be before we hear?" Dain asked as we rowed home.

"We mustn't reckon on hearing before a month," I said. "You see, the publisher doesn't read it himself first. It goes to a reader, and he makes a report on it, and if it's favourable then it may go to another reader. Then the man himself may read it, but it still doesn't follow that even if he likes it that he'll take it straight off. And remember that a man like Mr. Kaufman will get as many as a hundred books sent to him in one week. No. We've got to be prepared to wait."

"Yes. I suppose we have. But what a waste of time. Surely the man would only have to read one chapter of it to know how good it is, and to write you bang off saying he wants it, for fear some other publisher might take it. . . . And then another six months before it's published!"

"Perhaps even longer," I said, not too cheerfully.

Dain laughed.

"Well, it would be funny if the book was published and we had our baby on the same day, wouldn't it."

"I don't know. I'm not so certain about that."

"Well, I'm pretty certain now I'm going to have one."

I ought to have been thrilled (although there was no reason why I should have been surprised) by that remark, but I was not, just then. I had a sudden horrible foreboding. My God, I thought, supposing that we had both completely overrated the virtues of the book, that instead of being snapped up by Mr. Kaufman, it was turned down, not only by him, but by all of them, highbrow, middlebrow and lowbrow, that it proved to be just another patent lobster pot! I felt myself go hot and cold. What if we did not make a farthing out of it! What if my creditors got on my trail now? What if our only source of income, the live animal job, dried up. With only ourselves to think about, we could escape and fend for ourselves somehow. But with a baby we'd be in a terrible fix. What if instead of a single baby Dain produced two, or even three. There was no reason, except the law of averages, why she should have only one. The full implications of what we had let ourselves in for

momentarily staggered me. I nearly drove the boat full
tilt into the hulk of the *Amelia Hoskins*.

"Dain," I said, "what bloody lunatics we are. Why
didn't we wait until we were certain about the book, and
our having some money?"

"But I *am* certain about the book." Dain laughed.
"Absolutely. We're going to have just as much money as
we want. Everything's been wonderful so far, hasn't it?
Why should our luck change? Wasn't it luck finding the
hut, to start with, and Choo-i washing up like that, and our
getting that job. And haven't we been lucky about the
Fosdycks, coming so near to us and yet not finding us out?
Look at them, they must be going for a picnic up the Pol, or
to call on some of those other ships. Isn't it just marvellous
how they keep out of our way?"

My spirits began to rise again. Yes, by jove, we had been
lucky, and really there was no reason why we shouldn't
continue so. The Fosdycks (Grab was in a tropical white
duck suit with a panama hat, and his wife was wearing a
summer frock) were moving up the Pol estuary, well out of
dangerous range. They looked so very benign, yet what a
fright Grab had given me when I had first seen him and
when he and his wife had made their mysterious call. No, it
was no use meeting troubles half-way. The book *was* good.
We would sell it, and make money out of it. As for the baby,
the chances of twins or triplets were very remote indeed, and
it *was* thrilling we were going to have one.

We had fixed a letter slot in the back door, for the postman would use the flimsiest excuse for engaging us in
conversation, and he never had anything interesting to say.
It was a week later, and we were at breakfast, when we saw
him coming down the hill in a very leisurely fashion,
stopping every now and then to admire the view, or perhaps

the aspect of our garden. I was expecting the usual letter and postal order from the firm, but certainly nothing from Mr. Kaufman, and I laughed when Dain said:

"I wonder if he's got any real news for us. About the book. I bet anything he has."

"If he has, it will be good news then. He certainly hasn't got a parcel with him. Don't be daft. We can't possibly hear anything inside a fortnight. It's just our postal order for the wood-lice."

But my heart had started to beat quicker, as still taking his time the postman moved out of sight round the end of the hut. We heard his footsteps on the paving. Then they stopped, and there was a long pause before we heard him open the "door" of the slot, and then the sound of a letter dropping on the floor of the lobby. He gave two diabolically loud raps that brought my heart into my mouth. Then Dain whispered:

"There's two letters—I'm certain by the sound."

"Well, go and get the blasted things," I whispered hoarsely. "No. Wait till he's gone. Don't be a fool. I *know* it can't be anything from the publisher yet. What's the use of getting excited!"

We waited foolishly until the postman was in sight again, moving up the hill, then Dain rushed to the lobby. I took a drink of tea, but I could scarcely swallow it, for Dain was rushing back, crying:

"There *are* two letters. Yes. One of them *is* from the publisher. It's got his name on the envelope. Open it— quick—quick!"

She gave it to me. I looked on the flap, and sure enough it bore the name of Mr. Kaufman. But I daren't open it. I laid it on the table.

"For God's sake," I said, "don't let's get excited. It's

quite impossible for him to have made a decision yet. It's no good getting worked up about it. I know what it will be. It'll just be a receipt for the manuscript. That's what it is, just like when you order something by post from a big London store. You know, 'We are in receipt of your esteemed order, and remittance, and assure you——'"

"Oh, don't be so silly. You haven't sent the man any money, and if that's all it is, there's no need to be afraid of opening it."

"Well, you open it then."

"No. It's addressed to you. You open it. Oh, God, *do* be quick. I'm just mad with excitement."

I took another gulp of tea, and trembling all over I opened the letter, and read it in one glance. It said that Mr. Kaufman thanked me for submitting my book to him, but that he regretted that its subject matter was such as to make it unsuitable for his lists. And there was a postscript which said that as I had not included stamps for return postage, it was presumed that I would call personally for the manuscript. If not they would be glad to post it to any other publisher for me on receipt of stamps. It was signed by a secretary.

I did not read it aloud, but Dain must have known by my face that it was bad news. She put her arms round my shoulder. I gave her the letter to read, then she cried in fury:

"Oh, what a swine the man must be to write a letter like that. It's beastly, it's beastly! It's mean, horrible. Presumes you'll be calling for the manuscript! In a Rolls-Royce, I suppose. What a fool he must be. He can't have even read a bit of it, or he couldn't have helped not taking it, or at least he wouldn't have been so mean. Fancy bothering about a few penny stamps. I'm glad he hasn't taken it. He'll be sorry when someone else does, and it becomes a huge success. Let's keep the letter and send it to him when it does!"

I felt angry myself, but below that was an awful fear. Mr. Kaufman was not a fool. No publisher would turn down a book by an unknown author so quickly without good reason, and that reason was clearly stated, the subject was unsuitable. He, and presumably the readers he catered for, did not want books whose subject was the doings of inshore fishermen. And yet this would not have been a positive bar if my book had possessed an unusual literary quality. Mr. Kaufman, or one of his readers, must have read some of it. Obviously they had not found this quality. Obviously it was not there to find. I felt profoundly discouraged, and very badly frightened. If Mr. Kaufman had decided so quickly the book was no good, what hope was there of finding a publisher who would decide otherwise?

Mechanically I opened the other letter that had come. The sight of the expected postal order gave me only a vague and momentary reassurance, for there was an enclosing letter, and this too, as though my eyes had become specially sharpened for the perception of bad news, I read at a glance.

"My God!" I gasped. "My God!"

"Whatever's the matter now?"

"The firm. . . . They don't want any more animals till after the holidays, till autumn. . . . My God!"

We sat in silence for a while, both of us completely staggered, and Choo-i, taking advantage of the occasion, leapt on to the table, and helped herself to some milk. Then suddenly Dain cried:

"Oh, what does it matter! What does it matter? We're not beaten just because one silly publisher thinks the book's not suitable for him. Suitable—I like *that*. Just as though the book was a pair of shoes or a hat. It's a grand book. I just *know* it is, and nothing can stop it being a success. He's not the only publisher in the world. What about the other two we thought of. Let's send it off to one of them at once. There's that one who does the adventure books. Ours is adventure all right. Think of that bit where they're shooting pots and the gale comes on. That's adventure. That's thrill for you. It's *all* thrill and adventure. Don't let's wait for the first copy to come back. Let's send the stamps for it, of course, the mean beast, but let's post the other copy to the adventure book man, and put some stamps in with it, so as not to run any risk of annoying him, but I'm certain he'll never use them. Come on, let's get it packed up at once and go and post it."

I shooed Choo-i off the table and took another drink of my tea, which had grown cold. My hopes were rising again slowly on the tide of Dain's optimism. I thought about Mr. Parker. There was something about his advertisements I did not like. Obviously he was appealing to less intelligent tastes than Mr. Kaufman or Mr. Mackenzie. From what I remembered of his books they were not bound or printed very well, and they always had very gaudy pictorial jackets. But you saw them prominently displayed on railway book-stalls, and cheap libraries were full of them, and it was clear that he made large sales. Money, after all, was what we wanted. I had another sudden cold shiver as I glanced at the letter from the firm, and the postal order for fifteen shillings.

"Yes," I said. "We'll have to do something quick or we're going to be in a ghastly hole. Blast the man! He's lost us a precious week, and the only good thing is he didn't keep it a month before turning it down, and that's what the next one will very likely do. We've only got enough to keep us for a week. What on earth are we going to do? What a pity we can't sing or play some sort of instrument, or we might put masks on and go out in the harbour and serenade the yachts and at least make a few coppers. We might even invite people to throw coins into the water, so that we could dive for them like native boys in the tropics."

"How awful if someone threw us half a crown and it sank. No. I've got it. Let's sell fish to them. Let's go to that cove again and catch swarms of mackerel, and just sell them. We ought to get at least twopence each. Then we'd have the excitement of catching them as well. Much nicer than catching cockroaches or beetles."

"Don't be daft," I said. "It was only chance we got the mackerel there. We'd not be likely to strike them again. Besides, I think we'd better leave that cove alone at present. But it's an idea. We *could* sell fish."

"We could sell stuff from the garden too. Look at all the lettuces we've got. And the cauliflowers and peas and beans and raspberries."

I glanced through the window at our overstocked garden, at the rows of peas and beans and beds of lettuces, and I said:

"Good Lord! Why didn't we think of it before? We've got pounds worth of stuff we don't want. And flowers. We can start a bum-boat! Just go round hawking things from yacht to yacht. What a pity that big yacht has gone. I should think they'd have bought us out for a start, and they might have invited us on board and given us a cocktail too."

"There's heaps of everything. We ought to do the flowers up in bundles, and we could sell them cheaply, and still make money for really they've cost us nothing. We ought to be able to live all summer on what we sell. But I still think we ought to sell fish too. Come on, let's get the

book packed up, and you write the letter, and then let's go to
Porthkerris and post it off, and then go out and try and get
some mackerel. We needn't go as far as the cove. The best
time for business will be in the evening when the yachts
come in to anchor. Won't it be fun. We can arrange everything in little compartments, and make a lovely show of the
flowers. Shall we have to shout out to the people on board.
'Fresh mackerel' or 'lovely marigolds' or 'fine raspberries.' It *is* going to be fun!"

I was not so certain of that, and although the shock of
the morning's mail had passed, I was still deeply worried
about the book. Was Mr. Parker the right man to send it
to? Or should I send it to Mr. Mackenzie? Was the book
lowbrow, or had it got a literary quality that was more
likely to appeal to the publisher of the two distinguished
writers I admired and also envied? The devil of an idea took
possession of me. Why not send it to both? If Mr. Parker
took a month to turn it down then that would be another
precious loss of time, and we'd be starting all over again.
Perhaps they would both want it. Well, there would be no
harm in that. I was only offering it to them. I might be
in the rather enviable position of trading one against the
other.

The more I thought of it the more sensible it
seemed, and Dain thought it was a more brilliant idea
than the bum-boat. I got out the typewriter and started
my letters, while Dain made a jacket for the carbon copy
of the book.

"It's a lovely morning," she remarked. "Much too
lovely for us to be worried and miserable. I bet the mackerel
are biting like billy-o. We'd best take some food with us,
though, in case we have to land."

There were swarms of fish about that morning, and in

spite of the anxiety that gnawed me we had a very exciting time; for when we got tired of rowing and hauling in mackerel (we caught more than a hundred) we anchored in deep water, and using mackerel for bait caught some very large conger.

With the mackerel on strings of a dozen each, which we were prepared to sell for a shilling, and the well of the boat piled up with the choicest vegetables and bunches of flowers, we slipped down past the Fosdycks' ship to the harbour soon after tea. It was thick with anchored yachts and motor-cruisers, including one almost as big as the stockbroker's, and a magnificent racing schooner whose name was as familiar as that of the royal yacht. On the after-part of this yacht's immaculately-holystoned deck sat a middle-aged gentleman in white flannel trousers and a reefer coat and yachting cap. He had a deeply-lined weather-beaten face with a very dignified and solemn expression, and he was drinking whisky. Separated from him by a distance of about six feet sat a lady in navy blue trousers, and a shirt with a brightly-coloured scarf. She was tall and very slender, with a very beautiful aristocratic face and platinum-tinted hair that was exquisitely waved and curled. She too was drinking whisky, and smoking a cigarette, but the most peculiar thing about them both was that although they were so near they didn't speak to each other. The lady's expression was as solemn as the man's and they were both staring fixedly across the harbour. We rowed very close to them, but it wasn't until I coughed that they glanced at us, and then it seemed as though their eyes were coupled. They just glanced, and instantly looked away again, and their expression was exactly the same. We rowed round the yacht twice, and each time as we passed them the same thing happened, but the third time they looked a bit surprised, although they did not speak or look at each other, and I whispered to Dain:

"Look here, if we keep on doing this they'll begin to think they've got D.T.'s or something. We must look a bit queer, just going round and round. Let's try the motor-yacht."

"But isn't that woman lovely," Dain whispered back. "Do you think she's his wife, and they've had a quarrel. Look at her rings. Do ask them if they want anything. They must have pots of money."

I'd as soon have shouted "fresh fish" or "nice cauli-flowers" in the middle of a coronation ceremony. Indeed there was something quite regal about their appearance, their stony stare, as they sat on their splendid yacht, itself an aristocrat among the other craft that lay in the harbour.

We pulled along to the motor-yacht, which if opulent looked distinctly bourgeois, but evidently her owner or his guests were ashore or in their cabins. Her decks were deserted, and we had rowed round her twice before we suddenly saw, emerging from what was evidently the galley, a fat little man in chef's uniform. He had a red, jolly face, and it looked as though he was too hot, and wanted some air. We were quite close to him, and he saw us at once and gave us a genial smile, which encouraged me to say:

"Good-evening. Hot, isn't it?"

He said in Cockney.

"Bloimy, it ain't 'alf."

He came to the rails and looked down into our boat. And *he* seemed surprised.

"Bloimy," he said. "What's this—a blinkin' carnival? What's all the flowers for, mate? Bloimy, what a lot of flowers!"

"We're selling them," I said with anything but assurance. "Pretty cheap, too. Sixpence a bunch and make your own choice. We're market gardeners, you see. Got all these flowers left over, so we're clearing them cheap. I suppose you've got all the flowers and vegetables you want. But we've got some nice fresh mackerel, only caught this afternoon. Shilling a dozen."

I held up one of the strings of fish. The man grinned.

"Meckerel!" he said. "Meckerel! Don't show me another meckerel. I've been cooking meckerel for breakfast every day this blinkin' trip. Gents we've got on board have been catching meckerel all day long. The blinkin' fridge is full of 'em, and they don't 'alf stink. Don't show me meckerel, mate, for the love of Gawd."

I think the man must have felt sorry for us, for he went on:

"Don't think the boss wants any flowers, mate. He ain't that sort. He and the rest of the gents are ashore playin' gorlf. We're well-stocked with vegetables too. But I'll tell you what," he added quickly. "My old woman wouldn't 'alf mind a bunch of flowers. Give us a couple, lady, you choose them. I'll pack 'em up in a box and send them off to-night with some Cornish cream. She ain't 'alf fond of flowers, and you knows the sort of flowers you gets in London."

Dain selected two of the largest bunches, and added another for luck. The smiling chef took them, and said:

"'Arf a mo. I'll go and get you a bob." He walked back to the galley, and he had no sooner disappeared than out of the tail of my eye I noticed the Fosdycks, not more than a hundred yards away, Grab sculling as usual, and bearing for the racing-yacht. I yelled at the invisible chef:

"All right. We don't want any money for them." And

with that and a hoarse whisper to Dain, "Look out, the Fosdycks coming almost straight for us," I pushed the boat off, and pulled frantically so as to get on the other side of the yacht. I went on pulling then until we got sight of the Fosdycks again, well out of range, then swung round and bore down-harbour.

"Damn and blast them," I said. "They've done us out of our first shilling. We daren't go back there now, anyway. What the devil are they doing?"

It seemed that they were engaged on a round of sight-seeing, with the yachts their main interest, for like us Grab sculled slowly round and round the schooner and then moved towards the motor-yacht.

"I hope to God they don't speak to the cook, or anyway he doesn't speak to them. He must think we're lunatics. Oh damn! Let's go home and think of some less trying way of making money. My nerves won't stand it!"

Dain laughed.

"We're not going to give up yet. They're not going close to the motor-yacht. And there's no sign of the cook. I'm glad he's got his flowers, anyway. He was funny, and nice. Come on, there's dozens of other yachts this end of the harbour. We can dodge the Fosdycks all right."

It was true that Grab was not venturing within dangerous distance of the motor-yacht, and now it seemed a smaller sailing-yacht higher up the harbour was claiming his interest. We carried on more or less in the direction of Porthkerris, picking our way slowly between the anchored craft, hoping that someone would hail us, or at least give us an encouraging look that might lead to business. There was a great variety among the craft. There was a sprinkling of legitimate sailing-yachts of various sizes, and motor cabin cruisers. There were converted fishing luggers and smacks, and a number of "cruisers" which obviously were converted from ship's lifeboats, some professionally done, others obviously the work of amateurs, and probably powered with a motor-car engine. They hailed from ports as distant as Harwich and Liverpool. One of the ex-lifeboats had on board quite a large family, including two little boys, and as we passed near one of them pointed and shouted:

"Hey. Look. There's Robinson Crusoe!" A remark which I supposed was inspired by my beard and my ragged shirt. The parents and the wretched child laughed, but I was feeling far too discouraged and uncomfortable to relish the joke. No one else, however, took any notice of us until I turned the boat homewards, when we had to pass close to a moderate-sized but quite luxurious cabin cruiser. Two middle-aged and sharp-faced women were sitting knitting and talking together on the near-side deck, and I saw one of them nudge the other as we drew near, and they both stared hard.

"Shall we try them?" I whispered to Dain.

"Yes, do," she answered, adding rather unnecessarily, "We haven't sold anything yet."

"Then, you do the selling this time," I whispered grimly. "I've had enough."

We stopped and the women still stared. Dain said in very businesslike tones:

"Good-evening. Do you want to buy any fresh mackerel or vegetables. We've got some very nice cos lettuces and cauliflowers, and peas and runner beans. Straight out of our own garden and just picked a few minutes ago. The flowers are very cheap. Only sixpence a large bunch."

One of the women, her face was sharper than the other's,

looked at Dain and then greedily at the vegetables. Her voice was sharper than her face.

"I don't think sixpence is very cheap for a bunch of common garden flowers at this time of the year. How much are the cauliflowers?"

I gave Dain a nudge. "Say sixpence for the big ones," I whispered. "Mean devil."

"The very large ones are sixpence," Dain said sweetly.

"Everything seems to be sixpence," the woman snapped. "This is Cornwall, remember, not London. Sixpence is a ridiculous price. They're not worth a penny more than tuppence."

I was amazed at Dain's forbearance. She picked out the smallest cauliflower, it had a head at least eight inches across, and pushed it on to the deck.

"You can have that for threepence. Really we can't afford to grow them for less. Would you care for some lettuces? Shall we show you the mackerel? They're really very nice ones. Only sixpence for a dozen?"

"Thank you, but my husband, who happens to be the owner of this boat, catches all the fish we require. He's out fishing in our dinghy now, as a matter of fact. I'd like some lettuces, if they're not very expensive. Really, vegetables ought to be very cheap in this part of the world."

I lost my temper, for again I had caught sight of the Fosdycks well out of range, but bearing definitely down-harbour. The woman was already reaching out a sixpence to Dain.

"They *are*," I said, taking hold of two more cauliflowers and a huge bunch of lettuces and throwing them on to the deck. "You can have all these for sixpence. And a bunch of common garden flowers. Two if you like," I added, throwing them up. "Hang on to that sixpence," I muttered,

as before the women had time to recover from their astonishment I swung the boat out again, and then pulled across the
yacht's bows for the Porthkerris shore. I was too angry to
speak, and Dain was silent until I had put a dozen lengths
between us and the yacht. Then she said:

"What dreadful people. How awful to have to serve in a
shop and be bullied like that, and have to be polite too.
Never mind. We've made sixpence. It's mine, by the way.
I had to be polite to them. You were only rude. Do you
know what I'm going to do with it? Next time we go into
St. Jude, I'm going to buy an ounce of lovely blue wool, and
I'm going to start knitting our son a real fisherman's
guernsey, same pattern as the Lunns', cable and diamonds.
Won't he look grand!"

I was incapable at that moment of envisaging such a
spectacle as a child of mine, not only born but big enough to
be clad in such a garment, for I was thinking hard and
rather gloomily of the nearer future. Bum-boating was
obviously a failure. What the devil could we do to make
some cash? We had passed the last of the yachts. I was
rowing steadily for home, thankful at least that there'd be
no need to creep with heads averted past the steamer, for
the Fosdycks now were well down-harbour.

"We're not going home?" said Dain. "Are we? What
are we going to do with all the vegetables and the fish?
There's far more than we can eat ourselves in a week. Why
not call on Joe and Charley May and ask them if they'd like
some?"

"No, by jove!" I said. "I half-promised Charley I'd pay
some more off his account this week. I don't think I could
face him. Besides, the Fosdycks are down Porthkerris way
now. It would just complete the day's misfortunes if we
ran into them."

I continued pulling for home. We were getting near the ship. Then Dain remarked:

"Wouldn't it be a joke if we parked a lot of fish and things at the foot of the ship's ladder. What a surprise they'd get when they landed home. I say. *Let's!*" she went on eagerly. "It would be a joke. And a nice one too. I bet they don't often get nice fresh vegetables, and we've never noticed them fishing. They couldn't fish for mackerel, anyway, in that boat of theirs. It's too big."

For a moment I was staggered at the suggestion. Then suddenly I saw in it an ironic, paradoxical humour that appealed to me strongly. To avenge ourselves on Grab by showering on him all our unwanted and unsaleable fish and vegetables. Gorgeous!

"By jove, yes! Let's park everything, flowers too. . . . I know. Let's string the mackerel all the way up the ladder hand-ropes, and festoon it with flowers too. And put a cauliflower and a lettuce on every step!"

"No. That's silly," Dain protested. "They'd just know that someone was trying to be funny. I mean really *give* them the things, only we mustn't let them guess who'd done it. After all, they don't know how they've butted in with that cook. It isn't really their fault that they're here and have frightened us so badly——"

"—and made me grow this blasted beard!"

"Well, it's saved quite a lot in razor blades anyway, and it doesn't look bad when it's trimmed. Come on, do let's do it. I'd far rather our stuff was eaten by a real sailor and his wife than one of those horrible women on that yacht."

I felt no philanthropic leanings towards Grab and his wife, but I still saw a certain humour in the idea of us, broke and discouraged, making them a handsome present. They were now a good half-mile away, and still sight-seeing among the yachts. Glancing towards the steamer I observed that there were no rowing-boats near at hand or in the Pill Creek.

"All right," I said, "we'll do it. Give 'em a nice selection. But you'd better leave out the flowers. They'll have seen our garden, and they musn't know they're from us, or we'll have 'em calling again." I hesitated, then added, "It *is* a bit dangerous. Perhaps after all——"

"Oh, what does it matter if they do call. We can hide again. And they'll *not* know."

I made no further protest. With another glance down-harbour at the Fosdycks, I pulled in to the ship's side, to the foot of the companion, and quickly Dain flung a string of fish and a bundle of greens on to the landing grid. Then with a very guilty feeling I pushed off and pulled hard for our cove, from which an hour before we had set out with such high hopes of making money. Choo-i was on the shore to meet us, and she mewed loudly as I ran the boat aground, at the smell and sight of the remaining fish. By that time what kick I'd got out of the semi-practical joke we'd played on the Fosdycks had gone. I was assailed by a dreadful gloom.

"My God, what idiots we are," I said bitterly. "What an idiot I was to imagine that I could take on a job like this, without having a bean in the world. The responsibility of you, and now of a kid. What an idiot I was to imagine I could write a book that would be an instant success, that could have any quality at all. And what a pair of complete idiots we are to end up a day like this by doing what we've just done. I'll bet anything you like we'll have them calling on us to-night, or at any rate first thing to-morrow, and then what will happen? Won't Bramblewick just love hearing we're going to have a baby!"

Dain laughed.

"Oh, don't be so daft. How on earth do you think they'd know, even if we did meet them, and I'm sure we won't. Come on. Stop being gloomy. Look at our lovely little home. Not a sign of all those beastly yachts. We're not idiots to have taken such a place. We're a lot happier than those two old women, for example. How would you like to be married to the one who spoke to us? No wonder her husband goes fishing in the dinghy. It's a grand book. And it is going to be taken, and it *is* going to be a huge success, and we'll have enough money to have not only one but lots of babies. Let's hurry and have supper. Grilled mackerel again! Let's have pancakes for a sweet. There's only one egg left so we'd better share it. I'm glad we left all that stuff at the ship. It shows we're not starving, doesn't it? It shows we've still got something to give away. And besides, I wouldn't be a bit surprised if that's the very thing that changes our luck. Things like that sometimes do, you know. Cast thy bread upon the water."

We started to off-load our fish and vegetables from the boat. I felt a bit better for Dain's homily, and it was pleasant to think we were out of sight of the yachts and that we could have grilled mackerel and pancakes for supper; but I was very bothered about the Fosdycks, and wished to the devil we'd left them alone: and I couldn't see a gleam of real hope about the book or our future.

Indeed, things grew worse instead of better during the following days. The fine spell of weather broke with a southerly gale. It rained almost continuously for three days, then the wind veered to north-west, and, although we had less rain, we had no sunshine, and it was by comparison with the heat wave bitterly cold. We became increasingly vigilant about the Fosdycks. They did not come, but my heart nearly stopped beating one morning, a week after we had left the stuff at the ship, when we heard the sound of a boat actually coming into the cove. We were in the hut, and we bolted both doors before I rushed to the front window to see who it was. My fear was not allayed when I saw that it was Charley May: for he had never been near the place since we had taken it, and there seemed something peculiarly ominous in the way he walked slowly up the path to the front door, which I quietly unlocked. We had carefully avoided the shipyard since the day of our double calamity.

He was as polite and pleasant in his manner as ever, and that in itself increased my apprehension.

"I was just having a pull up the creek," he said, "and I thought I'd look in and see how you were getting on. Hope I'm not bothering you."

There was a cold wind and a steady drizzle, and I could not believe that Charley, normally such a busy and practical-minded man, should choose such a morning for a pleasure excursion. We invited him in.

"My!" he remarked in frank admiration. "You *have* made a difference to the old place and no mistake. I wouldn't have believed it possible. It's as good as a real house. You seem to have stopped the roof leaking too. And what a garden you've got!"

"Would you like a few lettuces or cauliflowers or peas?" I said quickly.

"Why no, thank you very much," Charley answered. "You see, I'm sort of lodging at present with one of my uncles, and he happens to have a bit of a garden, so he has all he wants of vegetables. Thank you very much, all the same. But I wonder you don't sell some of your garden stuff."

I dare not look at Dain when I said, rather tactlessly:

"Oh, I don't suppose it would be worth it, with almost every one round here having gardens of their own."

"No, perhaps not," Charley agreed. "Half the people in Porthkerris have pretty well nothing else to live on just at present. Vegetables and fish!"

"How's business then. No better?"

A really worried look came into Charley's eyes.

"Terrible," he said. "Terrible. The firm hasn't had a job of any sort the last six weeks. There's nothing doing anywhere. I put in a tender for a job the other day, similar to that trawler conversion, only smaller, and I've just heard that the man who wanted it done has gone bankrupt, and that the boat itself is being sold by the Receivers. Work on the clay jetties has practically stopped. There's more men on the dole now than ever. I'd be on it myself if I'd been a workman, and not a supposed employer. And, of course, every one is pressing for cash at the same time. I've got now so that I daren't open the morning's letters."

Apart from the rent we owed the firm about three pounds, and our capital was now standing at just over a pound. Something told me that Charley would never bring himself to a direct request for money, but it was obvious that money was the object of his visit, and his very decency put an unavoidable compulsion on me.

"Look here," I said, "it just happens that we're temporarily short of cash ourselves. Only temporarily, mind you. I'm expecting a pretty useful cheque in the course of the next few weeks, and when I get it I'll be able to pay up in full what I owe the firm. In the meantime, would it be any use if I gave you ten bob on account. I know it's a very small amount, I'll make it more if you want, but I don't want to run ourselves too close."

Charley beamed as though I had offered him a ten-pound note.

"Yes. Of course. I'll be glad to take ten bob. That is, of course, if you can really spare it. I don't want to inconvenience you. It seems we're all pretty well in the same boat, doesn't it? Thank you very much. It's really very kind of you. Mind, I think we've touched the bottom of the slump now. Things are bound to start picking up soon. And there's one thing, yachting and cruising's becoming more popular. In spite of the slump there's more pleasure craft in the harbour this summer than there's ever been. There's a lot of home-made craft, of course, and the people in them don't seem to have much money to spend ashore, but it shows that the idea's catching on. Honestly, if I had a bit of capital, I'd build a couple of cabin cruisers on spec. We'd sell them all right, when money started to move again."

"I'm certain of it," I said, with a rush of optimism that rose absurdly from the fact that Charley had been satisfied to take only half our capital. "I'm certain of it. And if things pan out as we're hoping they will, in the future, we may be wanting a cabin cruiser ourselves. It's a bit too early to say anything definite yet, of course."

That rush of optimism was spent long before Charley pulled out of the cove, and without any pretence of pursuing his pleasure trip turned down-creek for home. I counted the money we had left, and it came to twelve shillings. Dain, who had spent her well-earned sixpence on some wool, and had already started her diminutive guernsey, did not seem very perturbed when I told her. For the last few days, during which it had become increasingly certain that she was going to have a baby, she had been idiotically happy, and all she did now was laugh, and say:

"Well, when we've got so little money as that it doesn't seem very important whether we've got a few shillings more or a few less, and I'm glad you gave Charley something. I *do* like him. And he *did* look so worried, and thankful to get even ten shillings. We're all right. We're better off than thousands of people. It won't be so long before the postman brings us that precious letter saying the book's accepted. What shall we do when it comes? Shall we have another glorious picnic if the weather's fine?"

I did not regret having given Charley the ten shillings. I agreed with Dain that a few shillings one way or another did not make much difference when you are so close to the verge of absolute poverty. But I could not rise to her cheerful faith in the future. I could not rid myself of a growing fear that when news of the book did come, it would be bad. The postman had not been near us since that fatal morning.

Another week passed. The weather continued cold and miserable. We worked hard, in the hut when it was raining, outside on the garden and paths when it wasn't; but neither of us worked with that feverish joy that had possessed us in the early days. The strain of waiting was testing even Dain's high spirits. We practised a more rigid economy in our diet. We cut out bacon and eggs, and for meat allowed ourselves only one sheep's head for the week. We substituted margarine for butter, and made our own bread, although with this the saving was not great, for it was so nice the temptation to eat more was irresistible. We were far from starving, for we had the garden, and plenty of whiting and shellfish; but we were getting sick of the taste of fish and we missed our bacon and eggs dreadfully, and there were times when we'd have gone without breakfast and dinner and tea for a steak or a chop or a plate of roast beef.

The mornings, or rather that hour of the morning during which the postman had usually come, were the greatest strain. Try as we might, we could not keep our eyes off a certain clump of brambles on the ridge of the hill from behind which normally he first emerged on his descent of the path, and time after time we would mistake a wet leaf or a moving branch for the gleam of his cap or cape. But he did not come. At last I could stand the strain no longer, and I wrote letters to both Mr. Parker and Mr. Mackenzie, saying (quite untruthfully) that I did not wish to hurry them in their decision, but that owing to the rather primitive local postal arrangements, I would be glad if, when a decision was made, they would acquaint me of it by telegram as well as by letter. We'd no sooner posted those letters, than of course we regretted it, for instead of watching for the postman only, we now were alert for the coming of a telegraph boy, without knowing whether Porthkerris had a telegraph boy or not.

It was, however, the postman who came, towards the end of that third week. The wind had backed to south-west again that morning. The air was warmer, but it was raining hard. We saw him emerge from the brambles, and then very slowly (not because of the view, but because the path was thick with mud) move down towards the hut; and he wasn't half-way before I saw that he was carrying under his cape a flat brown paper parcel, which I knew could be nothing else but the book. He was late, and we'd had breakfast. I cursed the fact that I had not made the slot in the door big enough for a parcel. He rapped imperiously, and I was obliged to go to the door and open it. He seemed delighted that for once he was able to meet one of us in

person and have a chat. Although I knew that the parcel was
actually in his hand, he pretended to be fumbling in his
bag for it, while he said:

"What weather we be having! What weather! Mud be
almost up to your knees along the footpath. Time something was done about that path. What with mud and
brambles growin' everywhere, wonder anybody can get
along 'e. You be lucky 'avin' a boat to get about in. Have
you been doin' any fishing lately? Be plenty of whiting in
the harbour, but I reckons all mackerel be gone with this
wild weather."

My silence checked him and reminded him of his official
duties.

"I've got a parcel for 'e. From London, I think."

He produced it from under his cape, and rather reluct-
antly it seemed handed it to me, and started to fumble
in his bag again.

"I'll just see if there be anything else," he went on,
examining a bundle of letters. "No, I fancy that be the lot.
Had an idea that there might have been a letter, but I must
have been wrong about that. You ain't got anything to post,
have 'e? Might save 'e a journey, if 'e have."

With that grim-looking parcel in my hand it was not
easy for me to be polite, and close the door quietly. I went
back to Dain and flung the parcel on the table. I had already
observed that the address label bore the name of Mr. Parker.
Dain stared at it, but said nothing.

"Well, that's that," I said bitterly.

We both stared at it. Then at last Dain said quietly:

"*Is* it the book? I suppose it must be. Well, you'd better
open it, and be certain. You don't know for certain it's been
rejected until you've opened it and read what they say about
it. They may——"

"Yes, they *may*," I echoed ironically. "It may not be the book at all. It may be just a great wad of banknotes. Ah, well, we may as well know the worst."

I ripped off the brown paper covering, and revealed the all too familiar jacket Dain had made. And attached to that jacket was not even a letter but a printed slip saying that the firm presented its compliments, and regretted that they were unable to make an offer for the accompanying manuscript.

We were silent for a long time. Then Dain said, with what I knew was a brave effort at cheerfulness:

"Well, there's still the other man. After all, you weren't so very keen on this one taking it. You said he got his books up very cheaply, and made them look like boxes of sweets. I'm absolutely certain it's going to be taken. It doesn't make a bit of difference to what *I* think of the book. And, anyway, hasn't it happened like this with hundreds of writers who have become famous in the end. What about that man called Chatterton or something?"

I laughed ironically.

"Yes, by God. The man who died in a garret. And that's about the only thing he is famous for. Have you ever read anything that man wrote? Do you know what he did write? I'm damned if I do. Besides, I don't want to die in a garret, or an army hut. I don't want fame. I want brass. If this blasted man had taken the book, he'd have given us at least twenty pounds down."

"But the other man will give us just as much if he takes it, won't he?"

"If he *does* take it!"

"He will. He will. So just let's stop being gloomy about it. Let's think about something else. Let's do something. Let's make a new piece of furniture. I know. Let's

start making a cot for the baby. All we need do is to make a
sort of box, and then put legs to it, and put wheels on the
legs, so that we can move it in and out of the hut without
waking him up. He'll want to be in the garden all day, you
know, when the weather's fine. We can make wooden
wheels and make the whole thing lovely. Come on, do let's
start it."

Making a cot for one's own first child, however remote
his birth might be, was certainly a better way of occupying
one's time than moping, and I did my best to cheer up and
not think of the awful hole we were in, and to try and
believe that what had happened to us was just what had
happened to most unknown writers. We hunted round for
some suitable wood, and came across one of the soap boxes
that had washed up in the first storm. Dain, however, was
very contemptuous when I suggested that if we shortened
it and painted it, it would do.

"We don't just want something we can drop him into!
It's got to be a piece of real furniture, better than anything
we've made yet. Really we ought to have some special sort
of wood, and plane it very carefully and fasten it together
with little wooden pegs, and then sandpaper it all and polish
it with wax. It's got to be really lovely. I know where we
might find something for it. Let's go and have a look at
the hulk of Hoskins's old ship. We might find just the very
sort of wood we want."

The gale was blowing straight up the harbour. It was
still raining, but the tide was down, and in sea-boots and
oilskins we made our way to the hulk. The planking on one
half of her was stripped, and the forepart of her decking
was gone, but what had once been the captain's cuddy was
still protected from the weather, and there to Dain's intense
excitement we found two planks which looked as though

they had been locker lids, for they'd had hinges on them. They were stained and dirty and full of nail holes, but when I scraped them with my knife we saw that the wood was sound, and it looked very much like teak. I began to feel quite excited myself, and Dain shrieked when she found a large, four-sheaved block, with its standing parts rotten but its hardwood pulleys sound.

"Just what we want for wheels! We can make tyres for them out of rope. They'll look grand. The whole of his cot will be made out of a ship. Who says our luck's out?"

We took a good look at the steamer before we left the shore. The Fosdycks were not visible. We started cleaning the planks, and as soon as I'd got a bit of one of them planed our hopes that it was teak were confirmed. It was a lovely reddish-brown, hard as iron, and with a surface which would take a high polish.

"We'll not put a single nail in it," said Dain. "We must measure the joints ever so carefully, and if we can't use pegs, then we'll have nothing but brass screws. It's going to look grand."

I was excited while we worked, but all the time there was a lump like lead inside me, and I couldn't stop thinking and worrying about the book, and about what we were going to do to get hold of some money, and while I was glad that Dain was happy she was going to have a baby, I knew that I didn't want one myself unless I could successfully provide for all of us. I had no hope about Mr. Mackenzie. Not once while we worked did I look through the window to see if the telegraph boy was coming. He wouldn't come. To-morrow or the next day, or perhaps in a week, the postman would come, and again he'd have a parcel. That would be the final proof that the book was no good, and that I was no good as a writer. What the devil was I good at, then?

How could I earn a living? I didn't know, and I felt hopeless, and yet I was quite excited again when I finished the first pair of joints in the box part of the cot and the dovetails fitted like a glove.

We had only the soup left from our sheep's head for lunch. We put some more vegetables in it, and we had a bread and margarine pudding for a sweet that used up all our milk, so that we couldn't have any tea after it. We went on working at the cot all afternoon, and then as we had no bread left, or flour, or even any fish, and we were horribly hungry, we decided we'd better go shopping with the remains of our cash, and catch some whiting on the way. Luckily we had some bait. The gale had moderated a little, but it was raining hard as ever. As soon as we had cleared the bluff we saw that the Fosdycks' boat was fast to their ladder, (which for some reason or other, had been shifted from the port to the starboard side), and as we were well-hidden in our oilskins and sou-westers we didn't trouble to strike out for the far shore, but kept to the fairway. The wind was dead against us, and during the gusts I had to strain my hardest at the oars to keep even way on the boat. Undoubtedly it was that, and the fact that I'd made a new pair of very stout oars, and was transmitting all my energy to the rotten gunwales and to the thwart against which my feet were braced, that was the primary cause of our disaster. Yet, beyond a familiar creaking of the gunwales, I had no warning. We were almost dead abreast of the ship's companion ladder, when Dain who was sitting aft, muttered:

"Don't look up at the ship. He's there at the top of the ladder looking down at us."

She meant Grab, of course, and he must have just taken it into his head to have a look out, for he certainly hadn't been in sight before. I kept my head averted, and steered slightly away from the ship; and it was then, at the climax of a stroke, that disaster happened. In other circumstances it might have been quite funny. Certainly the experience was a novel one. There was little noise, no dramatic sundering of wood; but the sides just bent gently outwards and the boat simply split along its keel like a filleted fish, and a double cascade of water gushed upwards between our legs as she gently foundered. I had time to shout to Dain:

"Get your oilskins off."

I had just got my own off as the water swelled round my backside, and I felt myself half-floating. I kicked out, turned over, and the next moment there was no sign of the boat at all, except the oars and the baling tin, which was bobbing up and down in front of Dain's face, so that she looked ridiculously as though she were drinking out of it. We could swim too well for me to have any fears as to our actual safety. We were not more than two hundred yards from the bluff; the tide was flowing and the wind was in our favour. But the steamer was considerably nearer, and with the shock of immersion passed I was already thinking about Grab.

"You're all right, aren't you?" I said to Dain.

"Yes, but I'm damned wet, aren't you? How awful. The boat. Can't we get it somehow, can't we mend it?"

"Never mind the boat. Swim like hell for the bluff. There's Grab."

I hadn't dared to look up at the steamer. I had a hope that before the moment of disaster Grab had turned away. But that hope immediately went, for as we struck out we heard a loud shout.

"Hoy! Hold on there. I'll be to you in a minute."

I cried to Dain, who was slightly ahead of me, swimming a steady breast-stroke:

"Don't look round. Pretend we haven't heard him. He'll give it up when he sees us making for the shore."

But our clothes were impeding our speed, and already I could hear the sound of Grab getting into his boat: and anyway we could have been no match for him bearing down-wind. I was furious. It was bad enough for us to have lost our boat, on top of all that had happened on this fatal day; but to have had it happen under his nose, and now to have him rescue us! And yet it would have been a deeper humiliation if we had tried to ignore him, to continue swimming for the shore while he sculled alongside us, or even ahead of us. He shouted again and I turned, to see him not more than a length behind. I trod water. He forged down on us, swerved so that he passed me, and the next moment I saw him ship his scull, reach over, and seizing her by the shoulders and then by the waist haul Dain on board. There was nothing I could do but swim to the boat-side and submit to the same undignified operation.

So far I had not looked directly at Grab's face. The moment I was on board he had seized the scull again, and he had turned the boat and was sculling back for the ship's ladder, with his back towards us, for I was ahead and Dain amidships, and he was saying:

"It was a bit of luck that. If I hadn't just happened to take a look overboard just then to see if my boat was all right, I'd have never have seen you. I've never seen a boat go down so quick in my life. She seemed to split in two. I'd best take you on board. We've got a fire in the galley, and the missus will soon get you some dry things, and I should think a cup of hot tea wouldn't come amiss."

It was obvious that Grab so far hadn't recognised me,

but just as obvious that he would do so the moment I spoke and he looked me in the face. In the water while we'd been swimming, I'd been angry, courageous enough. Now, listening to that familiar voice at close range, I felt very much as I'd done in those days before I'd learnt to fight, when the sight even of Grab's figure in the distance would make me tremble with hatred and fear. The words were on my lips, but I was incapable of saying that I was grateful to him for coming to our rescue and offering us hospitality, but that we didn't want to go on board his ship but wanted to be landed on our own shore. And the next thing he said was:

"Watch out ahead, and get hold and hang on when I fetch her up. There's a strongish wind."

He brought the head of the boat in to the ladder. I got hold and made the painter fast, absurdly conscious of the fact that in my embarrassment I was tying it with a most unnautical knot. But Grab did not notice the knot. He said something and I turned, and we looked at each other face to face, and I don't think that his surprise was any greater than mine: for it was Grab I was looking at, and yet it wasn't Grab. The features of that face I had detested so were, allowing for age, the same. It was the same, slightly-hooked, domineering nose: the same mouth that used to half-open like a snarling dog's: the same hard blue eyes that used to sneer at me contemptuously; and yet there was nothing in his face that was cruel or bullying or even unkind. It was deeply-lined, weather-beaten, strong, above all dignified, the face of a fine sailor. His mouth for a moment was half-open while he stared at me and I stared at him. Then I said with an extraordinary assurance:

"Hallo, Grab; do you know me?"

He took a stride across the boat, and reached out his hand

to me, and uttered a name that I'd almost forgotten myself.

"Worms! I can't believe it. I'm damned if I can believe it." He held my hand in a grip so hard I felt my bones were breaking, while he stared hard at me. And then he turned and looked at Dain, and I said quickly:

"It's me all right. I spotted you when you first came in, but I'll tell you straight I didn't want you to spot us. We're living here, kind of hiding to tell you the truth. But since you know, there's no point in pretending any more."

There was indeed no point in keeping up the pretence, and with my hand still sore from the undoubtedly sincere handshake, I dared to be franker still.

"Look here. I'll tell you the truth. We *are* in hiding. We've done nothing criminal, but I owe a devil of a lot of money, particularly in Bramblewick, and I've come down here to write a book and get on my feet again. The book's finished and we're waiting now to hear of its being taken by a publisher, when we'll get some money. But we don't want any one here to know who I am, and I don't want any one in Bramblewick to know we're here at present. Can you keep it quiet? It'll only be for a few more weeks."

Grab laughed.

"Quiet? Who should I be saying owt to, in this God-forsaken spot. It's not my business anyway. And there's plenty of folks in debt these days. There's no shame in that. My but you've altered. It's that beard that made me stare hard. I can still hardly believe it, though. Damn it, was it you that left that fish and all those vegetables on our ladder the other day? My missus would have it was you folks. Eh—get on up the ladder. She'll be capped when she knows it was someone from Bramblewick. We'll say nowt to her at first. Do you know my missus? Old Captain Grainger's youngest but one, Elsie. You'll know Captain

Grainger, of course. Him that owns Bramblewick Gas-
works."

In the dramatic happenings of the past few minutes I
had forgotten that Grab had a wife. I said hastily and with
a new alarm:

"Aye, of course I know him, but I'll only know your
wife by sight. Look here, I don't think we'd better come on
board now. If you wouldn't mind just putting us ashore,
I think it would be better. It won't be so easy to explain
things to her bang off. She mightn't understand, and——"

Grab cut me short with a laugh.

"Garn. You've got nowt to be frightened of in Elsie.
Now she might be fed up if I told her I'd had someone from
Bramblewick half on board, and then let 'em go. Get up
that ladder, while I make the boat fast proper."

We climbed up on the deck of the ship, and as we looked
about us, waiting for Grab, Dain squeezed my hand and
whispered:

"Isn't it exciting? Haven't we been fools about him.
I think he's just marvellous. Isn't it thrilling to hear a
Yorkshire accent again?"

"Yes," I whispered back. "But there's his wife yet. Can
you imagine her not wanting to write home to Bramblewick about *this*?"

Grab joined us and then led the way along the deck
towards the galley.

"Walk soft," he said. "Let's give her a real surprise.
By——, she'll be capped all right."

He motioned us to wait outside the galley door while he
opened it and half-stepped in and shouted:

"Eh—Elsie, I've fetched someone to see you."

There was a sound of moving crockery within, and an
embarrassed feminine voice.

"Eh, what? Don't fetch any one in here. I'm so untidy. Take them into the captain's room. What a thing!"

Grab laughed.

"Garn. Never mind how you're looking. It's someone you know. Come on," he whispered to us.

We followed him in. The galley was arranged as a living-room, and Mrs. Fosdyck, with sleeves rolled up and her hands covered with flour, was standing by a table strewn with the apparatus of pastry-making. She was only a few years older than Dain, and she had a very well-shaped pleasant face which bore an undoubted resemblance to the more familiar face of her father. I couldn't help thinking instantly of him and that wretched gas account. She, however, did not recognise either of us in that first embarrassing moment. She just said:

"Why, you're the couple from the bungalow, aren't you. I hope you don't mind my being so untidy. We weren't expecting any visitors yet, although we are later on. That's why I'm busy baking. Can't you give them summat to sit down on, Will? Why, you're wet——"

Grab cut her short with another laugh.

"Eh—do you mean to say you don't know who it *really* is, Elsie? Haven't you spotted *him* yet? Never mind that beard of his. Take a good look at him. Damn it, any one might think you've never heard of a spot called Bramble-wick."

Mrs. Fosdyck stared hard at me, and then harder at Dain, and she went very red when she said to Dain:

"Why—I've seen you before at home. Yes, of course, I know you by sight. But you are the couple from the wood bungalow, aren't you?" She looked at me. "Yes, of course, I know you too. Well, what a surprise. I hardly know what to say!"

"Well, you can say thank you for that fish and all those greens and things they gave us the other day," laughed Grab. "But there's no need to ask 'em a lot of questions yet, while their clothes are dripping wet. Haven't you got summat you can lend that poor lass to put on. Take her into the cabin. Their boat fell to bits just close by the ship, and I hauled 'em out of the water while they were trying to swim ashore. And I can tell you, I was capped when I found out who it was. Me and him's scarcely seen each other since we were lads, and we had a fight down on Bramblewick sands; and by—he didn't half sole me that time. Haven't I ever told you about it, Elsie? But never mind now. Let's get them some dry things."

I saw Mrs. Fosdyck give Dain a quick feminine look which scared me, for I guessed what was flashing through her mind. But the next moment she was fussing Dain off to the cabin. Grab fetched me a pair of trousers and a shirt, and while I changed he made a pot of tea, and went on talking. I felt too bewildered to take it all in. I was more bewildered when Mrs. Fosdyck and Dain returned, and saw Dain in a dark skirt and blouse, for I scarcely recognised her with her legs and arms hidden. The whole experience was more like a dream than reality; and yet it was true I kept telling myself that this morning the book had come back to us, and that during the day we had been making a cot for our very unborn child, that we had set off for Porthkerris to buy some food, and our boat had foundered, and we had been (technically) rescued by a man I had regarded as an enemy and who was now behaving like a life-long friend. Elsie (I could not think of her any longer as "Mrs.") had made Dain sit down in front of the stove. She had pushed her baking apparatus to one side, and she had put bread and butter and jam and cakes and a tin of herrings in tomato on the table, and she was now pouring out the tea.

Apart from that one lightning glance, there was nothing in her manner to suggest any feeling of disapproval against us. The atmosphere apparently was one of complete friendliness, and the sight of a dish of Yorkshire cheesecakes brought a sudden lump in my throat. It was a real Bramblewick tea. And all the time Grab kept on expressing his astonishment and delight at our reunion. He told me that in the years-past, whenever he'd been home from sea, he'd hoped to find me at Bramblewick. It was queer how we'd missed each other, but then that was how it often happened with sailors. For instance there was his young brother Len, master of a Harrison boat. Hadn't seen him for ten years, although three times, in Cardiff and Capetown and Rio, they'd missed each other only by a matter of hours. And to think that if our little boat hadn't sunk like that this morning we might have gone on dodging each other. All of us from Bramblewick, and living within hailing distance of each other. And it was a queerer thing still that soon after Elsie had come down to live on the ship she found there wasn't any baking-powder one day, and she didn't want to go into St. Jude for some, and she'd noticed us and thought we might lend her some, and although he was a bit nervous about it they'd gone ashore and called at the bungalow, but they couldn't make any one hear. Then a day or two after they saw the notice-boards so they decided that we must be a bit standoffish, so they'd best leave us alone. Dain and I exchanged glances when Grab gave us this simple explanation of that alarming visit, but I thought it best not to tell him how we listened fearfully behind the bolted door. I did think, however, that it was time we explained the exact state of affairs to Elsie. I began to do so, rather nervously, for whenever I looked at her she reminded me of her father; but Grab practically took the words from my mouth.

"We've not got to say owt about them being here, Elsie. They want it kept a secret for the time being. You can trust both of us for that. Mum's the word. But I hope you're not going to go on giving us the go-by, now we know. You must be a bit lonely at times, same as we are. Come aboard whenever you like, and we can yarn over old times at Bramblewick. By—do you remember old Slogger, the schoolmaster, and the way he used to hide us. Do you remember Boozer, and Mike Regen? Do you remember the time that ship went ashore at High Batts, loaden with fruit, and how it all washed ashore, and we all played truant from school, and Slogger came out along the shore with a damned great stick laying in to us all, but he didn't get us back to school? Look here, you'd better stay on board and have supper with us."

"Eh?" his wife put in. "Don't forget about the superintendent and his wife coming. It's about time you went for them now."

"Damn it, aye. I'd forgot about him. The superintendent of the company's coming down to-night. Nowt but a lot of nonsense, inspecting the ship and finding fault with everything, just to justify his wages. But I've got to go and meet them, and we've got to put them up to-night. Where were you off to when your boat sank like that?"

"Porthkerris," I said. "We'd run short of milk, bread and butter, and meat and groceries. But if you can put us ashore, we can walk along the path."

"Why, if it's only things like that you want we can let you have plenty," Elsie put in. "We've got no fresh milk, but there's plenty of condensed. Wait a minute, I'll have a look in the larder."

She disappeared through a doorway, and Grab shouted after her:

"Give 'em some of that roast lamb we had for dinner. And a lump of that ship's butter. It's a bit salt, but it tastes all right. Fill a box full of things for 'em. There's plenty of tinned fruit, and sardines, and God knows what. Wait, I'll give you a hand."

"You'd best get yourself ready for off," his wife retorted. "If you miss meeting that man, he's likely enough to get you the sack. I know better than you what they'll need if they've run short."

I had to protest when Elsie returned from the larder with a box cram-full of food and groceries, and started filling another box with loaves and pastries. But she laughed.

"Eh, it's nowt. And think of that fish, and the other things you left us. I said at the time it was you, and I wanted Will to call and thank you proper, but he's shy when it comes to owt like that. I do hope you haven't caught a cold with your wetting. Will you take your wet things, or shall I dry them and you can get them to-morrow."

There was no mistaking Elsie's sincerity and good-nature, but again as we parted I saw her give Dain a quick sidelong look, and I was bothered. Was it possible for her to refrain from making any mention of what had happened when she wrote home, and she a Bramblewick woman? Grab, who had changed into officer's uniform, sculled us ashore. We asked him to wait while we got some things from the garden to take back with him, but he was too afraid of being late at the station, and with more protest-ations of delight at our reunion, he pushed off, and we were alone again on the shore of our cove, with Choo-i alternately rubbing herself against our legs and smelling the two boxes of victuals.

We watched Grab move out of sight round the bluff. Then I said:

"My God! Who would have believed it?"

"It *is* like a dream," said Dain. "To think how we've been dodging them all this time, and hating them so. I just love Grab. I like Elsie too, but she scared me when she took me into the cabin. She simply bombarded me with questions. She wanted to know when and where we were married, and she asked me straight out if I was going to have a baby. I'm just certain she couldn't tell, but it did bother me. I just laughed and said nothing. Yet she does look so kind, and I'm sure we can trust her. Just look at all the things they've given us. Won't we have a feast to-night. Didn't I tell you—cast thy bread upon the waters!"

"Yes," I said rather grimly. "But we've had to cast our boat and ourselves too. Damn it. What are we going to do without a boat?"

It was an unanswerable question, and carrying our boxes we made our way in silence up to the hut: and by the time we reached it a heavy gloom had sunk on me, which was not dispelled when we walked into the living-room, and I caught sight of the package containing the rejected book. The room was untidy and the fire, of course, was out. Uneasily we walked into the big room which was more in a mess, for it was there we had been making the cot. Dain looked at the cot, and said:

"I'd almost forgotten about it. It *is* exciting, you know. But it's a good job he didn't come up with us and see it, or he'd have guessed. Shall we get on with it to-night when we've had supper."

"I suppose so," I said without enthusiasm. "Come on, we'd best get the fire on and have something to eat now."

We went back to the living-room, but my eyes were drawn irresistibly to the book, and suddenly I was overwhelmed with an angry despair. I flung myself down at the table.

"Oh, to hell with lighting the fire!" I cried. "To hell with having a meal. To hell with the Fosdycks and their blasted generosity, and to hell with Bramblewick and everything connected with it, particularly that blasted book. Why did I write the blasted thing. Why did you keep on saying it was grand when you know quite well it's rubbish. Here, I *will* light the fire. Pass me that bloody parcel. Let's stuff it in the stove and have one good bonfire with it."

Dain was angry.

"Don't talk such rubbish. It is a grand book, and you know it is, and it's just silly to go on like that, particularly when our luck's begun to change. Think how awful it would have been if the Fosdycks instead of being friendly had turned out just as you'd imagined. Anyway, you can shave your beard off now, if you want to. That's something. It's no good despairing. What we both want is a good meal, and we're jolly well going to have one too. Mint sauce and roast lamb! We'll have chipped potatoes and runner beans, and they've given us two huge tins of fruit salad and a tin of cream, and a tin of coffee too. We'll have a real dinner. Do hurry up and light the fire. I'm going out to get some beans and mint, and then I'm going to have a bath and put a frock on. And you can have a bath too and shave, and it can all be very exciting!"

Dain, guessing perhaps that my comments on this suggestion would be ironic, did not wait for me to answer.

She rushed up the lobby to the back door. She did not open it. I heard her stop, and then I was startled by a peculiar cry. I jumped up.

"What's the matter?" I shouted.

There was a deadly silence, and then my heart seemed to stop beating, for she shouted:

"A telegram. Addressed to you. It's been pushed through the slot. A telegram—a telegram!"

I stood where I was, my knees shaking, while Dain rushed in towards me holding out a little orange envelope. Then holding it I leaned back against the table for support. I opened it and pulled out the piece of folded paper. Then I took a deep breath, and I said to Dain:

"Don't get excited. Don't get excited. It won't be from the publisher. It'll be from the firm. They'll want some animals, a special lot perhaps, urgently. It can't be about the book. Here for God's sake read it. I daren't. I simply daren't."

"But you've got to. You've got to."

I took another deep breath.

"All right," I said, "I will. But don't expect good news. Don't get excited."

I unfolded the paper. It was upside down and it nearly dropped from my shaking fingers as I turned it the right way and read it.

"My God!" I cried then. "My God. The book. Taken. Fifty pounds advance. Listen. 'Delighted make offer manuscript. Fifty pounds advance royalties. Usual contract. Letter following.—Mackenzie.' Dain, Dain. It's happened. The book's taken. It's going to be published. Fifty pounds. All in one lump. We're rich. We can pay our debts. We can get a new boat. We can get some lino. We can do the big room. We can get some new clothes. We can have roast beef for dinner every day. Read it. Tell me I'm not dreaming."

Dain glanced at the telegram. Then she looked at me, with her eyes filling with tears.

"It's true. It's wonderful. But I knew. I knew all the time. I knew it best of all, though, that day in the cove. When we sat in the sunshine, and you read the last bit, and we were so mad and happy. It was all so thrilling. It's thrilling we're going to have some money. But it's more thrilling to think we've loved each other. That we're going to have a baby. Aren't you thrilled about that? Aren't you thrilled about the cot we've started?"

I was not so certain even then that I really wanted a baby. The idea was still too vague, too abstract and remote. But I felt ecstatically and triumphantly happy and never so completely in love as I took Dain in my arms.

10

FIFTY POUNDS was not a fortune. When the cheque came I decided to defer settling my "Bramblewick" debts, for by doing so I would risk putting the other creditors on my trail; and now that the Fosdycks had proved friendly, it would have been silly to raise that bogey again. Both Elsie's father and the lady who owned my cottage would not be inconvenienced by waiting a little longer. Their account would be settled in full later on. But of course I had to pay Charley.

He and Joe were both overwhelmed when we went down to do this, and to give our order for a new boat, the keel for which Joe sawed out straight away, and set up in his workshop. We wanted it, we explained, large enough for fishing outside the harbour in fair weather, but small enough to be hauled up and down our beach, and on to the deck of the cruiser which we intended to have built later on, when we had the money. She was finished in a week, and we were as pleased with her as though we had built her ourselves. She was twelve feet long, with a good beam, and yet a graceful bow. She was so light the two of us could lift her off the ground: and pulling her out to the harbour mouth on a day when a heavy southerly swell was rolling in, we found her a splendid sea-boat. She cost us ten pounds.

There were many other things to be bought too. We got lino for the living-room and bedroom: plywood to line the walls of the big room, cement for the building of the fireplace. We saw in the papers that the decree had been made "absolute": but as there was no registry office in

St. Jude, we had to go to a town some miles inland to get married. We would have liked Grab and Elsie to have gone with us on this occasion, but of course Grab could not leave the ship. The town (which wasn't very interesting) was on the main railway route to the big seaport of Salmouth. As soon as the job was over we caught a train on to this place. We didn't feel much different, being married, but we were very happy, and rather reckless. There was a sale at one of the big stores. We bought yards of "material" for curtains, and some stuff for Dain to make some garments: and wool to knit things for the baby: and we bought underclothing and shirts and flannel bags. There was a fascinating marine store near the harbour where we bought new oilskins and sea-boots, and a fishing net, and lines and ropes. We spent nearly an hour in Woolworths, and we had a meal at a restaurant and a bottle of wine, and we went to the pictures, and discovered when we got home that we'd spent nearly eight pounds on top of what we'd had to pay for the marriage licence and a tip to the registrar: which was more than a year's rent, but I was not worried. Mr. Mackenzie had sent me the contract for the book. The fifty pounds was only an advance on a royalty of ten per cent on sales. It was a very fair contract. If left me the American and the foreign and film rights, which if the book was a success in England would probably be worth a huge sum of money. The firm wanted an option on my next three books, on more or less similar terms. And Mr. Mackenzie had written a personal letter saying he had read the book himself, and that he was in complete agreement with what his reader had said about it. It was an extremely interesting piece of work and it deserved to have large sales. He proposed to publish it early in the new year.

Why should we worry? In less than six months we

would be rich: and the firm of naturalists had written
asking me to continue supplying them with animals
throughout the autumn and winter. I had shaved my
beard, our clothes were no longer in rags. We had painted
our little boat lifeboat blue, with a red line round her gunwale and ivory white inside, and we felt intensely proud of
her as we rowed among the yachts of the harbour and we
did not envy any of them, because next year most likely
we would have one of our own.

The yachts grew thinner towards the end of the holiday
season. By the second week in September the harbour was
taking on a more normal commercial aspect, although there
were very few cargo steamers coming in for china clay,
and we were told that what was being shipped was merely
from the reserve stores, and that all mining and processing
had practically ceased. There were now no less than twenty
vessels laid-up in the Pol estuary, and it was rumoured
that even more were coming. The slump evidently was
getting worse instead of better. The papers were full of the
most depressing news as to what was happening, not only
in our own country but throughout the world; but I had
never been good at economics and I found it impossible to
comprehend the causes of it all although obviously the
roots of it were in the war. It seemed that even the economists
themselves were not much better off, for they all gave
different explanations, and offered different remedies.
Perhaps the whole business of civilisation had grown too
complicated for any one to understand or control; but it
was terrible to think about: for the poverty in Porthkerris
and St. Jude was very bad, and obviously it was nothing
compared with the poverty of the great industrial areas.

We could not blind ourselves to this. It worried us often
that we had found almost perfect happiness with so little

money, and that other people could not do the same. We were fortunate, first in our temperaments and tastes, in that we could enjoy things that would bore many people stiff; that we liked gardening and fishing; and we had the ability to contrive and make things for our own needs. We had been fortunate in finding a home and land at a rent that was probably a quarter of what an industrial worker would pay for a miserable gardenless cottage in a row in a dirty town: we were fortunate in that I had found a possible profession that made us independent of towns or factories or machines. But these workless and miserable men were tied temperamentally and economically to their machines. Even we could not have lived on the results of our physical toil alone; and it was likely that the majority of the men who were suffering from the economic slump would have shied at changing places with us; and one could not have blamed them, for a man deserves to be able to do his own job, and enjoy life according to his tastes, whether they take him to a pub or the pictures or the countryside.

And we *were* happy. We had an Indian summer, which with a few short interludes of rain, lasted well into October. The days were getting shorter, but they were warm and sunny, and if there was a chill in the evening air, it only made our fireside seem more cheerful and snug. The mackerel had gone, but we got some good bass fishing inside and outside the harbour, and our net was a great success. We caught grey mullet with it actually in our own cove, and occasionally salmon trout, and if the tides were too strong to use the net, and we did not wish to put out to sea, there were always the baby whiting to be caught in the harbour. The bracken and the oaks were turning brown, yellow and red, and the view from the new window we had made in the big room was enchanting when the tide was up and the creek was smooth. There was plenty of work to do in the garden. We weeded and cleaned and dug loads of wrack into the vacant plots. We lifted our "keeping" potatoes, and made a clamp of them, and we planted out the spring greens and broccoli we had sown earlier on. We pruned our fruit bushes, and planted cuttings. We sowed seeds of wallflowers and phlox and iceland poppies and sweet williams, and sweet peas for next year. We made a bonfire of the garden rubbish and it went on smouldering and giving off a delicious scent.

We carried on with our pavings. We cleared the spring, and made a deep, covered cistern for our drinking water; and trained the overflow into little shallow pools which we planted with watercress. At night, or when it rained, we made jam from the last of our raspberries, and scores of jars of bramble jelly. We made curtains for all the windows. We had finished the cot, of course, and we had sand-papered it and polished it with bees-wax until it was as smooth as porcelain: but we had to make a mattress for it; and we contrived it from the kapok stuffing of an old ship's lifebelt Grab gave us, so that we were still preserving the nautical idea!

The building of the fireplace in the big room occupied us many days, and offered many problems, chief of them being the very low eaves of the roof. We began by laying a stone hearth, and when this was done we found that the weight of it was so great that it was making the floor sag, so we had to get under the floor and nail extra joists between the piles that supported it. Then we built walls on the back and sides of the hearth, and formed a "breast" with two iron girders and a steel sheet we lugged up from the beach. We fixed two old bottomless buckets to slant up and towards the wooden wall of the hut from this, and packed them round with concrete, so that they gave us the beginning of our flue; and there ·we were stuck until we conceived the notion of getting outside the hut, and building the chimney stack as an independent unit, and connecting our bucketflue to it. We bought two drain pipes for the actual chimney, but to support them we had to construct a timber framework from the logs of Hoskins's unlucky "slip" and surmount this again with a concrete and stone foundation. From the outside it looked as Heath-Robinsonish as our water works, but inside, when we had pointed the stonework, it looked quite good; and from the anxious moment when we lit the first fire it behaved splendidly in its main function, for it roared away like a furnace, and did not smoke a bit. We had made the grate big enough to burn large logs. When we had finished the plywood linings, and got the curtains up, that room was as cosy as our living-room. We made a table for it, and a divan and an easy-chair, adapted from the seat of a derelict Ford we had found on a country walk one day; and later on we made what was, next to the cot, our best piece of furniture—a chair contrived from the elm slabs of an old-fashioned blacksmith's bellows we bought for a couple of shillings. One slab formed the back of it, the other slab cut in two formed the sides, and to support the cushion we plaited strips of motor inner tubes, which gave it a sensuous buoyancy.

Here, on at least two evenings a week we would entertain Grab Fosdyck and his wife; or rather Grab would entertain us, for he had more than an ordinary gift for yarning. From that first dramatic encounter neither he nor Elsie had given us any reason to doubt their sincerity or their good-will. They did not question us, although even about the baby we were frank enough. Whenever they came they brought us

something in the way of a gift, perhaps a pie, or a bag full
of cheesecakes, or a length of rope or a piece of canvas that
Grab had come across doing his daily round of the ship
and he thought might come in handy; and we reciprocated
with fish, or whatever they cared to have from the garden.
But the basis of our friendship was not material. We had a
common interest in Bramblewick, and apart from this we
liked them both immensely, and we were always excited
when we heard their boat ground on our shore; or as
happened just as often we called at the ship to have supper
with them in the galley.

I was surprised, for the ability and will to succeed of the
Bramblewick sailor, and particularly those of the Fosdyck
family, was traditional, that Grab had not already saved
enough " brass " to make himself financially secure; to hear
him state quite frankly that apart from his present job as
watchman, for which he only got three pounds a week, and
that he now owned the small villa in " Up-Bank " Bramblewick
where he and Elsie lived, he was no better off than we were.
It surprised me even more when he said that although he
had been at sea since he left school at fourteen, and got his
master's ticket at the age of twenty-one he had never yet
had the command of a ship. For the last twenty years he
had been sailing mate. One evening when, having had
supper, we had settled down in front of the big room fire,
I dared to question him on this curious circumstance. Grab
himself was sitting on an upturned box with his long shanks
reaching to the hearth; Dain and Elsie both of them knitting
shared the divan; while I (Grab having refused it) had the
blacksmith's chair at the opposite side of the fire, so that I
could watch his face the whole time. His eyes, which as a
boy I'd thought so cruel, were really grey, with curious
streaks of brown in them, and although they were bright

enough, the whites were bloodshot, and strained. Henry
Lunn's eyes, I remembered, looked like that after a night at
sea in bad weather; and in many other ways Grab reminded
me of Henry, but then a seafaring life undoubtedly tends to
create a pattern, physical as well as of character. Henry
Lunn's mouth was fuller, and would more readily break
into a smile, but the smile in each case was always faintly
ironic, and both had that determined, grim set of jaws and
lips when their mouths were closed. There was a great
strength of character in Grab's face. One felt instinctively
that his natural place was the bridge of a ship in full
command; and I had a further surprise, and a new insight
into the nature of my old enemy, when Elsie took up my
question and said:

"Aye, you might well ask him why he's never sailed
as master. He's too soft and tender-hearted is Will. He's
too backward in coming forward. He'll let any one take a
rise out of him, or over him, which is more important. He
could have been master years ago if he hadn't let himself
be taken advantage of."

Grab laughed.

"Don't talk so daft, Elsie. It's only been luck."

"It wasn't luck when you were offered the *Swallow Beck*!
I know you were offered it, coz father's got shares in the
company, and him and the *Swallow Beck* owners were great
friends, for they went to sea together. You could have got
her, and you could have been in her now, for she's not laid
up yet."

"Aye. I know. And that would have meant taking the
bread fair out of the mouth of poor Jimmy Henderson who'd
been sailing mate of the *Swallow Beck* nigh on ten years in
hope that he'd get her when the old man retired. Poor
Jimmy; who'd lost his ship and his ticket first voyage

he'd gone as skipper, and him just married too. And not his fault either. He'd been on the bridge twenty hours on end and he'd just gone below when she collided. It might have happened to any one."

"Yes. We were all sorry for Jimmy. But it's a pity you weren't married to me then," Elsie retorted. "I could have told they wouldn't have given him the *Swallow Beck* anyway, and that the owners would be mad with you turning it down, and give it to a stranger. . . . And then what about your brother Len? That was another chance you missed. You could have gone mate on the ship he's on now knowing for certain the master was going to leave her at the end of the next voyage, and that you'd drop into his shoes. But you stood by for Len and of course he's been master ever since, and him five years younger than you."

Again Grab laughed.

"It's nowt but luck, I tell you. Len's been lucky, and I'm glad of it, but there's plenty of chaps that's worse off than me. I've been lucky to hang on to a watchman's job, times like this. With that fleet of colliers that's layed up in the river they've only got one navigation officer and an engineer for the lot of them, and I'm standing all right for master's berth on this ship when things start to move again, as they're bound to soon. The old man, of course, was offered my job by the way, but he told me he's had enough of the sea, and that he was going to live as far away from it as he could, somewhere near Birmingham, and that he was going to buy a greengrocery business, and settle down proper. Well, I'm damned if I could do that, until I was old and doddering. I like a spell ashore as well as anybody; but when I've been ashore more than a month, I begin to feel there's summat unnatural going on."

"You're not being very complimentary to me," put in Elsie. "And it's true, you're always itching to be off."

"Aye. But don't forget, that when I get a master's berth I'll have you with me most voyages: and then it'll be you who'll be itching to be ashore. . . . You'll start pining for Bramblewick, as you do now. You'll be worrying as to whether the house roof's leaking, or the village lads have been robbing the garden or throwing stones through the windows, same as we used to do when we were lads. (Do you remember how we used to steal apples and pears, and smash folk's windows?" This in an aside to me.)

Elsie laughed.

"Why, it's true I'm not pining for a life on board ship. What I don't like on board ship is that try as you may, you can never keep things tidy. There's too many men about. No; a woman's place is in her own house, and I do long for it some times, particularly when we come ashore here, and see how nice and comfortable you've got things."

I observed a wistfulness in the sudden glance Elsie gave at Dain, who was unashamedly knitting a baby's vest. We had learnt that they had been married four years, and Elsie had confided in Dain that they were both very anxious to have children, and that although there was no physical reason why they shouldn't, it just hadn't happened to them yet. There was no doubt that that they were in love with each other, and well and happily mated. . . . Grab puffed at his pipe a while; then he said, meditatively:

"Life's nowt but luck, you know. It's nowt but luck; and it seems to me it's specially like that for a sailor, but that's maybe only because I am one. Maybe Elsie's right about me being a bit backward in coming forward, and being easily taken advantage of. It's very likely I could have been sailing master and saved a good bit of brass by

now, if I'd been smarter; for there's plenty of ways that
even a mate can pick on things if he's a mind to; you
know what I mean—letting stevedores and charterers slip
you a little packet of bank-notes for services rendered, and
things like that. I was once offered five hundred dollars,
that's a hundred quid mind you, if I'd let a chap stowaway
on a ship I was mate of, in Galveston, and drop him again
in Havana, saying nowt of course to the old man, for I
think they must have tried him first. From what I could
make out of it the chap was a gangster or summat. He might
have been a murderer. Anyway, I wasn't going to risk
getting the old man or my owners into trouble even for a
hundred quid. Same with rum-running. I know several
chaps, one from Bramblewick too, but we'll not mention
any names (although I'll say to see him going to chapel
on Sundays you'd think butter wouldn't melt in his mouth)
who made enough to retire on out of that game. I think
prohibition was nowt but a lot of daftness, but seeing that
it was the law, and that they were nowt but a lot of cut-
throats who were making brass out of breaking it, I kept
clear; although I'll admit I once got double pay when we
ran a cargo of rifles and war stuff into a spot in South
America where they were having a revolution; but then
there was no telling which side was winning, and whether
we were breaking the law or not."

Grab leaned over to the fire to knock the ashes out of
his pipe on the stone kerb; then, slowly refilling it from
his pouch, he remarked:

"You know, I practically *did* sail as master one voyage.
. . . I was as near being master of the ship as makes no
matter; although of course the master was on board."

"What happened?" I said encouragingly. "Was he sick?"

"Sick? Aye. I suppose he was in a way."

"Do you mean that time you went across the Atlantic during the war?" Elsie put in. "Now that shows how easily you let yourself be put upon. You ought to have got a medal for that, never mind getting your command, and a good lump of brass for what you did."

Grab grinned.

"Don't talk so daft. I did nowt but what I had to do to earn my wages. It was all in day's work. But it was a queer do, all the same. I've often wondered what happened that chap since."

"I should think that, like most of the others you've let walk over you, he's done very well for himself."

"Aye. Maybe. He was practically a youngster at the time. Maybe it wasn't altogether his own fault he was like he was. I don't think he'd ever been through the mill proper, like some of us had. He'd served his time on big passenger ships running out East, and he'd never been on a tramp before. It was his first command too. Only that wouldn't account for everything. No. There was summat rotten inside him. He was a fair-weather sailor. Maybe he should never have gone to sea at all. Certainly he oughtn't to have been given the command of a ship over the heads of old timers, but I think he must have had some influence with the company. It was a London ship, but of course she was on Government charter.

"To be on the safe side, I'll call him Smith," Grab went on, encouraged by our silence. "He was a tall, well-built chap with a pale actorish sort of face, and I should think he was a bit of a devil for the women. A swank. And he let me know it too, first minute I walked into the chart-room to report my arrival. That was in Southampton. He was in uniform. You know all ship's officers were supposed to wear uniform then, a sort of naval get-up, only with the braid on it criss-cross; and almost the first thing he said to me was, 'Where's your uniform, Mr. Fosdyck? I want the officers on my ship to be properly dressed, ashore and afloat.' He said this in a swanky sort of drawl; and I said to him, quick but polite, 'It's at the bottom of the North Sea, about ten miles north-east of Flamborough Head.' You see, I'd been torpedoed only a week before. A German submarine had got two of us, out of a convoy. The whole fore part of the ship I was in was blown out, and she was down under in less than five minutes, and as I wasn't wearing my uniform at the time, I didn't think of fetching it out of my cabin. I didn't even think about saving my sextant. It was a case of jump, and jump quick. And I'd no sooner got ashore from the ship that picked us up than I got orders to join this ship at Southampton. Well, I started to tell him about all this, in a chatty sort of way, same as you would with any one, but he soon cut me short. 'I don't want to hear about your adventures, Mr. Fosdyck,' he says. 'You've got time to buy a uniform before we sail, and kindly do so.'

"It's a queer thing, but our orders were to come to this very spot and load china clay for the States, and I supposed we'd bring back grain or war supplies. Apart from him being standoffish, and throwing his weight about, I didn't have much against Smith while we were steaming here; and while we were loading. As you'll have noticed, it's a narrow entrance here, and it's tricky too, when the tides are strong, and there's owt like a sea running in, and that night was real mucky. There was a southerly gale, and a hell of a sea. It was raining hard, and next to no visibility. We'd finished loading at dusk, and we reckoned we'd be sailing at daybreak, but along comes the naval embarkation officer with our orders and we were to leave at once. Submarines were reported to be hanging round outside, and we were to stand well out to southward before getting on our real course so that by daybreak we should be clear of them. No coast lights were being shown then, and we hadn't to show any lights ourselves, but that was no more than I'd expected having been running across the North Sea for the last six months. Well, I fancied the captain went a bit whiter than usual when he read the orders, but he said nowt to the officer, and it wasn't until he'd gone that he turned to me, and cursed the chap up and down, calling him a bloody naval stiff, swanking in his bloody naval uniform, and giving orders he knew he wouldn't have the guts to carry out himself. Then he went into his cabin and when he comes on to the bridge again, I knew by the smell he'd had a drink of whisky, but I didn't think much about it then.

"We had a pilot to take us out, and we were all on the bridge together; everything almost pitch dark by now except for our binnacle lights, and now and again a little light flashing on each side of the fairway, where there's a fixed light ordinary times. But you know there's not more than the width of a ship's bridge between the fairway and the rocks on the east side, and it was just there we got the swell, and I don't mind telling you I had a bit of wind up myself when I saw the seas breaking on those rocks under our lee quarter, but if you can't trust a pilot who can you trust? Smith sees them at the same time, and he gets hold of the pilot's shoulders and shouts:

"'You bloody fool, you're putting us aground,' and he shouts to the steersman, 'Port your helm.'

"When we came in here this time to lay up, and the pilot came on board, first thing I asked him was if the chap who took us out that time was still at his job, but he died a year or two ago. I should have liked to have asked him if he'd ever had any one do that to him before or since. Of course he told the steersman to hold on, and a few minutes later we were clear and slowed down for the pilot to get into his cutter. I've never seen a smarter bit of seamanship in my life than the way he did it. Our ship was rolling almost on her beam ends. We had nowt but flashlights to show him overboard and down the ladder, and he was swinging on to it like an acrobat in a circus, before he jumped. He never said a word to Smith, by the way. But when the cutter sheered off, Smith turns to me, and says, ' The bloody fool. Serve him right if he'd been drowned.' He brushed against me then, and I noticed he was trembling from head to foot.

"Well, I'd discovered that behind all his swank the chap was nowt but a funk, trying to keep his end up with whisky and blustering. Blustering; you know what I mean, shouting as many orders as he could to everybody, and finding fault and saying things that narked and vexed. He was scared stiff we were going to run into those submarines, or hit a mine, but he went on as though it was *us* that was scared, not him. As it happened we cleared the channel without seeing anything, and the gale moderated, and it looked as though we were going to have a fair crossing, and then, five days out, things started to go bad. The second mate, he was a Cockney, but a very quiet sort of chap, who'd scarcely ever opened his mouth since we'd left port, although he'd done his duties all right, was taken ill. From what we could make out it was pneumonia, but, anyway, he was dead in less than twenty-four hours, and we had to shove him over. We didn't carry a third mate, so the bo'sun had to take over the second's job, but as he knew nowt about navigation, he wasn't much use to either of us. And that

was only the start of our bad luck. Next thing that happened
was that the wireless room was burnt out. We had only one
operator, and it seems that he was cleaning summat inside
the room with some petrol, and the stuff exploded. He
dashed out with his clothes all on fire, moaning with pain,
and although we managed to save his life and stop the fire
spreading, he was so badly burnt that he was in his bunk
the rest of the voyage; and of course we were left without
wireless. I'll say this for Smith. Although he cursed and
blinded about the operator having been so careless, he
dressed his burns for him, and ordered the steward to give
him the best of everything. But that's about the only decent
thing he did do that I can remember. The very same night
the wind piped up from the west, and we were for it.

"I've crossed the Atlantic scores of times, in mid-winter
and all, but I've never hit owt like that weather, an' I hope
I never shall. It blew and it blew, and I can tell you the
seas were like mountains dropping on us. Sometimes it
rained, sometimes it snowed, and one day it was so warm
the sweat was running down my legs into my sea-boots,
but we never saw the sun or the stars, and it never stopped
blowing. I didn't tell you she was a brand-new ship. She was
one of those standard ships they'd started building then, all
the same size and shape so that we used to say they were run
out of the shipyards like strings of sausages. But as ships go,
she was all right, I've been in dozens worse. For the first
three days and nights Smith did make some sort of a
show, but I knew he was drinking hard all the time. He'd
never take his watch alone; and at nights, anyway, I'd
never get stretched out on my bunk for more than a few
minutes before he'd send the acting second or a seaman
down to fetch me up again, and when I'd get on the bridge
he'd look at me as though he was going to ask me summat

important, then he'd say summat that wasn't important
at all, or ask a question he could have answered for himself,
and then he'd mutter it was all right, and I could go down
again. He was in blue funk, but either it was the whisky,
or he wasn't far enough gone yet for him to tell me he was
beat. There was still some swank about him, but not much.
He never bothered to ask me if I was wearing my uniform
under my oilskins. I was wearing a fisherman's guernsey,
and a scarf, if he had but known, but as I never had a chance
of getting my oilskins off he never did.

"It was a devil. Decks were awash with green seas all
the time. One of our boats had been washed clean off its
derricks; and we had to cut another adrift in case it pulled
its derricks out of the deck. She was bashed in, anyway.
Fo'c'sle was flooded, for the ventilator and the stove chimney
had been washed away. Same thing happened with the
galley, so that the only hot stuff we or the men, and that
poor devil of a wireless operator got was coffee or tea from
the stokehold; the steward was a hero the way he fetched
it up and shared it round. And then just after daybreak
on the fourth day of that gale, the chief engineer speaks up
to the bridge to tell us that water was coming into the
stokehold and engine-room, and that he thought we must
have sprung a plate. Smith went down. I'm not likely
to forget the look of his face when he came back. It was
snowing then. We were going fair into the weather, and
she was pitching and rolling so that you couldn't stand
without holding on to summat. I heard him shout and
there he was half-way up the bridge steps, holding on to
the rails with both hands, and it looked as though he darn't
come any higher. I hung on to the top of the rails, and
looked down at him. He must have fallen somewhere,
for he'd got a great cut on his forehead, and the blood was

trickling down his cheek and dripping from his chin, but it
wasn't so much that that struck me at the time but the
look in his eyes and the way his lips were twitching, just
like a bairn that's beginning to cry. Swank! There was no
swank about him then. He just hung on and he says, in a
shaking sort of voice:

"' Fosdyck, we're in a bad way. I don't know what to
do. I've never had anything like this ever happen to me
before. I'm a sick man. I can't think . . .'

"And then he puts one hand to the cut on his brow, and
be damned if he doesn't start crying like a bairn. Well, I
knew where I was with him then, and I wasn't thinking so
much about him as about the ship.

"' Get up on to the bridge,' I shouts at him, as though
he'd been an ordinary seaman. ' And don't alter her course.
Keep her straight into the weather.'

"I climbed down past him, and I went down into the
engine-room as fast as I could get. It wasn't the quantity
of water coming in that had put wind up the chief. What
bothered him, and me, was that it was coming through
the bottom of the bunkers, and it was white, like milk. It
was coming from the hold. It was white because of the
china clay, and we knew damned well it was hopeless trying
to find the leak let alone stop it. There wasn't so much,
anyway, no more than you'd get from a couple of rivet
holes. If it got no worse it could do us no harm. But if
it was from a sprung plate, and the plate itself was rove off,
then another would go, and it wouldn't be long before half
the ship's side was out. You see, they were building those
standard ships in a hell of a hurry, and there was no telling
what stuff they were putting into them. Well, there was
nowt to do but carry on as we had been doing. We'd have
done no better if we'd turned and run with the weather.

That might have changed the strain on her hull in such a way as to have made the damage worse, and the chief agreed that we'd best keep her to it. There was nowt wrong with the engines, anyway. I went back to the bridge, expecting of course to find Smith there. The acting second was in charge, and he told me Smith had sent for him, and then gone down to his cabin. I didn't knock at the cabin door. I burst in, and there he was sitting on his bunk with a whisky bottle in his hand, and he was already as tight as makes no matter.

"'Have a drink,' he says, holding out the bottle. 'Have a drink.'

"I knocks it out of his hand, but all he did was grin.

"'Are you coming on to the bridge?' I says. 'We're in a tight place, and you're the master of the ship.'

"'No,' he says. 'Sick man. No good sick man master of ship. Ship sinking. You master of ship.'

"And with that he rolls over into his bunk, and I reckon if he hadn't I'd have landed him one that would have laid him there quicker.

"He could have been gaoled for what he'd done, of course, and I suppose if I'd done my duty I'd have seen he was gaoled, but then I wasn't in shape for doing owt when my job was finished, for there was still three more days and nights of that gale to go. It was the engineers and stokers that saved that ship. The leak got worse, and in the end the stokers were up to their boot tops in what looked just like milk, and we all knew that any minute it might start coming in in floods, but they kept the fires and the engines and the pumps going. All I had to do was stay on the bridge, turn and turn about with the acting second—I never thought of promoting him to acting mate, although I'd got another seaman, as well as the steersman up with us, in case either of us dropped; and if we were just about frozen stiff, there wasn't once when I'd have changed places with those below. I shouldn't have liked to have been shut in. So long as I could see the weather, I didn't feel so bad, and I suppose that in a way I was glad I was master of a ship, after all the years of sailing only mate. I didn't bother about Smith. The steward told me he was still drinking when he was conscious at all. I think what would have finished me though would have been if he had come on to the bridge, sober, and told me he was going to take charge again.

"She was saved, anyway. The gale moderated on the seventh day. The sky cleared and I got our position, four hundred miles east-south-east of Ambrose Light; and I was in the chart-room, just checking my figures, when I suddenly felt dizzy, and I dropped, and I believe I was delirious for the best part of a fortnight after, and it would be another fortnight still before I really knew I was in a hospital in New York. Aye, and they wouldn't tell me even then all that had happened after I'd dropped. I'd had brain fever, it seemed. I wasn't altogether surprised when I did hear, that Smith having got to the end of his whisky, had sobered up, and that he'd just taken charge again, and fetched the ship into New York. I learnt this from the company's agents, and that he'd put it in the ship's log, that he had been disabled by an accident, and had been obliged to hand over the ship to me for three days. But he'd had the sense not to try and brazen it out, and he'd cleared off the minute he'd drawn his wages from the agent. I should think I'd have had his berth on that ship all right for the homeward voyage, if I'd been up and doing. She was dry docked, and it was found she'd actually split a plate along a line of rivets, but she was repaired and away again, before I was really conscious, and I had to sign on as mate on another ship later, and I was on her till the end of the war."

He stopped, and started to fill his pipe.

"Didn't I tell you he was daft?" said Elsie. "And he hasn't told you half of what he really did. I wouldn't have known if the wife of the second engineer hadn't come to Bramblewick for her holidays one summer, and we got on talking about it. It's a wonder the engineers and the rest of the crew didn't murder that man. He did well to clear off. It might have been him that dressed that poor lad's burns, but it was Will who saved him from being burned to death when the fire happened, and it was Will and the steward who looked after him after. According to the second engineer's account, and he'd got it from the sailors, Will never once left the bridge after the so-called master had thrown things up; and all the time he kept the others encouraged and cheerful. And he got nowt for it—nowt at all. . . . He *is* daft—isn't he?"

I saw Elsie look at her husband when she asked this question. She *might* have thought him daft, and slow, and, being a Yorkshire woman, it might have exasperated her at times to think how much better off they could have been if he had been truer to the Bramblewick tradition. Yet her look was full of quiet pride, and I knew that she did not misunderstand me when, using a familiar Bramblewick idiom, I said:

"Aye. He ought to be locked up."

Grab laughed as he lit his pipe.

"Aye. I know. But Elsie hasn't told you everything the engineer's wife told her. That ship struck a mine just as she was in sight of Brest where she was taking a load of shells for the American Army, and I believe the second engineer was one of the three chaps who were saved. All the rest of them including the master and the mates were blown up. It shows after all I was lucky."

It was a morning towards the end of November, and Dain and I had just washed up from breakfast when we heard the sound of a propeller and then the strident blast of a horn, just over the hill where the steamer lay. The tide was half-way down, and we had planned that we would do our shopping in the afternoon when it flowed again, and then fish in the harbour, and call on the ship on our way back and stay for tea, and persuade the Fosdycks to come back to supper. The sounds startled us. Did it mean that another ship was coming in to lay up? Several more, including an enormous tanker, had arrived during the autumn, but all of them had gone to berths up the Pol, where special dredging had been carried out. We had been told, however, that there was still room for another ship of moderate tonnage alongside the *Heather Wyke*. We dashed up the hill to our old look-out place, and we saw a cloud of black smoke emerging from the *Heather Wyke's* funnel, and alongside her one of the harbour tugs and a coal lighter. I felt a sudden lump in my throat.

"My God! She's taking on bunkers. Her furnaces are lit. She must be sailing."

We had got so used to the sight of the idle ship, so resigned to the continuance of the trade slump, that never once in the months of our friendship with the Fosdycks had we seriously considered the possibility of her going. Like the ships I had seen on my first arrival at St. Jude (they were still there) the decks and the funnel of the *Heather Wyke* had rusted, and everywhere the paint was blistered and peeling off. Except at high tide her hull was really aground and even when she was afloat there had only been the faintest tremor to tell you so when you were on board. She had indeed become part of our land to which she was attached, and even now with the smoke belching from her funnel it was not easy to realise that her fires were turning water into steam that would energise her cold engines, and make her into a living ship that would move away from our shore and out of sight for ever. And it was harder still to realise that Grab would move with it.

Dain said nothing, as we hurried down to the cove and launched our boat. The tug and the lighter was clear of the companion ladder. Already there were men on board, and steam was coming from one of the winches, and we saw Grab in his shirt sleeves busy preparing a derrick for the hauling up of the coal. But he did not see us, and as we walked along towards the galley we saw Elsie, just going in with a basket of washing.

"Hallo!" she greeted us. "I was wondering if you'd noticed all the commotion, and hoping that you'd come along. . . . Eh, can you believe it, after all these months! . . . You'll have guessed she's sailing. . . . I had some shirts of Will's that I washed this morning hanging out, and I thought I'd best get 'em inside before they started coaling. Come inside. He'll be coming as soon as he's rigged that derrick. I'm going to mash a pot of tea."

We went inside, and sat down in that place which had become as familiar to us as our own living-room. We were both feeling very glum at hearing that our surmises were correct, yet I was thinking that it must be very good news for Grab, for no sailor can be really happy on a laid-up ship.

"What's really happened, Elsie?" I said. "Is trade improving at last? Is Will getting his captain's berth?"

She smiled ironically.

"I only wish he was, if only for this one trip. But he's

had his usual luck. It isn't because trade's improving that she's going. It's the other way round. She's been sold to the Greeks, and she's sailing now for Cardiff, to be taken over by Greek officers and crew. You see the Greeks, for some reason or other, can run ships much cheaper than we can, and so they can charge cheaper rates and get what little trade there is. Will can tell you more about it than I can. He's trying to make out he doesn't care, but really he's very fed up about it. Fancy! He's been with this company five years, and yet they've decided to send another captain down just to take her to Cardiff, and he's still to sail mate. You know it would have done him a lot of good to have got it. It might have made him feel that his luck had changed at last. As it is, he won't even have his watchman's job, when the Greeks take over. It'll be Bramblewick for us until the slump ends."

Grab came in. He might have been "fed up," but he gave little outward sign of it. His brow was moist with sweat and he was full of energy and importance.

"I'm glad you've come aboard," he said briskly. "For I doubt if we'll get a chance to come ashore again before we sail. Has Elsie told you?"

"I was just telling them," said Elsie, busy making the tea.

"I think it's filthy, them not letting you go as captain," Dain said indignantly. "It's just filthy."

Grab laughed.

"Why, that's no more than I expected. The chap they're sending is their senior captain. His ship's been sold too. The company itself is selling out altogether, and winding up. Never mind, I'll be able to do a bit of gardening when we get home. I've never yet had a go at that garden of ours, for it's always been the wrong season when I've been home.

Do you think we could grow cauliflowers and lettuces like yours up there, or will it be too cold. I wish I'd learnt summat about it, while we've been here, but it seems we've spent most of our time yarning. . . . By gum, we'll miss you."

It was not easy for us to tell Grab and his wife how we were going to miss them; and besides we still could not realise that they were going. Yet there was plenty of evidence to convince us it was so, apart from what they had told us. The iron decks of the ship, usually so silent, rang with the footfalls of men, and there was a terrific clamour as the first sack of coal was shot into the almost empty bunkers.

"By——" said Grab as he hurriedly drank his tea. "We've had a night of it. We got the wire at seven o'clock last night. I went ashore with the chap who fetched us it, and I had to talk over the 'phone with the owners up in London, and then get hold of a donkeyman in St. Jude, and see the coal agents and fix up about our bunkers, and then come back and get the fires on. We've got to sail by five. And now I've got to get over to St. Jude, and talk to the owners again over the telephone. I hate telephoning worse than owt. But it's got to be done, and the ship's got to be victualled for a two-days' voyage, and fresh water put in the tanks, and I don't know what else, and the master and other officers and the crew won't get here until three this afternoon."

There was nothing we could do to help, and, as it looked as though we'd only be in the way if we hung about the ship, we went home and tried to find some consolation for our sadness in making a last selection from our garden; but there was nothing really exciting left in it except chrysanthemums, and as Dain remarked when we had picked a huge bunch of them, they were very beautiful but very sad, and it was just as though they'd been picked for a funeral; and we couldn't help thinking of the day we'd left the things on the ladder, and wishing we could have all the months of our friendship over again.

All through that morning we could hear the noise of bunkering and the shouts of the men, and while we were having lunch there was a new hideous noise, the blowing off of steam from the safety valves. We set off in the boat soon after, taking our last gifts with us, but we rowed past the ship without calling, and went straight to Porthkerris and did our shopping, and then we shot our net close in to the Porthkerris shore, and we were lucky enough to get a couple of nice bass and about a dozen mullet. All the time we had been afloat there had been a constant traffic of rowing boats and launches between the ship and St. Jude, and about half-past three two launches, crowded with men, left the St. Jude quay, and at the same time the tug left the ship's side, towing behind it the empty coal lighter. We were still nervous of being in the way, so we pottered about the harbour until four o'clock when the tide was nearly high, and we observed a pilot boat moving in to our shore to the ship's moorings. Then we rowed to the ladder, and climbed on board. There were men everywhere. Some we recognised as belonging to St. Jude: tradesmen and harbour officials; but the crew had arrived, and when we went to the galley we found a cook with an apron over his shore togs busy peeling potatoes. We found Elsie at last in the mate's cabin busy packing her things. She looked hot and perplexed, but very glad to see us.

"Oh, it is nice of you to have brought us all those lovely flowers. They're lovely. . . . But they make me wish we weren't going. Do you know, I hated this spot when we first came, and I did long for Bramblewick. But somehow or other I've grown to like it, and Will and I have been so happy. It's the first time since we were married that we've had more than a month together. It's just awful having all these men on board, making such a mess. And poor Will's almost out of his mind. The captain hasn't turned up yet. You see, he's coming from London and the train doesn't get in till four. Will's gone to meet him, and it's such a bother, because Will wants me to go with the ship, but he can't let me without asking the captain first, and he's likely enough to be awkward about it. So I've got to be packed all ready. . . . By the way, we've got a lot of things for you. Will says that as the ship's sold to the Greeks, he's not going to leave any of our stuff on board at Cardiff. They're only odds and ends, but they may come in useful. I do hope he's back soon, so that I'll know what I'm going to do."

We suggested at once that if the new captain did object to Elsie going she might at least spend the night with us; but before she had time to consider, Grab burst into the cabin. The sweat was streaming down his face, but his eyes were sparkling with excitement and happiness, and to our amazement, for we had never once seen him make any physical demonstration of affection towards his wife, he took her in his arms and kissed her.

"Hoy," he shouted then. "Do you know what's happened? The captain's missed his connection at Exeter. Can't get here till seven o'clock. I've 'phoned the owners again, and they say we mustn't lose the tide. I've got the ship myself. I'm sailing master."

An hour later, we stood together, Choo-i with us, on the ridge of our hill, from which so many months ago we had watched the *Heather Wyke* creeping into her moorings, and I had made the terrifying discovery that Grab was on board.

Again it was nearly dusk. The ship's navigation lights
were lit. Smoke was pouring from her funnel, and with
a light wind blowing up harbour, and bringing the smoke
in our direction, we could scarcely discern the figures of
Grab and Elsie (Elsie standing well apart from him, on the
bridge). But we could hear his voice, as we had heard it on
that other occasion shouting orders, only it seemed to us (it
may have been only our imagination) that there was a
different quality in it, something just a little more authorita-
tive, as befits the man in supreme command of a ship. There
was a tug on each side of the ship. Below us at the moorings
the harbour boat waited. We heard Grab shout the command
to cast off astern. We heard an officer on the poop repeat
the order. The moorings were cast off, breaking the last
physical link between the ship and our land. The winches
rattled as the slack ropes were hove in. Then the horn of
the *Heather Wyke* sounded, three times, making our hearts
jump with the close volume of it, and through the echo
of the last blast we heard Grab shout another command
for the true anchors to be hove in. The tugs' propellers began
to churn the water. Very, very slowly the ship began to move
ahead. We heard a bell ring. The ship's own propeller moved.
There were more orders. Then we saw Grab lift up his
megaphone and his voice came to us, with an uncanny
power and modulation.

"Good luck to both of you from both of us. A merry
Christmas when it comes, and a happy New Year, and plenty
of brass."

"Good luck. Good luck," we shouted at the top of our
voices, but Grab already had turned to shout an order,
and, anyway, they could not have heard us against the
wind and the noises of the ship; and Dain suddenly gripped
my arm, and said:

"Oh, this is just too awful. I can't stand it. Let's go back."

We did not look at the ship again.

We walked down in silence, and through the back door into the living-room, for we both felt instinctively that, for to-night at least, we could not bear sitting in front of the big room fire. I lit the lamp, and at once we noticed the hamper of things they had insisted we must take when we had left the ship. There were tears in Dain's eyes.

"Oh, they have been good to us," she cried. "I just can't bear to think they'll never come in again. And yet it's wonderful that he's going captain. That does make it a bit easier to bear."

"Yes, by God," I said. "Even if it's only for two days. . . . Come on, let's see what they've given us. There's a piece of brand-new sailcloth for a start. Just what we wanted to make a hood for the cot. . . ."

I knelt down by the hamper and took out the piece of cloth. Under it were some tins of fruit, jars of mincemeat and sardines and a bottle of wine and some paper parcels of what looked like pastry, but before I touched another thing I saw an envelope lying conspicuously on the top. I picked it up. Dain's name was scrawled on it in a very feminine hand. She opened it. And then, in a very shaky voice that broke completely when she got to the end, she read it aloud.

"DEAR DAIN,—Only this is really to both of you. There was something I wanted to tell you before you left, only I hadn't the nerve to, and so I'm writing this short letter to tell you what it is, and I expect it will come as a great surprise, and you'll be the first to know, and I'd like you to keep it secret for the present, same as we'll keep it secret about you when we get home to Bramblewick. It's only that I find myself in the same condition as you do yourself, so it's going to be nice for both of us, only you'll have yours first, and I hope you have a son.

"Yours loving,

"ELSIE."

11

WE MISSED the Fosdycks dreadfully. The going of the *Heather Wyke* was the prelude to a sudden reduction in the number of laid-up ships. All three of the original steamers I had seen on Christmas day went in the following week. Again it was not a sign of a revival of trade. One of them had been sold to the Greeks as a going concern. The other two had been bought by the Government of Japan, to be broken up and resmelted into steel that would probably be used for the building of war vessels. Another steamer, which had been laid up in the Pol estuary only six weeks, had been sold to the Italians for the same purpose, and according to Joe, the only reason why more ships didn't come to take their berths was that there was practically none left sailing. Yet we had got a hurried letter from Elsie, at Cardiff, with the news that on arrival at Cardiff, Will had run unexpectedly into an old shipmate of his who was the superintendent of a small line of colliers running regularly to Ireland, and he'd been offered the master's berth on one of them, and had sailed the very same night, so he hadn't even been able to see her off at the station. She was a very small boat, of course, and the pay was only what a mate would get on a tramp, but it was better for Will than being unemployed, seeing it wouldn't be so long before there was one extra to provide for, although it was a wrench leaving him, and he had seemed disappointed about the garden, for he'd quite made up his mind to try and grow things like us.

It would have been better for us, if a ship had come to

take the *Heather Wyke's* berth; for when the tide was low
we could see the deep trench her keel and bilge plates had
scoured out of the mud, and the marks left by her mooring
ropes, and that gave us a perpetual reminder of our loss.
We missed them in a more practical way too. There had
been no specific arrangement between us, but we had
supplied them regularly with fish and vegetables, and they
had repaid us from their larder, making an appreciable
lightening of our weekly food-bill. Our rent was payed,
we had cleared off our debt to Hoskins, but we had spent
all of the fifty pounds advance, and we were dependent
entirely again on what we got from the firm of naturalists,
and, bearing in mind our experience of summer, we had
to be prepared for a temporary cessation of this when the
Christmas holidays came.

Yet, apart from the intense longing we got sometimes,
for the sound of their feet coming up our path, and Grab's
formal and quite unnecessary knock on the door, and his
breezy "Ship-ahoy" as he opened it, and Elsie's equally
unnecessary "Eh, we're not disturbing you, are we?" we were
happy. The present small inconveniences of poverty would
quickly pass. The slump itself which had not yet directly
affected us would undoubtedly be over by the spring. All
the excitement of the publication of the book lay ahead;
the day when the six presentation copies arrived, the day
when we'd see it advertised in the Sunday papers, and the
reviews would start coming in, and (our confidence was
supreme) the day when we'd see it listed among and perhaps
heading the season's best sellers, and our success was assured.
And then, farther along that rosy path that reached ahead
of us, was the birthday of our first-born, even to me more
profoundly exciting now than the birthday of the book.

We spent many pleasant evenings in front of the big

fire weaving plans for the future. We decided that however rich we might become, we could never leave our present home. I had taken the precaution of getting Charley to extend our lease for another year. But we thought that it would be much better if we bought it. We gathered from him that there would not be much difficulty in doing this. Like the rest of Hoskins's property it belonged to a sort of trust; and he assured us that if the trustees ever did decide to sell it, we should have the first offer. We must certainly buy it when our money came in. But it was equally important that we should have our cabin cruiser.

We made many sketches and plans of our cruiser, without, however, coming to a final decision, for that would depend so much on the amount of money we had to spend. But we were agreed that first and foremost she must be a real boat, and not like some of the craft we had seen in the harbour during the summer, merely a floating caravan in which we could sleep, and in calm weather, creep along the coast from harbour to harbour. She must be capable of standing up at least to fairly rough weather; she must be capable of sailing, but at the same time a motor was essential so that when we were embarked on a long cruise we should not be at the mercy of calms and unfavourable winds. Cruising, above everything, was what we wanted her for. Joe one day, when we had called at the shipyard for some paint, had taken us into his "shop" again, and rummaging among some of the *Amelia Hoskins's* gear had come across a bundle of charts. They were obsolete, for navigation purposes, and he gave us the lot; but to us they were as exciting as a treasure chart, and we spent hours poring over them and planning where we should go. There were scores of places along the Cornish coast which, at least on a chart, looked as glamorous as any places abroad.

Many of them like Chardmouth, had huge estuaries, with innumerable creeks that might take one months to explore. These might be the objective of our first cruises, and perhaps it would be as well, with our baby only a few months old, to confine ourselves to the south coast next summer. But the charts covered all the coasts of the British Isles, and the coasts of Western Europe, and really there was nothing to stop us going where we wished, to France and Holland and Germany, even to the Baltic provided we had the money to pay for fuel. But we thought that perhaps the most exciting cruise of all would be to sail east and through the Straits of Dover into the North Sea, and north along the coast of Suffolk and Norfolk and Lincolnshire; past the mouth of the Humber, and along the Yorkshire coast to Flamborough Head, from which on a clear day you could see the headland of High Batts on the sky-line; and steam at last into Bramblewick Bay, where the Lunns might be fishing; and we'd hail them and go alongside them and show them our baby; and then, not caring how the local folks stared (for all our debts would have been paid), go ashore with them and meet not only their families, but Elsie Fosdyck and perhaps Grab and certainly their child; and perhaps we might stay there quite a while before setting off on our return journey home. That, undoubtedly was the most pleasant of our dreams, but in it there was no disloyalty to our hut and our cove, and the happiness they had given us and continued to give us throughout the early months of that first winter. We dreamt, it was true; we lived very much in the future, but we worked outside and inside, preparing new flower-beds, making more paths, building walls and fences, hauling firewood from the shore and splitting and sawing it, gathering wrack for manure, making more furniture; and Dain knitted and sewed for the baby, and I, not yet with a complete enthusiasm, for I lacked the stimulus of proved success, began my new book which was to be the ironic story of my patent lobster pot.

Only at the close approach of Christmas did we have a sense, or rather an apprehension of loneliness. The shops in St. Jude and Porthkerris were making a brave show in defiance of the slump. The spirit of Christmas was in the air. The temptation to spend and celebrate was strong, but my fears about the firm had been realised a week before I had guessed; and we were back to our sheep's head again, and with just enough cash in hand to see us through the holidays if we practised the old economy. Just a few days before they had sailed, the Fosdycks had given us a definite invitation to Christmas dinner. Elsie's mother had written saying she was going to send them a goose, and the mince-meat Elsie had put in the hamper was some of what Elsie herself had been making in anticipation of that meal. Now, not only were we to dine alone, but it looked as though we must content ourselves with the plainest fare, even sheep's head, for on one of our shopping trips to Porthkerris we had been obliged by conscience to contribute quite a good lump of our cash to a fund that had been organised by some local religious body for providing a Christmas tea and party for the children of the unemployed, to which, however, we were not invited, probably because of Dain's now obvious condition, and because it was still generally thought that we were living in sin.

It was not a serious problem. Many people were destined to have poorer fare than sheep's head that Christmas day, and with little to hope for in the days and weeks that followed. At the same time many people would have just as good a Christmas as they'd had in years of plenty, for the fortresses of the rich were strong, and I did feel that we deserved something a little more exciting, particularly as Christmas was the anniversary of my lucky arrival at St. Jude.

It was three days to Christmas, and we were on our way home from a fishing trip late in the afternoon, and on the flood tide, when, a little higher up the creek than our cove, we saw a number of darkish birds swimming close to the far bank. At first I thought they were puffins or guillemots; but as we drew near I saw that they were wild duck. My heart beat fast with a mingled excitement and exasperation, and my exasperation grew more intense as we got nearer, and all they did was to continue swimming very leisurely so that at last we were not more than fifteen yards from them, a range at which, had I been armed with a shot-gun, I could have got at least a brace of them with positive certainty. But I had no gun, of course, and looking round the boat I saw no missile except a spare fishing lead, and it was my exasperation, rather than any hope that I might do damage with the thing that caused me to pick it up, and as Dain rowed, take aim at the nearest bird. I did not hit it. Actually the lead dropped nearer to another bird than the one I aimed at; but the splash of it caused the lot of them (there were about a dozen) to take flight, and away they went up-creek, and for a moment or so they were out of sight behind the oaks, and I presumed we had seen the last of them. I took the oars and began to row across to our cove, now dead opposite to us; but I hadn't pulled a couple of strokes before Dain shouted:

"Look. They're coming back again. . . . Oh, what a pity you haven't a gun!"

I stopped. They were flying down-creek again, but nearer to our own shore. They passed the cove, and got almost to where the *Heather Wyke* had been moored, then they turned again, up-creek, and to my astonishment, flew back actually into the cove and alighted on the very place close to the stream where we usually landed when the tide was high. Had I been ashore, and with the gully rocks near to hide me, I could have thrown a stone among them which could hardly have helped hitting one. Clearly my first attack had not alarmed them very much. Would they stay there long enough to let me do this? Dain could land me at the bluff. I could climb the cliff, creep along under the trees and down into the gully of the stream, and there was a jutting rock there would give me perfect cover until I took aim. Surely I could hit one out of a dozen birds!

We pulled in on a slanting course for the bluff, quietly, and watching the duck all the time. They were now crowding into the very place where the fresh water entered the cove, and shortly one of them, a drake, landed and began to waddle up the very stream where it coursed over the shingle, and the rest followed in a procession, in the way of ducks and geese, snuffling among the pebbles for fresh-water food.

" God," I whispered hoarsely. " If only they'd stay there. If I was behind those rocks now I could almost grab the first one with my hand."

Stealthily we crept in to the bluff. We had only a couple of lengths to go before it would hide us, and the duck apparently were still unalarmed. The drake was actually waddling past the very rock where I hoped to hide, and we could hear them quacking softly and contentedly. And then suddenly there was a terrific commotion. We saw the drake flapping his wings, the others fly up, and come straight towards us, quacking frenziedly, swerve over our heads and fly up-creek again, and we had

watched them almost out of sight before I realised that
the drake was still by the rock still flapping its wings and
apparently struggling in vain to release itself from something that held it.

"It's fast on something," I yelled excitedly, as I pulled
the boat round and in. "A hook, or a bit of net. God, if
we can only get to it in time!"

I pulled madly. The boat grounded. I leapt out, rushed
across the beach with one thought in my mind, to get that
duck, and ready, I think, to have made a stupendous leap
into the air myself if the bird had suddenly flown up. But
it didn't fly up, and as I reached the rock which had
momentarily hid it, I saw first, not the duck, but Choo-i,
lying full length in a shallow pool of the stream, spread-
eagled across the now completely motionless bird, her teeth
clenched in its neck.

We had no false sentiment about that duck. Choo-i,
who must have come down to the shore in anticipation of
our return with some fish, and taken hunter's cover behind
the rock when she'd seen the birds alight so near, had killed
it as swiftly and as painlessly as a well-aimed charge of shot.
Nor had I any scruples at depriving her of her prey, although
she snarled and cussed, and did her best to stop me with her
teeth and claws. But a nice whiting which Dain hurriedly
fetched from the boat, and almost pushed into her mouth,
consoled her for her loss and for the wetting she had got;
and after all, she wouldn't have caught the thing if we
hadn't thrown the lead which had so miraculously caused
the birds to alight in the cove. I held it up triumphantly.
It was a young bird, fat as butter, and it should be in perfect
condition by Christmas day. Stuffed and roasted in front
of the big fire, with bread sauce, and baked potatoes, and
brussels sprouts, we'd have a dinner that any one might envy,

and if we were obliged to go easy on the sweet, and cut out most of the conventional "good things" of the season, and confine our gifts to each other to things that were useful (and we'd have to get, anyway): and we were going to dine without our friends: there was the bottle of wine in which to drink to them and their happiness, to the book, and our unborn sons.

12

THE PROOFS of the book came at the end of January.
Publication day was fixed for a Tuesday, late in the following
month. The pages were made up exactly like a book, except
that they were printed on rough paper with narrow margins,
and were bound with a paper cover. There were two copies.
One had to be corrected and returned to the publisher.
The other, with the original manuscript, we were allowed
to keep.

We were thrilled when we handled them. In spite of the
rough paper, the print was very clear, and it was hard to
believe, comparing a "proof" page, with a page of the
manuscript (with its messy type and many corrections),
that they were the same thing. It was like looking at a
new house when all the scaffolding has been taken down.
It was a real book at last. And still it was not finished.
This was a mere whetting of our appetite for the day when
the presentation copies came, printed on proper paper with
wide margins, bound in stiff covers with a dust jacket
bearing most likely a fascinating design.

But when I began what promised to be the agreeable task
of correcting the publisher's copy, I was assailed by an
abominable reaction. Almost from the opening of the
first chapter, I had a sense of boredom, and this quickly
grew to one of repulsion as I made myself read on. It was
much worse than when we had been engaged typing the
thing. Then, I had consoled myself with the thought that
we were harassed and tired, and exasperated by the behaviour
of the machine. Now there was nothing mechanical to

disturb the flow of the story. There were very few spelling
or printer's errors. The actual type, the spacing, the para-
graphing, looked very good, but the story itself seemed to
move at the pace of a glacier. It was heavy, stodgy and dull.
I was possessed by a deadly fear that after all the book was
going to be a failure.

Dain laughed at my fear. Hadn't we got Mr. Mackenzie's
letter to show that her opinion of it was right? Wasn't
the fact that he had taken it, and given us the fifty pounds,
and was going to publish it proof that it was good? Surely
a man like that wasn't such a fool as to publish something
that wasn't good? To this I retorted that the best publishers
made mistakes, otherwise every published book would be
good, and even if ours *was* good, that was no proof that it
was going to be a success; in fact, almost everything was
against it: its subject, and having no real plot, or sex
interest, and above all, that it was dull. Hadn't the other
publishers turned it down? Would they have done so if it
had been so good as we'd imagined? Dain was angry.

"Don't be silly. Any book would seem dull if you'd
read it as many times as we've done this, never mind having
written it, and typed it on that typewriter, and then corrected
the typing, and now having to read the proofs. . . . The
other publishers turned it down because they were fools,
and they'll know it too, very soon."

I felt ashamed for having let myself go. But my fear
increased, when, having corrected the publisher's copy, I
made another effort to read the whole thing through, and
recapture my confidence, for it seemed duller than ever.
It seemed to me that I had missed everything I'd wanted to
say about Bramblewick, and the Lunns and the Fosdycks:
that incidents which themselves had been exciting enough,
and had seemed exciting when I'd read my description of

them aloud to Dain, were simply boring; and that the
writing itself was no better than that of a schoolboy doing
a composition on the subject of Yorkshire fishermen.
Damn and blast! Why hadn't I *written* the bloody thing?
Why hadn't I made a real novel of it? Why hadn't I
given it a plot, and a love interest? Why hadn't I made the
quarrel between the Lunns and the Fosdycks really violent;
heightened it to murder. That was what a really competent
novelist would have done, using the place and the people
and the actual incidents of their lives merely as raw
material. . . .

In fairness to Dain, I did my best to keep my fears to
myself, and I tried hard to believe that they were imaginary.
I gave up trying to win back confidence from the book
itself. The very sight of it filled me with loathing, and I
packed both the spare proof and the original manuscript
away in a drawer containing things we were not likely to
want, but that wasn't much use, for I knew the book off
by heart, and I'd find myself repeating whole passages of
it, and loathing them, while at the same time I knew that
these were the very bits I'd once liked, and that Dain had
raved over.

This was awful: and yet, I suppose it was better than
the overwhelming confidence I'd had in my patent lobster
pot when I'd set out to find a financier to back it. It was
better than thinking the book was a work of genius, and
that its complete success was assured by the very fact of its
being published, that nothing but a path of roses lay ahead
of us. Subconsciously at least, I was bracing myself for a
shock.

The days dragged slowly on.

Fortunately Dain had no similar misgivings about her
baby or if she had she kept them to herself. It made no

difference whatever to her physical activities. She was perfectly fit, and, I thought at times, almost stupidly happy, for she could not or she would not see what a ghastly fix we were going to be in if the book was a failure and we had no money at the time the baby arrived.

The days of February dragged slowly on. My acute pessimism yielded to a dull resignation. The book was not so good as we'd imagined it to be when I'd read the last chapter of it on the beach of that sun-drenched cove; but it could not be so bad as I'd thought when I'd read the proofs. From the point of popularity it had its manifest defects. But it was original and honest, and it was quite likely that some of the critics would recognise this, and praise it, and as luck played a very important part in the financial success of a book, it might sell moderately well, and give us enough to pay for the baby, and keep us going while I finished the next one, on which I was still progressing slowly.

Yet when the presentation copies arrived, a week before that fatal Tuesday, my feelings underwent another violent reversal. Dain unpacked the parcel, and she shrieked with excitement when she tore the inner wrapping and the books were revealed. She picked one up, and kissed it.

"Oh, it's just like seeing your baby for the first time! Isn't it *thrilling*?"

Repressing my excitement at first, I picked up a copy, and made a critical examination of it. It was beautifully printed, on very good quality paper, beautifully bound, and the dust jacket, although it was not pictorial, was tastefully printed in two colours, and looked very attractive. On the back was a short and discreet biographical note which at Mr. Mackenzie's request I had myself written, and on the inside leaf a short description of the book itself, very modest yet pleasing. I *was* pleased, and perhaps my voice was a trifle unsteady when I said:

"Yes. It looks pretty good. I certainly like the way it's printed and got up. And I like the jacket. Much better than having a picture on it."

"I love it," cried Dain. "It's just right!"

She suddenly opened her copy, and smelt between the pages and cried again:

"It's got a heavenly smell. . . . Ooo! One of those smells you can never quite get hold of in one breath—that makes you want to go on smelling. . . . It's grand—it's grand. I love the jacket; and with your name bang on the front. And just think that in four days' time all the booksellers all over the country will have it in their windows, and people will be asking about it and buying it, and reading it!"

Her enthusiasm at last infected me completely. I took the remaining copies, and I arranged them on the table in a row, as they might be arranged in a window, and we both stood back, and I shouted:

"By jove. They look grand. That jacket couldn't help but catch the eye, particularly when they're grouped together. It all depends of course on how he puts it out, how many copies he lets the bookshops have for display, but he's not going to be a fool over that. He'll be just as keen on selling it as we are. Of *course* he'll want it to be a best-seller!"

"You bet he will. . . . And it's going to be one too, don't you worry. But I wish it was Tuesday. What shall we do on Tuesday? We've simply got to celebrate. It'll be just like all one's birthdays and Christmases rolled into one. We ought to have a turkey or at least another wild duck, and champagne, and go on celebrating all day long. What a pity we can't go up to London for it, but I suppose we haven't even got the fare, and never mind, it will be just as exciting here."

But that day was very different from what we'd expected it to be. It was our habit to turn Choo-i out last thing at night and not let her in until we had started breakfast; otherwise, while we were getting breakfast ready, she would follow us about, rubbing herself against our legs, mewing and generally annoying us. And she had formed the habit of springing up on to the sill of the back window of the living-room as soon as she knew we were up, and sitting there watching us through the panes until I opened the door to let her in. It was a cold, gloomy, rainy morning, and it was nearly nine o'clock when we awoke. We dressed hurriedly, for (although I had no positive reason for supposing he would) I guessed the postman would have a large mail for us, perhaps a parcel, and I hated going out to him in pyjamas. We had lit the fire, before we noticed that Choo-i was not in her usual place. I went out to fill the kettle, expecting to find her mewing impatiently at the door, but she wasn't there. I left the door open. I called her, repeatedly, all the way to the spring and back and, having put the kettle on, I went out again and shouted, "Choo-i, Choo-i, Choo-i!" We were not deeply alarmed at first. Once before we had missed her in the morning, and later she had turned up, looking extremely pleased with herself and a half-devoured rabbit she had dragged almost to the back door. But we were worried, and we ate our breakfast in silence, and as soon as we'd done we both put on our oilskins and walked up the hill, shouting as we went.

"Perhaps the postman may have seen her," said Dain. "Let's go on until we meet him. It's time he was here now."

We carried on up the path to the boundary of our land but we saw neither Choo-i nor the postman, and we turned back again with the hope that Choo-i had already found her way in to her breakfast, but she wasn't there, and we started washing up, with our eyes constantly on that point on the path where the postman usually came in sight. I tried to appear cheerful.

"I expect she's been hunting, and perhaps she's got a rabbit, and it's too heavy for her to drag back. Perhaps she's even got another duck. What luck if we got another for our publication-day dinner! I wish the postman would hurry up. He's bound to have something for us this morning."

But the postman did not come. It continued to rain, and by midday both of us knew that something had happened to our cat, for she loathed rain, and no rabbit or duck would have kept her away from the shelter and warmth of the fireside so long, particularly as she could have eaten all she'd wanted of it. We'd planned that we'd have our celebration meal in the evening, and that we'd go to Porthkerris and St. Jude in the afternoon and, if we could get one at a reasonable price, buy a chicken, and also a bottle of wine. There was a multiple bookshop in St. Jude. We'd noticed that during the holiday season copies of new novels had been displayed in the window, and there was a chance that we should see ours; and, anyway, we could buy some newspapers and see if there was any reference to it, although of course it was much too early for reviews. We had a scratch lunch, and before setting out in the boat, we walked up the shore of the creek as far as we could go, shouting, "Choo-i, Choo-i," and then I ran back to the hut, just to make certain she hadn't got in through the window we'd left open.

We went to Porthkerris first. We found Joe in a shed, chopping firewood, with his terrier sitting patiently beside him, just as I had found him on that first Christmas afternoon, but in a more pessimistic mood. We should have liked to have told him about the book, but we only told him we had lost our cat, and he said:

"Ah, cats be like that. You can never depend upon a cat. Cats do wander, 'tis their way, specially shes. Maybe she go huntin' on one of they farms after chickens, or maybe chasin' game. Maybe some farmer or gamekeeper have shot she with a gun, or she maybe have got caught in a rabbit trap, for there be a lot of rabbit traps set this season of year. . . . Dogs baint like cats. You ought to keep a dog for a pet, like this little one of mine. Dogs don't wander like cats, provided you'm kind to them."

There was no other activity in the shipyard. We couldn't find Charley May. We went to the grocer's shop, and we wrote a notice, offering a reward to any one finding and returning Choo-i, which the man promised to put in his window, and we made our way gloomily across the harbour to St. Jude. There was no sign of the book in the bookshop window. We went inside. The manager was away on his holidays, and the female assistant in charge hadn't a very friendly looking manner. She had the uncomfortable habit of not looking at you when she spoke, and having bought some newspapers, it took me quite a lot of courage to ask her if she had a copy of the book. I did not identify myself with it. It was clear at once that she had not heard of it, but she went into the manager's office, and looked at some catalogues and letters, and then she came back, and said, still without looking at us, that no copies of it had arrived yet, but she would be pleased to order me one, if I'd give her the name of the publisher. There was a shelter near the quay, and we went to it and looked through the papers, which were full of bad news about the slump, but had nothing in them about the book.

The chickens in St. Jude were all very dear. We bought a boiling fowl for three and six, thinking that if we boiled it for an hour and then roasted it it wouldn't be too bad, and we paid another three and six for a bottle of claret; but we couldn't forget about Choo-i, and what Joe had said, and we couldn't look forward to our dinner with that on our minds.

"*Do* you think that someone could have killed her?" Dain said as we rowed back. "Isn't it awful? Do let's hurry. She may be there, waiting for us. If she isn't we'll just have to go off looking for her again. We must go round to all the farms and ask every one if they've seen her."

She wasn't on the shore when we pulled in, and she wasn't in the hut. The milk we had left for her was untouched. We set off at once to explore the countryside. We called at two farms without success, and we shouted, "Choo-i, Choo-i" into every copse, and along every hedgerow we passed. It was still raining heavily, and by the time we got back it was almost dark. We shut the window but we left the back door open. We lit the lamp, and the first thing we noticed was the six copies of the book that we had arranged on top of our bookshelf, and I think that just then I'd have bartered not only them but the book itself for the sight of Choo-i lapping her saucer of milk, in which I observed a cockroach had drowned itself.

But we did our best to be cheerful, to invoke a spirit of conviviality and celebration. We made a huge fire, and we put the fowl on to boil, and then, as it was too late to have tea, I opened the bottle of claret, and we ceremonially clinked our mugs (we had no glasses yet) to the book, and publication day. Whatever that claret lacked in bouquet and flavour, it made up for in potency. The first drink was a small one, and it was to have been an appetiser only, but I poured out another at once, and as neither of us was accustomed to alcohol, and we'd had practically nothing to eat all day, it was not surprising that when we'd drunk that one we were nearly tipsy. We didn't forget about Choo-i, but our anxiety was temporarily allayed. We were certain that nothing tragic could have happened to her, and that any moment we'd hear her mewing at the living-room door, or see her spring on to the window-sill, and after we had started our third drink Dain swore that she could hear her, and we both ran out and shouted, and we were not seriously distressed when she did not come. Nor were we distressed when, returning to the living-room, we found it full of fumes, and discovered that the water in the pan had boiled dry. Such was the power of the claret that we decided not to continue the boiling process, but to put some fat in the pan, and then shove the whole thing in the oven to roast, and when we had done this we continued drinking, and we took the books and arranged them on the table, and we both imagined that we were wildly happy, and that everything was going to come right. We laughed at the idea that Choo-i could have been killed or caught in a trap. She was far too clever a cat for that. Think of the way she had escaped drowning that night of the storm! We laughed about the girl in the bookshop and the way she had told us she would order a copy of the book if we would tell her the name of the publisher. *She'd* know the name of the publisher, and our name, too, all right in a few days when the book became famous. We'd been silly to expect anything startling happening to-day. To-morrow probably or the next day there would be a letter from the publisher, telling us how things were going, and then the reviews would start coming in in earnest, and editors of newspapers and magazines would be writing, or perhaps wiring asking us for articles or stories, and film companies would be wanting the film rights and everything would be splendid.

The fowl was not a success. We forgot all about it until it started burning, and while bits of it were cooked they were so tough we could hardly get our teeth into them. We forgot to put salt in the vegetables, and the pancakes we made for a sweet tasted of fish, as we had used the wrong pan; but the claret sustained us throughout the meal, and we were still happy when we went to bed somewhere past midnight.

But there was no sign of Choo-i next morning. It was raining harder than ever. The postman did not come. We both felt ill and unutterably depressed. The wind was south-west, and too strong for us to use the boat. We set off across country again on another search, and by devious paths arrived at Porthkerris in the afternoon. Our notice was in the grocer's window, but as it was Wednesday, and early closing day, we couldn't ask for news. We couldn't buy any newspapers either, and as it was early closing day in St. Jude too, we made our way home to make a belated lunch off the remains of that miserable fowl.

Obviously Choo-i was dead. I had been very fond of her. She had been lovely to look at; fascinating to watch whether she was stalking a mouse in the garden (her whole body quivering with passion) or curled up sensuously in front of the fire. It had always given me a peculiarly agreeable sensation to have her rubbing herself against my legs when we landed from the boat and I had a fish for her. But I had no false sentiment as to her feelings towards me. Unlike a dog, whose affection could be absolute, transcending even human love in its sacrifice of self, a cat would always choose the best life that offered. Their affection, if you could call it that, was directly related to food and comfort, and no sense of loyalty or devotion would keep a cat in a home where it did not get a good measure of both, unless indeed, it could find nothing better. But we had treated Choo-i well. She'd always had plenty to eat, and except at night, when she'd prefer to be out, she could be as warm and comfortable as we were. I could not believe that she would find a better home on any farm or in the village of Porthkerris; and I could not believe that she had taken to the "wild," not in weather such as we'd been having. She might have been shot. She might have been killed in a trap. She might have eaten something that had washed up on the beach and been poisoned. But I was certain she was dead; and on Friday morning I was equally certain that all our hopes about the book were going to end, like my hopes about my lobster pot, in disillusionment, for the postman came at last, with a single letter that had been sent care of the publisher. It was a circular from a firm of money-lenders, with the information that sums ranging from ten to five thousand pounds could be advanced to suitable clients without security. The book had been published three days. We hadn't received a line from Mr. Mackenzie and this ironic communication was the first sign that the existence of the book (with myself as author of it) was known to the public. Would a money-lender have written to us if the thing looked as though it were going to sell? Would the publisher have merely re-directed it (and not enclosed it with a letter from himself) if he'd had any good news to report?

It was still raining, and blowing from the south-west. We hadn't the heart to go that day to St. Jude, for I knew that we wouldn't see the book in the bookseller's window, and that the woman would most likely be ruder to us than ever if we made inquiries about it. We went to Porthkerris. Our notice about Choo-i was still displayed, but the grocer

had no news for us. The only paper we could get was one of
the popular dailies. It had a small section devoted to books,
but there was no mention of ours. We didn't call at the
shipyard. We bought another sheep's head, and we went
home, and the first thing I did then was to put the six
copies of the book away in the same drawer that contained
the manuscript and the proof; for I couldn't bear the sight
of them any longer.

Dain went to bed early. I made up the fire, and took
out the manuscript of my new book, and read through
what I had written. I thought that in my whole life I had
never read such rubbish, and I tore it up and thrust it in the
fire, and then with a blank sheet in front of me I tried to
make another start: and I put my mind back into the days,
long before I had met Dain, when I'd first conceived the
idea of the collapsible lobster pot. There *was* a good story
in the thing, I told myself. In spite of its ultimate failure,
the early experiments with the pot, the practical tests, had
been terribly exciting, and my adventures in the business
world with it had been almost as exciting, and at times
extremely funny; and the whole story had an ironic significance that appealed to me very strongly at the present
moment. But there was no more plot in it than in the first
book: no love interest, no sex. Its atmosphere, its characters
(except that I would be obliged to show something of
myself) would be the same; and if the first was going to be
a failure, what chance would this one have, especially as so
much of its interest would depend on the reader compre-
hending the technical details of lobster fishing and the
manufacture of lobster pots?

I tried to think of some way of getting round these
problems; of making it less technical, of giving it a plot
and some sex interest, without interfering with the main

theme. But my mind kept wandering back to the present, to Dain and the baby, and the book and Choo-i, and I couldn't help looking at the place by the fire where, up to bedtime, Choo-i invariably lay sleeping! I couldn't shake off the awful depression that was on me, and I couldn't write a word. But the fire was hot, and the blacksmith's chair, which I'd pulled in from the big room, very comfortable. I fell asleep, and when I awoke, the fire was out; the lamp was burning low. Turning up the wick, I had enough light to see that it was nearly four o'clock. I got my flashlamp, and moved to the bedroom. I had no sooner opened the door than I was arrested by a sound coming from outside through the open bedroom window.

It had stopped raining. The wind had dropped, but the stream was swollen and noisy, and I wondered at first if my imagination hadn't tricked me; if the sound hadn't been made by the stream itself. Then I heard it again, an unmistakable mewing.

"Dain," I shouted. "Wake up! It's Choo-i. Outside."

Dain jumped up in bed, her mouth wide open, her eyes startled.

"What's the matter?" she cried. "What's the matter?"

"Choo-i," I shouted, as I made for the door. "Can't you hear her. It's Choo-i."

I didn't wait for Dain. I dashed out of the back door, shone the light across the stream and up the path. Then, just as on the night of the storm, I saw her eyes, glowing, a few yards away from the path, and I heard her mewing piteously. I leapt towards her. She was lying in a clump of dead bracken, and at first I could only see her head. She mewed, but she made no effort to move. I pushed the bracken aside, and then I saw that one of her hind legs was stretched

out behind her, that it was held between the jaws of a steel
trap, and that the chain of this had fouled a bramble. Dain,
carrying another flashlight, had joined me. We had no time
then for pity or anger or rejoicing. I released the chain from
the brambles. Dain picked Choo-i up, and I held the weight
of the trap from her leg, while she carried her inside to the
living-room, and laid her on the table. I fetched another
lamp.

But for her eyes, we could have hardly believed then that
it was Choo-i. Her fur, caked with soil and blood, was
plastered to her body. Her body was so emaciated you
could have counted her ribs and the joints of her spine down
to the very tip of her tail. But it *was* Choo-i, and, despite
her four days of starvation and agony, despite that she
must have dragged herself and that diabolical trap from
some distant copse or hedgerow we had missed in our search,
she was still very much alive. She snarled when Dain held
her down firmly, while I examined the jaws of the trap.
I could feel a definite muscular resistance in that hind leg
when I gripped it, and then, swiftly as I could, I opened the
jaws and set it free. I told Dain to hold on to her tight.
The teeth of the trap had cut through the fur, and there was
an open wound about three inches long reaching from the
paw upwards, exposing the ligaments and the bone. But
the bone, so far as I could tell, was not broken. I washed
the wound. Dain let go; and at once Choo-i turned her
head to the damaged leg, and started licking it.

I put the fire on. We warmed some milk. We set her
down in front of it, with a cushion under her leg, but she
balanced herself perfectly on three legs and the milk disappeared from the saucer as though there was a hole in the
bottom of it, and she at once mewed for more. We gave
her all we had, and as we had no ordinary fish, we opened

one of the tins of herring in tomato the Fosdycks had given
us. She cleared it, tomatoes and oil too. Then she started
licking her wound again, and we arranged some cushions
close to the fire, and helped her on to them, and she started
purring.

"Dain," I said. "*Is* that Choo-i purring there, or am I
dreaming?"

Dain was crying.

"I feel it's a dream too. But it can't be. Look, there's
that awful trap on the floor, and she's licking her foot again.
How can people be such brutes as to set traps like that.
And yet we've got her back. Oh, it's wonderful. Dear Choo-i.
Dear Choo-i. Hadn't we better open another tin of herrings
for her before we go back to bed."

We were asleep next morning when the postman rapped
loudly at the door, and my first thought then was not of him
but of our cat, and before going to the door I took a glance
into the kitchen, and there she was, with her fur dry, but
still a bit bedraggled, licking the last drop of oil out of that
second tin we had left for her; and I had opened the door
and said good-morning quite genially to the postman before
I had a thought of the book, and of what bad news he might
have of it; which encouraged him to a more than usual
garrulity.

"Ah, we've got a bit of better weather at last. First time
for nearly a week, I've been able to set out without my
oilskins. Maybe we'm in for a spell of real fine weather.
Be a real pleasure to be out, this mornin'. I've got a big
lot of letters for 'e this mornin'. Nearly all of 'em re-
directed too. And a lot of newspapers and things. Couldn't
have got all of 'em through the letter-box, so that's why I
knocked. Hope I haven't got 'e out of bed, though. I can't

remember having such a lot of letters to one address since there was a yachting gentleman staying at Porthkerris, and he do have as many as fifty in one post. He be a famous film actor or something like that. Most of they letters had been re-directed from Elstree, but all of yours be from someone in London."

My patience was at an end for the man was still only fumbling with the straps of his bag.

"Well, for God's sake let me have them," I said.

He was startled into a sudden activity. He opened the bag and he gave me first a large packet, then a bundle of newspapers tied up with string; then, glancing at each one as he handed them to me, about a score of letters. He searched into his bag again and produced another packet, and then he said, slowly fastening the strap:

"That be all, I think. I told 'e there be a 'andsome lot."

I hurried inside. Dain was sitting up in bed, looking very astonished. I threw the packets and letters on to the bed in front of her. I got into bed myself, and for a moment we just sat staring at them. Then Dain said:

"Surely they're not all for us! What's happened? Are they about the book. Open something. See what it is. Does it mean the book's a success? What are all the newspapers for? Look, all those letters have been sent to the publishers. There must be some good news in all that lot. Don't you recognise the handwriting? Look, that big packet. That's from the publisher himself." And then she said inconsequently, "What about Choo-i, is she all right?"

"Choo-i's all right," I said. "That's not a dream, anyway. But this looks as though it was." Then my old caution asserted itself. "Look here, don't let's get too excited. All this must be about the book, but it doesn't necessarily mean it's good news. Let's keep calm about it. Those papers may have reviews. It doesn't mean they'll be good reviews. It's more likely they'll be bad ones."

"I don't believe it. Open one, anyway. No, open the thing from the publisher first. Then we'll know straight away."

She handed the packet to me. I had a sudden spasm of terror.

"Look here. Let's have breakfast first," I said. "Or at least a cup of tea. I'm absolutely certain we're in for a horrible shock."

"Oh, don't be silly. If you won't open it I will, or anyway, I'll open one of the newspapers. Look, one of them's a Yorkshire paper."

A sudden courage possessed me. I took hold of that paper, a very well-known Yorkshire daily, ripped it open, and spread it out on the bed. I turned the pages until I came to one with a small column headed NEW BOOKS, and with my heart thumping I glanced down that column. There was no reference whatever to our book. Mechanically I turned to the next page, and to the next, which gave the feature news of the day, opposite to what is called the magazine page. And there, bang in the middle of the magazine page, was a reproduction of a photograph I had sent to Mr. Mackenzie at his request, and above this, top of the page spreading across four columns, and in large type, was printed:

EPIC OF THE NORTH-EAST COAST

and under this:

YORKSHIRE AUTHOR'S FIRST NOVEL A SENSATIONAL
SUCCESS

We didn't stop to read what was said below. I opened the packet from Mr. Mackenzie. There was a short letter from Mr. Mackenzie himself. It said that he had very great pleasure in sending me a selection of some of the early reviews of my book, all of which had been favourable. It was too early yet for these notices to have effected the sales of the book to any great degree, but the sales so far had been very satisfactory, and he had ordered a second printing, the first now being exhausted. In addition to the reviews he was sending me a proof of an advertisement that would be appearing in next Sunday's newspapers, and in several well-known weekly journals. He trusted that this advertisement would stimulate sales, and that the book was going to prove a success.

We looked at the proof first. It was a double column size. Four other books were listed in it, including that famous best-seller, but ours was on the top, and it was headed:

IMMEDIATE SUCCESS

and under the title were quotations from reviews by three famous critics, writing in famous journals, and under these, was printed in large type:

SECOND PRINTING

I gasped when I read what those famous critics had said. We turned to the cuttings, and saw that, in each case, the critic had put our book on the top of his list, and devoted most of his review to it, and although we were too excited to read one of them through, they seemed to have nothing in them but praise. We glanced through the others. Except for the Yorkshire papers (nearly all of which had made "news" of the book, and were dated Tuesday) they were all dated either Thursday or Friday. Some were newspapers. Some were weekly literary journals, and one was a famous society magazine which did not give a review, but published the photograph with a caption "Author of one of the season's hits."

"My God! My God! Can you believe it?" I gasped.

"Of course I can," cried Dain. "I just knew it would happen. Although I didn't think it would be quite as exciting as this. Listen to this. 'The book gains much of its strength from the deliberate exclusion of several elements usually held necessary in a modern novel. There is no plot, the feminine interest is almost absent.' Now what about sex, and the whole thing being just like a schoolboy's composition on inshore fishermen? Listen to this. 'Excitement flavours every chapter, not the garish excitement of the police court, but that intensification of feeling that comes from sharing in the victories men filch from the huge peril of the sea.' Now what about it being dull and boring. And listen to this too. 'A masterpiece of simplicity is here achieved by a British author who rivals the Scandinavian novelists' skill in grappling with big human issues and the changing moods of nature, and transcends them in fluency and descriptive ability.' What do you think of that, and there's nearly a column more of it. Shall I go on reading?"

"No. For God's sake don't," I protested. "Let's get up and have some breakfast. Let's have two eggs each. Let's——"

"But we haven't read any of the letters yet. Do let's open everything. . . . I've never been so excited in my life. Look, here's one from Bramblewick, and here's another."

I glanced at the two letters Dain held out to me. I knew without opening them that they were bills, and I put them on one side, with the swift and comfortable reflection that they'd be settled very soon; and I opened a letter that contained a request from a Bond Street photographer for a complimentary sitting. There were two other similar invitations. There were two letters from literary agents offering me their services. There was a request for an autographed copy of the book from a charity organisation, who wanted it for a bazaar; several money-lender's circulars, and a prospectus of a newly formed company which had a gold mine in Canada and wanted a lot of money to work it. And there was also a letter from the firm of naturalists, evidently containing our weekly postal order, and this we didn't trouble to open at all. I turned to Mr. Mackenzie's letter, and I held up the proof of that advertisement.

"Immediate success," I shouted. "Immediate success. Look at it, Dain. We've done it at last. Money. Pots of it. No more worries. No more bloody sheep's head. . . . God! Come on. Let's have breakfast. Let's go and see Joe and Charley May, and show 'em the plans of the boat. Let's go to St. Jude and buy a real chicken and damn the cost, and let's have a bottle of champagne. . . . And Choo-i's back too. I'd clean forgotten about Choo-i."

I had also forgotten about my patent lobster pot, and the pessimistic wisdom of the saying, that there's many a slip twixt the cup and the lip. I got out of bed, and went to the drawer where I had hidden the copies of the book, and I took one out and gazed at it with passionate affection; and it seemed to me then that instead of the title there was blazoned on the jacket the single word—SUCCESS!

13

THE BOOK in one sense was a success. Almost every newspaper and journal of note in the country gave it unstinted praise. We got scores of letters from readers too, some of them very famous people. All were full of praise. We got one from a lady who lived in a castle in Scotland, and she said she had never read a book she liked so much, and she felt that she would very much like to meet me, and would I care to come and stay with her at her castle. When I wrote and told her about Dain and the baby, she wrote us another charming letter, and sent us some marvellous baby clothes, and said that we must all three come up as soon as we could.

We had sent copies of the book to Henry and John, and Marney Lunn, giving them of course the publisher's and not our actual address. A fortnight later we got a long letter from Marney himself, although evidently it had been written by his wife at his dictation. It began by expressing his surprise at not hearing from me for such a long time, and he hoped that I was keeping well as he and Amy and the bairn were at present, although they'd all had bad colds, and it had been a bad winter for weather. He'd have written before this to thank me for sending the book only they'd had a very busy time of it, and a lot of things had been happening. The chief thing that had happened was that they'd had a stroke of luck with a trawler that had gone ashore in a fog at High Batts. They'd managed to put a kedge out for her, and get her off, and they'd got a hundred quid for the job, and with that they'd bought an old Burnharbour mule, and they'd started fishing at Burnharbour, and he and Amy had already decided to flit there and try to persuade John and father to flit there too, but the biggest job was getting mother to shift, but she'd have to agree in the end that it was best, as at present he and John and father were sleeping on board her all week, and only getting home for week-ends, and that made mother worry as to if they were all getting enough to eat. Burnharbour was an all-round better spot for fishing than Bramblewick, and besides, they could still fish Bramblewick grounds, without having to think about the landing bar. And there was plenty of life at Burnharbour too. They'd got two picture houses, and as they changed the programme twice a week that meant you could go four times a week if you wanted to.

He'd just finished reading the book. He thought it very interesting. Father had read his copy, and he'd been fair capped with it, especially the bits where the Lunns had got the laugh against the Fosdycks. He didn't know whether John had read his copy, or not. When was I coming back to Bramblewick? Had I made a lot of brass out of the book? He hoped so. They'd been doing very well since they'd got the mule, earning six times as much as they had done in the coble. They all sent their best wishes, and he and Amy looked forward to seeing me soon. . . .

That letter made us both very homesick, and I couldn't help thinking how thrilling it would have been if we'd had enough money to go up to Yorkshire for a week or so, anyway, and see them all again; and that it would have been even more exciting if we could have bought them a brand-new boat, although I knew that if we had been millionaires, they would not have accepted it.

But the book was not a best-seller. The first printing, which had been so quickly "exhausted," was only a thousand copies. A fortnight passed before the second printing was sold, and the advertisement contained the phrase "third printing." But by then the advertisement was much smaller, and lower down in the list, and by the end of the month all that appeared was the name of the book and no mention as to how many printings it had gone into, and soon after this there were no advertisements at all, and Mr. Mackenzie wrote me quite frankly to say that the early brisk demand for the book had now slackened. We must not however think of the book as a failure. It was always difficult to establish a new author with a single book, particularly if its subject was as original as mine. Its reception by the critics had been most gratifying. The chief value of this lay in the fact that when my next book was ready, the firm's travellers would have something very concrete to show to the libraries and booksellers (who were the *real* buyers of books) so that the success of the new book should be immediate, and would probably rekindle a demand for the first. He advised me strongly to get on with the new book as fast as I could, so that it could be out before the first was forgotten.

We received no inquiries for the film, or translation, or American rights; no letters from editors asking for articles or short stories; but the total sales when Mr. Mackenzie wrote to us were just under three thousand, making the total royalties about a hundred pounds; and he obligingly agreed to pay me this at once less the fifty already advanced so that I was able to pay off the last of the Bramblewick debts and still have something in hand for the baby.

It was a pity about the new boat; particularly as Joe and Charley had been most enthusiastic about our plan; and Charley had offered to build it at practically cost price, in order to keep the yard busy, and because it would be a

very good advertisement for him. They had not had a
single job all winter. But they took it philosophically, and
we consoled ourselves with the thought that it wouldn't
be much use while the baby was very small, and that we
were only postponing the idea, not abandoning it. The new
book would undoubtedly be a huge success, financially, as
well as "artistically." I had solved the problem of how to
construct it. I had invented a slender but feasible plot. I
had seen how I could introduce a moderately exciting sex
interest as a balance to the technicalities, and I was making
swift progress with it.

However disappointed we might have been with the
financial results of the first book, we couldn't have helped
being happy, for spring had come. The weather was dry
and sunny. The banks of the creek and of our valley were
starred with early primroses. The wild daffodils we had
planted along the stream in the autumn raced the primroses,
and before either had passed their full bloom, masses of blue-
bells thrust themselves out from under the dead bracken to
take their whack of air and sunshine before the greedy shoots
of the new bracken burst the soil and overwhelmed them.
Close by the hut we had planted out the wallflowers and
polyanthuses we had sown last spring. The scent of them
drifted in through every window, and every morning we
were awakened by the passionate singing of a blackbird,
perched on the garden fence, and when he paused for breath
we'd hear chaffinches and bullfinches and tits, warbling and
twittering in the nearby copses, and the more distant cries
of the gulls and curlews and herons in the creek.

But one morning before the blackbird had piped up we
were awakened by a peculiar tat-tat on the wall of the
hut, close to our bedroom window. It sounded exactly like
the postman, but it was much too early. We went to the

window, and looked out, and we were amazed to see the tail
of a sand-eel hanging down from the gutter, just above the
window, and flapping against the uppermost pane. Then
we saw that it was held by a kingfisher actually perched on
the gutter, and that the noise was made by the bird's beak
as it slapped the fish against the pane to kill it. On the path
below sat Choo-i (who had made a complete recovery from
her wound) lashing her tail and watching bird and fish
with passionate interest.

The garden soil was warm, and it had a stronger and
more exciting tang when you broke it than in the autumn.
You felt that it was alive and breathing. We planted our
early potatoes, and made sowings of peas and lettuces and
carrots, kohl-rabi and leeks and endive according to the
instructions of the gardening book; and we sowed many
new varieties of flowers. Armed with the experience we had
gained last year, we renewed our fight against the weeds
and pests and diseases, although we soon discovered that
such things move in cycles and that a pest that is prevalent
one year may not appear at all the next, and that there is
always something ready to take you by surprise. For example
there was no sign of the tiny grey slugs that had attacked
our peas last year; but there were swarms of small, hairy,
whitish insects which we identified as springtails that were
just as destructive until we choked them with soot. There
was no sign of club-root among our greens. But our cos-
lettuces, instead of shooting up, and thickening at terrific
speed as the first lot had done, began to wilt when half-
grown and we found an unidentifiable grub in the heart
of each one; yet the ordinary cabbage lettuce grew without
hindrance.

We gardened and fished, and went on collecting animals
for the firm; we painted and joinered, and I worked at the

new book, and Dain sewed and knitted. All the time a deeper
excitement was growing in us, for it wouldn't be long now
before our baby was born. I had no fear as to what was
going to happen. Things often went wrong when women
had babies. Sometimes the mother died. I knew that Dain
might die. But that knowledge only came from what I'd
heard, or read in books, and against it was an instinctive
confidence (which may have been partly communicated to
me by Dain herself) that everything would go well.

Yet, so far as modern science and our financial resources
could assist in the natural phenomenon of birth, we took
no chances. We saw a doctor in St. Jude. There was a
nursing home in the town, but when he made an inquiry
to the matron by telephone, he discovered that every bed
in it would be occupied on the anticipated date. The
alternative was to have a qualified nurse come and live
with us for the time, and we agreed that this would be best.

I went to St. Jude station to meet this lady (she came
from a distant city) one afternoon in early April. She was
short, slender, with silvery hair and a pink face with very
bright blue eyes. She wore a dapper uniform, with starched
cuffs and collar, and she looked so clean and dainty, I thought
at once that she'd get a shock when she saw the home she
was coming to, and I wished I'd engaged a motor-boat to
take her across the harbour, for although the weather was
fine, there was a stiff south-westerly wind and the water
was very choppy. I thought that probably she was going
to be a most difficult person to live with. She'd be fussy,
and want to run everything just as though she were in a
hospital, and expect to have someone wait on her hand and
foot, and she'd be horrified when she saw our Heath Robinson
bath, and discovered we had no water-closet. I was certain,
too, in that first moment of meeting, that she strongly dis-

approved of my personal appearance, and I wished I'd put
a collar and tie on. And when, a few minutes later (our
conversation so far had been confined to platitudes about
the weather) I led her down some slippery steps to the boat,
merrily bobbing up and down against the quay-side, and I
glanced across the choppy harbour, I should not have been
a bit surprised if she'd refused to get into the boat, and told
me she was going to take the next train back to the city.

All my first unfavourable impressions were completely
wrong. She was certainly nervous; but she got into the
boat without protest. I dried the stern seat, and folded my
coat for a cushion, and when she had sat down I gave her
my oilskin to protect her clothes from the spray. I apologised
for the strong smell of fish in the boat bottom, and she
astonished me by saying she liked it. When the first choppy
wave hit the boat side and the wind whipped the fine spray
almost into her face, she astonished me more by laughing
and saying:

"What an adventure. *What* an adventure!"

She thought the harbour was lovely with the sun shining
on it, and the water so blue where it wasn't whipped white
with the gale. When I pointed out the creek to her, with
the oaks bearing now a half-formed leafage that was nearer
gold than green, she cried:

"Oh, what a lovely view. What a picture!"

When I rounded the bluff into the cove, and she saw
the hut and the garden, she seemed as excited as Dain had
been when I'd first shown her the place.

"Oh, how lovely. Is that really your little house? Isn't
it romantic! All by yourselves. Not another house in sight.
I've always dreamt about a place like this, but I never really
imagined I should ever stay in one. I *am* glad I've taken
on this case."

Mother Macree (as I had already christened her in my mind), liked everything. She thought the sink and the bathroom plumbing most ingenious and efficient. It didn't bother her that our "sanitary" arrangements were outside. She liked drinking tea from a mug. She approved of all our labour-saving devices for cooking and washing up. She liked her own bedroom and the bed, and the built-in wardrobe cupboards, we'd specially made for her. She was enchanted by the sound of the stream, and the singing of the birds, and the scent of the flowers. She liked Choo-i, and above all she liked Dain, the cot and the garments Dain had made. Like Joe, she said that the whole place was like the garden of Eden, but the only thing wanting was what we were going to have, and that was a baby—she just knew it was going to be a lovely one, it couldn't help but be, born in such lovely surroundings. What a pity all mothers couldn't have their babies like this.

She told us her story while we were having supper that night. She was a widow. Her husband had been a civil engineer, and they'd had a family of two sons and three daughters, the youngest of them ten when the war came. Her husband had got a commission in the Royal Engineers. He had gone to France in 1916, and was wounded three times, and finally gassed, a month before the Armistice, and he actually died on Armistice day. Her eldest son had joined the Royal Air Force from school, in 1917, but he had been killed in a crash before he had seen active service. Her other son had been too young to join up. He had followed his father's profession, and had got a very good post in India, and had married out there, and now had two children. The two eldest daughters had married soon after the war. One was in Australia, the other in South America, and they too, had families which she had never seen. The youngest daughter, who had trained as a children's nurse was now with a family in France, and very rarely came home. . . .

Well (she told us), she had her widow's pension (her husband had been a major when he died) and with only that youngest daughter's training to pay for in the early days of "peace," she could have sat back, and grown old in comparative comfort, but that had never been her idea of life. She loved children, especially babies. Her own were fledged, and she was too old to think of marrying again and having any more. But she wasn't too old for a profession that had always interested her, one that she would have entered if she hadn't married. So she had taken a course in general nursing and midwifery at a famous hospital, got her diplomas, and she had been in private practice ever since, and she was certainly happier doing that than being a good-for-nothing old woman. But this was the last case she would take for a long time. She had been saving up, from her pension and her professional fees, and in about six weeks' time she was going to set off on a grand tour, to visit all her children and grandchildren. She was going to France and then to India, and then to Australia, and then to South America—all round the world. She was going to have a glorious holiday.

But if Mother Macree had an amiable, easy-going disposition, and carried with her an aura of happiness, she soon proved herself a professional martinet. She assumed complete command of the whole establishment, and of us. There were only three of the calculated days of waiting left. Dain was put on a strict routine of rising, and meals and exercise, and bedtime at ten o'clock. As Mother Macree herself retired then and she was a light sleeper, and the floors of the hut creaked with every footstep, I felt myself under a dreadful constraint, and so, when that third day came, I rigged myself a tent out of a piece of sail-cloth, and pitched it at the cove end of the garden. Nothing had happened, or looked like happening, by official bedtime that night; but Mother Macree assured us that a first baby was usually late, so that there was nothing to worry about. If anything did happen, she'd let me know at once, but the best thing for every one was just to go to sleep. I took a hurricane lamp with me, and hung it from the ridge pole of my tent, and tried to get on with my book, but I couldn't concentrate, and as I could not go to sleep at that ridiculous hour, I went down to the cove, Choo-i following me and wondering what the devil was the matter. The tide was up, and I had some bait. I launched the boat, leaving Choo-i to mew her bewilderment on the beach. I rowed slowly across the creek to a spot practically opposite to the cove where, at high tide, we'd sometimes caught flounders and occasionally bass. I dropped the anchor and started fishing.

I wasn't frightened. I had a perfect confidence in Mother Macree. She had told us that if everything went normal she could manage the whole job by herself. If anything did go wrong, I could get the doctor from St. Jude in less than half an hour. It was queer, however, being in that boat by myself. It was queer, looking across the creek at the dark hut, and thinking of Dain being asleep by herself, and my not daring to venture inside my own home lest I should wake her, or Mother Macree. I wasn't frightened. I kept on telling myself that what was going to happen was a perfectly normal process of nature, as normal as breathing, or eating and digestion; yet it was no use my pretending that *I* felt normal. I could not concentrate on fishing for one thing. I could not stop looking towards the hut, although I knew that so long as there was no light in it, nothing could be happening, and that I was near enough to hear Mother Macree's voice if she merely opened the door, and called softly to my tent.

There were no fish, anyway, although there were plenty of crabs to eat the bait. When the last of the bait was gone, I hauled in my line and I wondered if it would be any good getting the net and shooting it, for I still didn't feel sleepy. But I just remained where I was, looking towards the hut. The air was still. I could hear, quite distinctly, the sound of trucks being shunted on the far away and invisible "clay" jetties of St. Jude, but in the creek there was no sound. The tide was full. The water might have been a solid block of ice, immobile, and completely silent, in which even the boat was fixed, for I could not detect the faintest gurgle from stem to stern. There was an icy pallor on its surface, the reflection of the stars, dimmed and diffused by a thin, low-hanging water mist I could feel but could not see. But the stars themselves were clear, and my view towards the almost indistinguishable hut must have comprised nearly half of the eastern dome of the sky. There was one star, it was not a particularly bright one, and I did not know its name, which hung almost immediately above the hut. I was not, normally, superstitious. I thought of the star of Bethlehem. The association was inevitable. But I was concentrating my attention more on the hut itself, looking for a practical, and not a symbolic sign of an approaching earthly event. Besides, any house where a baby was expected, might be found to have a star of some sort shining over it, if it was a fine night, and the observer looked from the right position. Suddenly a sign did come. I saw the gleam of a light, in what I guessed was Mother Macree's bedroom. I forgot about the star. I stood up, and I could feel my heart thumping wildly. The light went out, and it appeared in another window. It might have been the living-room, or our bedroom, I could not be certain, but it was a proof that someone was out of bed, moving about, that something was happening or about to happen. Should I pull ashore—or should I wait until Mother Macree shouted? With my eyes glued on that light, I stepped forward, and felt for the anchor rope, and as I touched it there was a flash in the southern part of the sky. Involuntarily looking up, I witnessed the astounding spectacle of a meteor moving from the south, upwards, and northwards, and then curving down towards that very star which hung above the hut, and there apparently explode with a flash as brilliant as a distant thunder-bolt.

I did not wait for that expected shout. I saw that the light in the hut was still burning. I hauled the anchor, and I felt myself trembling as I grasped the oars, and pulled in for the cove. Choo-i was waiting for me, and I cursed her violently when she tried to rub herself against my legs. I dashed up the path and up to the front door and opened it, and looked into the big room. I couldn't see any light, but I could hear footsteps and I shouted in a voice that I knew was hoarse:

"It's only me. What's happening? Do you want me?"

The door leading into the living-room opened, and there was Mother Macree in her nightgown, and her silver hair down her shoulders, with a candle in her hand, looking a bit startled, and certainly very vexed.

"Hush, hush," she admonished. "Nothing's happening. I just got up to get a drink of water. You gave me quite a fright, coming in like that. I told you that I'd call you, if I wanted you."

I was crestfallen. "I saw your light," I explained. "There was a meteor, flashed across the sky, and burst clean over the hut. Did you see it? It was as bright as a flash of lightning! You see, I was out in the boat fishing."

"Of course I didn't see any meteor and what have meteors got to do with it? You ought to have more sense than be sitting out in a wet boat this time of night. You expectant fathers are all alike. You're much worse than the mothers. Now you get to bed, and stop worrying and fussing. It may be a week yet before your baby comes, and until it does we've all got to keep calm, and get all the rest we can."

Actually it was three nights after I had witnessed that seemingly portentous spectacle in the sky that the event took place; and, just to show how impotent, and completely unnecessary the father is on such occasions, I was not aware that it was happening; for after three comparatively sleepless nights spent partly in the boat, and partly in my uncomfortable tent, I turned in at ten o'clock and fell asleep instantly. And it was somewhere round five in the morning that I was awakened by Mother Macree shouting from the hut door. I shot up from my mattress, and answered hoarsely:

"Yes, yes; I'm coming!"

She answered: "It's all right. No need for you to be alarmed. It's all over. You've got a lovely little daughter. You can come and see it if you like, but you must be very quiet, and not disturb your wife. She's just been splendid, and now she's fast asleep."

I suppose that I realised then that I had been frightened after all, more frightened than I'd ever been in my life before. I didn't think of the baby. I only thought of Dain, safe and fast asleep, and I was glad that Mother Macree had shut the door, and that she could not hear me sobbing my relief as I hurried to follow her.

14

To an unbiassed critic, a newborn human baby is not beautiful. Its head is too large for its body. It slopes back, and seems unnaturally elongated. The nose is flat. The mouth of course is toothless. The eyes have no apparent pupils, no expression. The hands and feet are purplish, the legs are bowed, so that you'd wonder how the devil they could ever grow straight. The general appearance is that of an ape, and compared with the young of the domestic fowl, for example, a human baby is monstrous and repulsive. There's a saying that a baby arrives in the world wrapped in its own love, and it is a more obvious psychological truth that parents are blind and that to them their own child, especially if it be their first, is a paragon of beauty and the other virtues.

To us Amelia (it was inevitable that we should name her after Hoskins's ship, seeing that she owed so much to it) was perfect from the start. True that while I had seriously, and with fear, considered the possibility of twins (even triplets) neither of us had imagined that Dain would produce a daughter, and that we were both surprised. But we were not disappointed. I might have known, from my scientific training, that the factors which determine the sex of offspring are beyond parental control; that Nature is concerned only with the production of sufficient numbers of both sexes to maintain the continuance of the race, and that the chances of any particular mating producing male or female are exactly the same as a tossed coin falling head or tail. It didn't matter how much you were in love with each other. It didn't matter how healthy you were, and least of all how much you wanted a son or a daughter; you got what was sent to you, whether you were a king or a beggar. The exciting thing was that our baby had arrived without scratch or harm, a brand-new human being, complete with eyes and ears and nose and mouth, and limbs and lungs and a voice, all, especially the voice, in working order. She'd got ten little fingers, complete with finger-nails, and ten toes complete with toe-nails, all perfectly manicured; eyelashes and eyebrows, and a funny sort of down on her head that at least looked like hair, and she could open her eyes even if she couldn't focus them. She was *alive*. If I was privately worried about the shape of her legs, I accepted Mother Macree's assurance that they would grow straight, as we both did her assurance (although I had no doubt she said the same to every parent) that Amelia was the loveliest child she had ever "borned."

"You ought to see some of them," she told us. "Talk about being ugly. I borned a boy once, who was just covered all over with long black hair. And his face! You'd think he was a son of Satan. I was just terrified of showing him to the mother, poor dear, because for one thing both she and her husband had been praying for a daughter, and she was so certain that she was going to have one and, I think, she'd imagined it would be born with golden curls. It was a shock to her; and her husband never said a word when he saw it, not one word. He just looked completely disgusted. Yet, before I left that case they'd both gone quite crazy over the poor little mite, and, anyway, he grew into quite a lovely boy."

Before Mother Macree left us for her city, and to make her final preparations for her voyage of family visitations round the world, she gave us a lot of advice as to how we should bring up Amelia. As a mother herself (*and* a grand-mother) she didn't hold with everything in the modern methods of mothercraft. All this Freudian stuff, for example, was disgusting and horrible. Fancy any one suggesting that because a father, when he was bouncing his baby up and down, and happened to hurt it, was really *meaning* to hurt it, because he was jealous of the baby stealing his wife's love! There were a lot of so-called modern thinkers who put down everything that went wrong with children to sex, and what they called complexes, and fixations and inhibitions and goodness knows what. Yet a good deal of what was being taught was sound common sense, and a great improvement on the old-fashioned methods. What we must watch out for from the first, especially as Amelia was such a *lovely* baby, such a little *darling*, was not to spoil her, for her sake as well as ours. We mustn't underrate a baby's intelligence. They knew far more than grown-ups about some things, and they'd be very quick to take advantage of it too. You must never, never give in to them. The main things, of course, were feeding and fresh air and sleep. A baby should sleep by itself, in the open air by day and in its own room at night if that was possible. It should be fed at regular intervals, strictly by the clock, and not as in the old-fashioned way, when it cried for it. But it was just as wrong to believe that it was natural for a baby to cry a great deal—that it was simply exercising its lungs. It shouldn't cry at all, except when it was hungry, and never at night if it was fed at the proper times. A baby should be a joy to its parents, not a source of irritation and anxiety. You had to give up a lot for them, and they'd take it and a great deal more if you were weak-minded, and that was as bad for the child as it was for you.

It was sound advice, and strong-mindedly we followed it.

Amelia was fed by the clock. She woke us up once or twice during the night, but as Mother Macree had warned us that she would do this to try it on, Dain simply gave her some boiled water out of a spoon, and she soon discovered it wasn't worth it, and she slept without break from ten to six. Apparently she was quite satisfied with the cot we had made for her. We pushed this out on to the little lawn at the back of the hut, and except at food time she slept there all day long in the flower-scented air, with the birds singing and twittering all around her, and the robin actually perching sometimes on the cot side; and, although we were careful never to let the sun shine directly on her face, her skin was soon tanned to the colour of honey; the down on her head was gradually replaced with real hair, the colour of straw, and her eyes, which at first had been an indeterminate blue, darkened, the pupils contracted, and if they squinted horribly at times their expression became quite intelligent.

Dain had made a swift recovery. There was plenty to do in the garden. We were still collecting animals for the firm. I had restarted work on the book, and but for the time that had to be spent feeding her, and bathing her and the extra washing, it seemed that Amelia was to make little difference to our ways of living. There seemed no reason either why we should spend all our time ashore. We made a sort of shallow box that would just fit between the middle and forward thwart of the boat, the size, too, of the cot mattress, and one sunny afternoon in May we carried Amelia down to the cove, tucked her up in her bunk, and away we went down harbour on her first voyage. We had a bright-red blanket for her top covering and she looked lovely with her tiny honey-brown face peeping out of it, and we felt very proud of her. We called at the shipyard, and we hailed

Joe and Charley to the quayside to have a look at her, and they were both quite enthusiastic, although I could see that Charley's mind was very preoccupied, and that he was more than usually worried. Joe beamed when we told him we had named our first baby Amelia.

"Why, that be a lovely name, although I hope 'twon't mean she'll be unlucky like that schooner of ours. She be a lovely little maid, though; lovely. Damned if I wouldn't like to have she for myself. You've got a proper garden of Eden now. Reckons you'll want a lot more too, now you've made a start like this."

I had brought the money for the rent, and leaving Dain and Amelia in the boat, I went with Charley into his office. At once he started to unburden himself about his worries. Things were getting worse and worse. Here they were with the summer season drawing close, and there was still no prospect of any work coming to the firm. Nobody wanted motor cruisers, or if they did they couldn't afford it, least not to have new ones built. And yet the cruising idea was catching on. Quite a number of people he knew were buying ship's lifeboats, and converting them, putting in a second-hand car engine for power. You could buy these lifeboats for next to nothing at Salmouth and Chardmouth, and he'd thought of investing in a few of them and converting them, for re-sale, but even that meant capital, and Joe was dead against it. It offended his pride.

To make things worse, the trustees of the "estate" had started dropping hints. I guessed what Charley was leading up to, and I was not alarmed when he asked me if I'd thought any more about buying the bungalow and the land. The trustees would, he was certain, be willing to break up the estate and he was just as certain they wouldn't ask a very big price for our bit, probably not more than three or four hundred pounds. He didn't want to hurry me about a decision, but he hoped I'd let him know as soon as I could.

I told Charley that we did want to buy the place, and that I'd intended to broach the matter if my first book had been more of a financial success. As things stood at present of course it was out of the question, but I was engaged on another book, and there didn't seem to be any doubt that this would enable me to buy not only the hut and the land, but to give the order for our cabin cruiser; and he seemed quite satisfied when I paid him the rent, and the subject dropped. I didn't mention it to Dain when I rejoined her. I knew that I could trust Charley. I knew that there was not the slightest chance of our being turned out so long as the rent was paid. Only I felt sorry, however, that I hadn't enough money to help him with this new idea of his which, even if it did offend Joe's pride as a master craftsman, would be better than idleness and the dole.

We did our shopping, and then as we had no bait, we pulled up the Pol estuary to the china-clay jetties. The only ships loading there were a small English coaster, and a Finnish "auxiliary" steel barque, with a number of tall flaxen-haired sailors on board, who looked over the rails as we passed slowly alongside, and showed a great interest in Amelia; one of them suddenly disappeared down a hatch and came back with a toy reindeer and sledge, clearly "home-made," which he handed to us with a broad smile.

"For your baby, yes?" he said. "Very nice. Very pretty. I got babies of my own. Very nice. You give her little toy, yes? From me."

It might have been that foreign ship, with its romantic-looking and kind-hearted sailors or it may have been the hot spring sunshine, but we both experienced a sudden and powerful attack of wanderlust as we continued up the estuary.

"We simply must get that cruiser," said Dain. "Won't it be exciting, putting all our things on board, and taking in supplies, and setting off for the unknown. I don't see any reason why we shouldn't make cruises abroad. Amelia's not going to make any difference. She'll just love it as much as us, particularly when she's big enough to take a real interest in things. Just fancy being able to go to a place like Finland, all on our own, and going into queer harbours and seeing people in their native costumes, and wandering through the market places, and buying toys like this, and queer shoes and baskets, and pottery and rugs. And it would be just as thrilling to get home again, and unpack our treasures, and then when we were home we could be planning our next cruise."

"With a decent boat, we could certainly go pretty well where we liked," I said. "There's nothing to stop us except really bad weather, and as time would be no object, we could slip from one harbour to another, and we could make some pretty long voyages, entirely in sheltered water. Rivers for example. I believe it's possible for a small boat to travel by rivers and canals practically across the whole of Europe. You can get from the Rhine to the Danube and then to the Black Sea. You could come through the Dardanelles into the Mediterranean. There's Greece and Italy and the Riviera, and I think you can travel up the Rhone and somehow or other get to Paris and the Seine, and back home that way."

"How exciting! Amelia would learn to talk in at least a dozen languages. I suppose there's no real reason why we shouldn't go to the South Seas one day, and the Caribbees. We might take Amelia to the very island where her far-away relations lived. Imagine the sunshine there, and swimming along the coral reefs, and seeing the queer fish. And coconut palms, and parrots, and butterflies as big as birds, and all sorts of thrilling fruits, and black people all naked."

"She'd have to be a damned good boat of course to get all that way. And we'd want some practice in navigation. But we've simply got to get one, the moment we can afford it. By next summer, anyway. Then make a few experimental voyages not so far from home, but going farther every time."

"Yes. I suppose we will have to do it gradually. Just think, Amelia will be more than a year old then. She'll be able to walk and talk, and she'll have teeth and be able to eat ordinary food. . . . I suppose by then, too, we'll be thinking about having another baby. If it's a girl this time it simply must be a boy next. That's the law of averages, isn't it? I should think she'll love having a baby brother."

At any other time I might have been alarmed at that remark; but the sun beat hotly on my face, and looking at Dain, and the little head of our sleeping infant poking out of the blanket in her bunk, I was incapable of a gloomy thought. We were, but for the "collecting job," completely broke again, with no prospect of getting any more money until the new book was finished. Yet we were immeasurably better off than we had been this time last year. However hopeful we might have been about the first book, nothing had been certain. There had been the anxiety about my debts, about the Fosdycks recognising us. There had been the fear that at any time we might have had to clear out of the hut. Now, even if the first book had been a comparative financial failure, I'd paid my debts out of it: we'd got our little boat, and many things we had needed for ourselves and the home: we'd got our baby. I could think of what the critics had said, and what Mr. Mackenzie had prophesied.

The success of the second book was assured. It was only a matter of time before we'd have enough money to do all the things we wanted; and if it did flash through my mind that a second baby might prove a difficult complication on a cruise to the South Seas, it was not a question of immediate importance.

That first voyage with Amelia was such a success that it justified our going on lengthier trips outside the harbour, and soon, although we were more cautious about the weather, we were doing most of the things we had done when we'd been alone. We fished, with lines and our net. We made a waterproof canopy for the bunk so that Amelia wouldn't get splashed when we hauled our gear or fish on board, and if occasionally a drop or two of spray did touch her face, or a fish jumped by accident into her bunk, she didn't seem to mind, but just went on calmly sleeping. How simple it was having one small baby, who slept, and, exactly five minutes before her feeding time, opened her eyes, pursed her lips, and yelled; then chuckled and fed with her eyes blissfully shut, and her little fingers and toes clawing ecstatically, then yawned, and drooped her head like a drunken man, and slept again until roused by that accurate internal alarm clock of hers

We dare not, even when a spell of really settled, fine weather came in June, risk venturing as far as our mackerel cove, but west of the harbour mouth we found within comparative easy reach of home one that was almost as exciting. It had a sandy beach where we could make a fire and picnic, and rocks from which we could dive into deep water; and close under the cliff were shallow pools so warm that we could hold Amelia in them for a brief bath when she woke up, and shorten her regulation spell of yelling; for she chortled with delight and hated coming out until she realised that what was next on the programme was the thing she had really woken up for.

The summer drew on. The harbour filled with yachts. The Saturday afternoon and Sunday high tide boating trips up the creek again robbed our valley of some of its peace and seclusion, and again, through the remarkable acoustics of the creek, we were able to learn something of what the local inhabitants were thinking of us. We gathered that there was still considerable doubt as to whether we were married, and there were one or two "families" who still kept well out into the fairway, as though there might be something infectiously dangerous in the air of our place. But on the whole, it seemed that our stock had gone up since the publication of the book and the arrival of Amelia. There seemed to be no doubt now as to my profession. No one seemed to know much about the book itself (although the St. Jude bookshop had had three copies on show and had actually sold one), but evidently some of the press notices had been seen and vaguely remembered, and we heard someone saying that I was a very famous author, and that I must be making thousands of pounds a year, and that I was living this sort of life only because, like most authors, I was a bit queer in my head. But the chief topic of these overheard discussions (which usually faded out in most tantalising manner at a most interesting point) was our baby, and it was wonderful the way the women stared in a vain effort to catch sight of the cot. It was clear that Joe (and the postman), must have done some talking about her in the local pub, for often we heard them quoted as the authority for such remarks as, "She be a lovely little maid, brown as a berry, although she do have whitish hair." . . . "No. They don't dress her in ordinary clothes. She be naked mostly, and lyin' in the sun, but she be a healthy 'un." . . .

"They don't keep her in no pram. They've made a box for she, and do actually take she in their little skiff, and even go fishin' outside the harbour, miles away." These remarks amused us and pleased us, and we were quite hurt when we heard uncomplimentary things such as, "Poor little maid, they ought to be ashamed of themselves." And, "'Tis all wrong the way these queer folks look after their little 'uns."

I finished the last chapter of the book in another all-night sitting; and I read it to Dain next morning as she sat outside on the lawn, feeding Amelia. She was as excited and pleased as she had been when I had read the last chapter of the first book on the beach of the mackerel cove. She said that she even liked it better. I was not so sure that I did myself; but I believed that I had done the chief thing I had set out to do, which was to show the fierce independence of my fisher-folk, their resistance to a commercialism, which might have spelt the uprooting of all their traditions, their ways of living; to broaden the picture I had tried to give in my first book of a people who found happiness not so much in the "brass" they won in their fight with the sea, but in the fight itself. This was all right. But in order to establish that hard conservatism of theirs, I had been obliged to establish my own conflicting character, and weave it as a cross-thread throughout, and I was bothered by the thought that perhaps I had made this too conspicuous. Again I thought that perhaps I hadn't made it strong enough, and that the personal "sex" interest I had introduced was far too slight for the presumed strong appetite the public had for such matters.

But Dain's enthusiasm overcame my doubts and fears. It was a *grand* book—better than the first! Mr. Mackenzie would be delighted with it. No awful waiting this time to know whether it would be accepted or not. No doubts as to its success. Money—money! And the new boat, and the Baltic and the Danube and the South Sea. And what about to-day? How should we celebrate? Wasn't it time the mackerel were in again? Couldn't we risk a trip to the famous cove?

The weather was warm, but there seemed to be a risk of thunder in an indefinite cloud-mass that hung low in the sky away to the southward. I compromised. We'd take food and gear for a meal, but we'd wait until we got outside the harbour before settling where we should go. Setting off for a trip with Amelia, however, was not quite so simple as when we had only ourselves to think about. There were so many more things to think about, so many more things to take, apart from the bunk and her bedding, and by the time we were pulling down the harbour that cloud-mass to southward had perceptibly risen higher, and my fears of the weather had likewise increased. Dain agreed at once that it would be too dangerous to venture far beyond the harbour mouth. But she said vexatiously:

"What a nuisance! It would have been just heavenly in the cove. Oh, if only we had our big boat now. We could have gone to the cove as easy as winking and not bothered what the weather was going to do. If it had turned bad we could have got back to the harbour just as easily. But we needn't turn back yet, need we? We've simply got to have some sort of a celebration!"

It was August now, but as it was morning there were not many pleasure craft at anchor. The sea outside the harbour, although grey under the shadow of that rising bank of cloud, was dead smooth, and undoubtedly most of the yachting people would be enjoying themselves with a complete indifference to the threat of the weather. Rain, even if heavy, would make no difference to your comfort in a decked boat. The squally wind and choppy sea that usually accompanied a thunderstorm would do little more than make the boat pitch and roll, and with an engine you could make for shelter if this got too much for you. Unconsciously the minds of both of us were being primed for (and not against) the temptation that was to confront us very shortly.

We had intended to do our Porthkerris shopping, and post a parcel of animals, on our way to the sea: so we carried on to the village, and, as we approached the shipyard, we noticed three, long, grey, naval gigs, and a smaller craft that looked like a ship's lifeboat, moored together in a line, just off the jetty: then, as we drew near, we saw that a fourth gig was drawn up on the landing slip. Charley May was standing close by, gazing at her so intently that he did not at first perceive our arrival. We had seen Charley several times since the day he had mentioned the matter of selling the hut. He had not raised the question again, and I had taken it for granted that it was not seriously troubling him. But he had referred again to his idea of investing in some ship's lifeboats, and converting them for re-sale; and the gigs suggested that he had at last put the idea into practice.

The sky now was entirely clouded over, and there was a rumble of thunder. It was spotting with rain. We lifted Amelia (in her bunk) on to the jetty, and moved into the shelter of one of the sheds; and at once Charley came over to us, and we saw that he was in excellent spirits. He looked at Amelia and politely admired her, and asked us how we were getting on, and made a remark about the weather. Then he pointed to the gigs, and said:

"See those boats? I went to Salmouth the day before yesterday, and bought the lot of them at a sale, for thirty pounds. We've had a stroke of luck at last. There's a retired

business man—although he's a major too—who came to
settle at St. Jude a few months ago. He came over here to
talk about having a cabin cruiser built, but although he's
got plenty of money, he decided, when we went into it,
he'd wait till things got better. Well, I talked to him about
my idea of doing conversions, and he got interested, and
said he'd have one for himself and help us do one or two
more as a sort of speculation, and told me to go ahead. I've
been scouting round for days looking for a ship's lifeboat.
Then I heard of the sale and as those gigs seemed a better
proposition than any lifeboat, as you'll know when you
look at one, all larch and English oak and copper fastened,
I put in a bid, and I can tell you I was surprised to get them
at that price. I'd been prepared to go up to ten pounds
just for one, but keep that quiet. I got that other boat,
which is a ship's lifeboat by the way, came from a Norwegian
steamer that was sunk in a collision, for another three quid.
This conversion job is bound to be a good advertisement for
us. I'll show you the plans in a minute. It's going to be a
tip-top job, not like one of these home-made affairs. I've
even got Uncle Joe—he's away at Salmouth now getting
some timber—quite interested in it. And if we can do one,
why not another, why not all four? Of course it's not so
good as building a boat from the keel, but it's better than
nothing. It's a start, that's the main thing."

There was a closer clap of thunder, and it rained heavily
for a few minutes. Then the sun came out again, and leaving
Amelia in the shed we walked over to the boat that was
hauled on to the slip. I don't think that Charley was trying
to do business with us. I doubt if he had an inkling of what
was passing through our minds, as he showed us the plan
of how the craft was to be converted, the rowing thwarts
taken out; the timbers braced; the sides of the forepart

built up to take the decking and roof for a cabin. I was not
enamoured by the boat herself. She was about thirty feet
in length with a beam of eight. There would be ample
room for a lavatory and two-berthed cabin, a wheel-house
amidships, a cockpit aft. The engine, Charley explained,
was going to be the only seriously expensive item. Lots of
these amateur-built cruisers had car engines in them with
reducing gears, but they were very heavy on fuel, and their
parts were inclined to corrode with salt water or even sea air.
The major was not going to economise falsely in that
particular. He was going to have a real marine engine that
would cost £120; but even with that the whole job would
only come to £200, whereas a new cruiser with the same
accommodation couldn't be built for less than £400.

Four hundred pounds! When we had discussed the plans
of our own proposed boat with Charley and Joe, we had
never asked its possible cost. Money, then, with the
stupendous success of the book so certain, had seemed to
us a minor matter. Taking the size of the gig as a guide
(ours would have been ten feet longer), and thinking of the
many ways in which our plan improved on Charley's, then
the cost would probably have been close to £500. How daft
we had been ever to think of such a thing. And yet I couldn't
fight back the envious excitement that was possessing me.
I saw the same excitement in Dain's eyes, as she looked at
the gig. I couldn't help thinking of the absurdly low cost
of the boat itself and that, with no customer to satisfy, and
no time limit for its completion, we could probably carry
out the conversion of such a boat into a cabin cruiser
ourselves. Why not, if we could get hold of one? Raising
the sides, the laying of a three-quarter deck, the building
of light bulkheads and bunks and floors was not a highly
technical job like the building of a hull. We had proved in

the making of Amelia's cot, that if we took our time, and disciplined our desire to see a thing finished, that we were tolerably efficient craftsmen. It was only a question of being careful about your measurements, and not guessing them, and making certain that you planed or sawed a piece of wood dead square, and resisting the temptation to drive in a nail, instead of using a gimlet, and countersinking a screw. We *could* do the carpentering. Given the hull, we could build a cabin cruiser; but there remained the far more vital matter of the engine, and looking at the gig my heart sank. It would take a very good engine to drive a boat that size through the water. You might get one cheaper than the figure Charley had mentioned; you might get one second-hand, but even so we wouldn't be justified in getting one until we had substantial proof of the book's success, and by then we might be able to get our dream boat built. It was as though Charley had read my thoughts just then, for he said:

"You know you ought to go in for a job like this. It would come out a lot cheaper than that one you showed us."

I laughed, perhaps a trifle bitterly.

"Not a hope at present," I said, adding with an air of superiority I did not really feel, "Besides, when we get the money, we'll want something much better."

Perhaps Charley did not hear me correctly; or perhaps he was a better psychologist than I'd thought, for he answered slowly:

"Of course. Of course." Then he said, "By the way, did you notice that ship's lifeboat? She's a bit small for a cabin cruiser, no good for what I've got in mind. But she'd be all right for just two people, and she's sound as a bell. Come and have a look at her."

The storm had passed away to the east, and the sun was

still shining; but more clouds were gathering, and we knew that we must finally give up the idea of a trip to sea. Amelia was sleeping serenely, and we walked to the quayside, and looked at the lifeboat. We had not really looked at her when we came in, for she had been partly hidden by the gigs. I was struck at once by her unusual lines. She was quite unlike the "regulation" British ship's lifeboat. She was clinker built, with very wide planks, and her gunwales had a high lift, almost like a whale-boat fore and aft. She was painted a dingy green, inside and out, and this was made dingier still by what looked like a coating of coal dust, congealed with sea water and oil. She was small, not more than twenty-six feet, I guessed, with a beam of about seven. But at first I did not think seriously about her size. The striking thing was that she looked a real sea-boat, and not merely designed to comply with official regulations, as part of the furnishing of a ship, for use in an emergency, like a lifebuoy or a raft.

Dain was silent, and so was I while Charley hauled her alongside. We got in. In addition to the ordinary thwarts, she had continuous seats along both sides, under which would have been the copper buoyancy tanks, but these had been removed. There was a thick coat of congealed muck on the seats and on her bottom, but apart from a little rainwater she seemed bone dry. With my knife I scraped some of the muck and paint from her gunwale, and from one of her planks. The wood was sound, and I noticed that she was copper fastened, apparently throughout. . . .

All this time it was as though there were two voices speaking inside me. One was saying that the boat was in no way the sort of craft we wanted, for the voyages we had planned. Even the gig had seemed too small for that, and yet the gig, because of the engine it would require, was quite beyond our present means. And the other voice was saying, she's a fine sea-boat, she's sound, and she'll be cheap. Suddenly it was Dain who seemed to read my thoughts, to hear that inner voice of temptation arguing against the voice of caution and common sense; and, devil's disciple, she said:

"She's lovely. Isn't she? She reminds me of a coble, in spite of her having a sharp stern. Wouldn't she look grand, with all the dirt and that gloomy paint scraped off, and painted, say, a lovely pale blue. . . . She'd be big enough for a cruiser. Surely there's room for a cabin and two bunks, and a little one for Amelia?"

I measured her with my eye. With all the seats removed and the sides built up there *would* be space for a fair-sized sleeping cabin. It would leave us a smallish cockpit, which would have to be partly filled with the engine, but that would not be a fatal disadvantage. There would be no room for our little boat on deck. What would stop us towing her, however? The voice of reason grew very faint inside me, and Charley joined in:

"She's a nice little boat, and I wouldn't say she's too small for a cruiser. It depends what accommodation you want, of course, but the smaller your boat, the smaller the engine and that's the main consideration, if you want to save money. . . . Don't think I'm trying to persuade you to have her. You know your own business best. But there's one thing. If you did want a bigger boat later on, you'd be able to get your money back on this. I only bought her because she was a bargain, and I knew I could sell her here for at least a quid more than I gave for her."

"Do you mean you'll sell her for four pounds?"

"To you—yes. She's cheap at that. I'd keep her myself, only she's too small. I want to specialise on the gigs."

She was cheap; but even so I knew that we could not afford to get her. The fifty pounds that was due when the book was accepted would have to last us at least six months. The "animal" job had again stopped for the summer. We did not know for certain it would continue later on. If we did buy the boat, we certainly could not afford an engine, however cheap. She'd be no use to us without. All that we'd have would be the excitement of owning her, of cleaning and painting, of making her into a cruiser, and dreaming of the time when we might have an engine, and take her out to sea. It was madness thinking of it. But we'd done plenty of mad things before, and somehow or other they'd turned out all right. I glanced at Dain, and I knew that already she was picturing the boat hauled up on our beach, with the fun of cleaning and scraping started. We'd had to give up our "celebration" expedition, and certainly we deserved some sort of compensation and reward for the work we had put into the book. I said to Charley:

"Look here, do you mind waiting a week or two for your money if we take her?"

He grinned.

"Of course not. Tow her away now if you want to."

Again I glanced at Dain, and I knew from her excited eyes I had got too far now to turn back, so I said to Charley, with a calmness that I did not feel:

"Right-o, then, we'll have her."

15

WE GOT A letter from Mr. Mackenzie enclosing the cheque, saying that the new book quite came up to his expectations, and that he trusted that this time it would have the success it deserved. It was too late for the Christmas publishing season; but if all went well he would bring it out early in the new year. In the meantime he hoped that I had got a third book under way.

It was not a very exciting letter. In fact, it quite depressed us for a time, for I couldn't help thinking that if he had read the book and enjoyed it, he'd have thought of at least one positive descriptive adjective to express his feelings about it. And again, the new year was a very long time to wait. But then Mr. Mackenzie undoubtedly was a very busy man, and he was probably assuming that since I'd written the book I knew more about its virtues than he did, and that praise was unnecessary. And anyway, the cheque was certain evidence that he liked it enough to put his money on its chances, and the fact that he was keen on still another, was or at least ought to have been very encouraging. Actually I could not think of another book just then and did not wish to. I could scarcely think of anything except the boat.

Even the garden and the hut suffered in our eagerness to get on with the job. We neglected our weeding, our vigil against parasites and pests. The bullfinches and blackbirds and our cock-robin (and their numerous season's progeny) gorged themselves on our rasps and currants, for we had no time to mend the nets, and they were quite contemptuous of Choo-i. Slugs browsed undisturbed on our greens. Our lawn became a miniature meadow. Docks, nourished by the richly fertilised soil, grew like palms among our lettuces and carrots and in the flower-beds; and although we had perforce to keep the living-room and bedroom tidy, and wash and cook, we had no time for any other inside chores.

We had taken advantage of a spring tide to beach the boat close in to the cliff of the cove, so that she was dry all day long when the tides neaped. We made a ramp down the steps to the beach wide enough to take the wheels of the cot; and as soon as we'd had breakfast and Amelia had been bathed and fed, we'd take her down, and put the cot in a sunny corner of the beach, and start work. If she missed the perfume of the flowers and the droning of the wild bees; the smell of the sunbaked weed when the tide was down, the cries of the closer sea-birds evidently were not distasteful to her, for she slept as soundly as ever when she *was* asleep. When she awakened (as she did now as long as an hour before feeding time) she would just lie wriggling her arms and legs, with her blue eyes staring up at the sky, and making queer chuckling noises which had no note of uneasiness or vexation in them until she began to feel hungry.

Whatever doubts I might have had as to our wisdom in acquiring that boat when our finances were still in such a precarious state, I had none as to the qualities of the boat herself. We scrubbed the muck from her first, with soda and fresh water from the stream. We borrowed a blow-lamp from the shipyard, then, starting from the keel, and working upwards plank by plank, we scraped the paint from her. It was a slow, laborious, back-breaking process, but we had our reward in finding every inch of wood without crack or flaw, every nail copper and free from corrosion. Only her keel plate was iron, and this and its fastenings into the oak keel were galvanised. In every detail, she was well and truly built, and when at last we had got all of that dingy paint removed from her outside, her lines were more satisfying and exciting than ever.

We had measured her hull carefully, and made a scale drawing and, although it looked as though we'd have to forgo most of the conveniences we'd planned for our "real" cruiser, we found that we'd have room for all that was essential for at least a lengthy coastal cruise. The actual length from stem to stern was twenty-seven feet. We could build up the sides for the forward two-thirds of this and deck it in. This would give us eighteen feet of "cover." The first five feet in the bows could be partitioned off with a light bulkhead and door for a store-room. Then would come the cabin, with locker-bunks each side, six feet in length, two feet three inches in width, with a gangway between them of one foot six inches. That left us with five feet of covered space. We could have a galley (a shelf and a primus stove would be all we'd want for cooking) on one side, and we could make a bunk for Amelia on the other. The engine (when we got one) would go in the cockpit, and of course be boxed in. The fuel tank, and perhaps our fresh-water tank could go in the stern. We might make an awning to cover in the cockpit in rainy weather, but this really would be our navigation and promenade "deck," and with the cabin to shelter in we needn't be too fussy.

I knew better than start on the real job of "conversion" without getting some technical hints; and so when the hull was clean we went down to the shipyard, and watched Joe and the two workmen the firm had been able to keep on, at work on the gig. If Joe had conveyed to his nephew that he was "quite" interested, in this idea for re-establishing the firm's fortunes, he certainly did not show it to us.

"Why," he said, "this be a job for a man workin' in his backyard in his spare time. Bain't a job for real shipwrights, not even boat-builders. Who'd built a craft like this yer, to take an engine? They be built for oars. All right for the navy, and for what they'm meant for, landing a lot of jack tars from a ship. Be all nonsense thinking you can make a proper motor craft from one of they, to behave and look proper. And then doin' everything on the cheap! No teak nor mahogany nor brass work, says Charley. There bain't nothin' in a job like this to encourage a man when he's a doin' of it, and gladden his eyes when it be done."

In spite of this Joe seemed to be taking just as much pains with the job as he had done with the "trawler" conversion, and while we envied nothing about the gig but her extra space, it was clear that when finished she would look extremely good. He willingly gave us all the advice we wanted. The thwarts (or seats) of an open boat are not merely planks for the oarsmen or passengers to sit on. They play a very important part in the boat's construction, for they brace the sides together. Remove them, and the sides would splay apart, like the ends of a bow with the string cut. In converting an open boat into a semi-closed one, this structural function of the thwarts must be transferred to the beams which support the deck, and to the deck itself. Therefore (Joe explained), the sides of the cabin must be built up, the beams joined, and the deck laid, before the original thwarts were removed; and we must remember that the sides would not only have to take the weight of the deck but also this fundamental strain, and be braced accordingly. It was not just a case of building higher walls for our cabin! The original gunwale of the boat must be carefully removed. The original "timbers" (or ribs) must be extended to the height of the deck, and in continuance of their curve; they must be tied to what was virtually a new gunwale running from the heightened stem to the after bulkhead of the cabin, and it was to this gunwale that the deck beams must be securely tied.

We had some misgivings as to whether all this was not beyond the range of our skill as carpenters. I could, if I took pains saw or plane a piece of wood dead square; but it looked as though in boat building, a dead square "join" was the exception rather than the rule. The deck beams which which had already been fitted to the gig were curved, so as to give the deck itself a camber from side to side. This was as necessary as the slope of a house roof. The planks of the new sides would have to be bent to the curve of the boat, and not only that, they would have to be tapered towards the bows. They would have to fit close enough together to make a watertight join by sheer contact, easy enough if their edges were straight, but devilishly difficult when tapered at an uncalculable angle. I was indeed tempted to propose to Charley and Joe that we should bring our boat down to the shipyard, and have them do at least the frame-work for the deck and cabin, but while I knew they would have done this at the mere cost of time and material, it would not have been fair to them, and however cheaply they did it, it would mean an unjustifiable bite out of our precious store of cash. And Dain was dead against it. It would be far more thrilling, she said, to do the whole job ourselves. Seeing that there was no chance of our getting an engine until the book was published, and that we could not use her without, there was no hurry. Even if it took us all one day to shape a beam to the proper curve or fit two planks together, it would be worth it for the cash we'd save and

the thrill we'd get when it was done. We had the whole
autumn and winter before us, hadn't we?

Charley let us have our timber, yellow pine for the sides
and deck, oak for the timbers and beams, and bulkhead
frames at cost price. Amongst the junk in his "shop" we
found four portholes which belonged to the wrecked yacht,
and also the frame of a deck skylight which had belonged
to a smaller boat, and was just the right size for ours, and
we got the lot for ten shillings. We learnt from Joe how to
make the oak "ribs" pliable by soaking them in an iron drain-
pipe full of hot water, so that they could bend like lead; and
the correct way of "clenching" copper rivets. We acquired a
few more necessary tools, and very slowly the framework
of the cabin began to grow, and take shape.

Although our interest in the boat never really declined,
it became less feverish as time went on. We disciplined
ourselves to definite and regular hours of work on it, and
transferred some of our energies back to the garden and the
arrears of weeding, and hoeing and digging. We gathered
and sawed a huge store of logs for the big room fire, against
the coming winter nights. We made jam from the fruit
the birds had left us. That August was wet and cold, but we
had some glorious warm days in September, when abandoning everything we'd set out for our sandy cove, and bathe
and fish, and lie with Amelia in the sun. But when we
talked, it was usually about the boat, and of the voyages
we'd make when we'd got our engine and she was fully
equipped; and when we talked about the book, and publication day, we were thinking chiefly that it would be then
that we'd be able to decide definitely about the engine, and
it just worried me a bit, that perhaps the book would be
such a terrific success that after all we'd want to have our
big boat built. Still, that boat would take a long time to

build, and if we had as much money as that there'd be no harm in getting an engine and installing it, and using our first cruiser until the other was ready, when of course we could sell her, and get back perhaps more than she had cost.

By the end of September we had heard nothing from the firm, so I wrote to them, and we got a letter by return of post to say that for reasons of economy they had been obliged to discontinue their regular purchases of specimens from outside sources. They would, however, communicate with me if any special things were required. Our bread and butter job was gone. The slump had at last struck home. It was a shock but we made the best of it. The job, if it had continued, would have meant less time for the boat. We were thankful, however, that we had gone very carefully with our fifty pounds, that I had not yielded to the temptation to have Hoskins build the cabin framework. We'd paid for the boat herself and for the material; we had bought some very necessary clothing for ourselves, and some things for the hut, and we still had enough, if we went back to our sheep's head and fish economy, to keep us going until the book was published when, even if it went no better than the first, I'd be able to get another fifty from Mr. Mackenzie. And as Charley had never mentioned again the matter of our buying the place, I was not worried on that score.

But the night of that day the letter came I didn't feel much like bed, and when Amelia had been fed and "settled," and Dain had gone, I pulled the blacksmith's chair up to the big room fire, on the hearth of which Choo-i lay comfortably curled (probably thinking that if she remained like that, I might forget to turn her out); and it wasn't surprising that I should start thinking about Grab and his wife, and of the nights, just a year ago, when we'd all four sat like this in front of the fire yarning. From that my mind began to wander back to Bramblewick, not to the Bramblewick of my late experiences there, but the one of my childhood, to that life which had been dominated chiefly by the youthful bullying Grab himself. I thought of that fight, in which I had avenged myself for all the humiliations and sufferings he and his gang had wreaked upon me, my only sin (apart from a certain cockiness) being that I was the son of a poor but respectable, and teetotal artist, who'd come to settle in the place and earn a living selling his pictures to the summer visitors, and of a woman who "kept herself to herself," whose religious views were Calvinistic in their ardour, who regarded drinking and bad language and "coarseness" as mortal sins, whose chief aim in life was to save me from the "contamination" of the village boys with whom perforce I had to go to school. I thought of our cottage, whose back windows looked sheer down a shale cliff into the sea, and whose foundations rocked, as though with the vibration of heavy gun-fire, on a winter's night when the sea was rough; whose living-room window overlooked a narrow cobbled street, which, within sight and hearing had three of Bramble-wick's nine busy pubs in it, and on any Saturday night when the pubs turned out was full of singing, quarrelling, swearing, drunken fishermen or sailors, among whom I'd always be able to pick out the voice of the infamous atheistic Captain "Boozer" Matthews, or that of my one grown-up friend, Mike Regan, himself a foreigner, but the biggest and strongest and most feared man in the place. . . .

Staring into that fire of wood which Dain and I had gathered from the shores of the creek or fetched back from our excursions along the coast, there came vividly to my mind a picture of Bramblewick beach, with a gale blowing and the ebb tide just leaving the cliff foot, with every little depression in the line of the cliff piled up with wrack and things that had been washed up. I remembered my breathless excitement, when beating the beachcombers because of my agility in climbing, I'd be the first on; and how, provided I was not robbed by them or by Grab and the gang, or by the coastguards, I'd get back home, trusting that my mother would either not notice, or at least forgive my wet boots or soiled clothes, in her own surprise or pleasure in seeing the firewood or other treasures I had brought her. I thought of my miserable, but faithful little pal, Chicken, himself the son of a down-and-out drunken pedlar, who'd come to Bramblewick about the same time as my own parents had done; who, although a foreigner, was too small, too weak, to be worthy of Grab's physical attentions; and of how Chicken and I, as much as anything to keep out of Grab's way, had built a wigwam for ourselves among the whins on the cliff a mile from the village; and how Grab at last had found us out, and smashed up our wigwam and given me a hiding into the bargain. I suddenly felt a surge of wild excitement inside me. In all this was the makings of another book.

The story of my boyhood in Bramblewick! My feud with Grab, my friendship with Mike Regan, and Chicken, the adventures we'd had with the wigwam, and poaching trout in the squire's stream and climbing for seagulls' eggs on Low Batts Cliff. My father's struggle for fame and fortune, his portrait of Mike Regan that he painted specially for the Royal Academy, but was rejected, and "bought" later by a "gentleman" summer visitor, who, however, suddenly vanished before he'd paid for it, after he'd borrowed a pound from Dad, on the excuse that he'd left his purse in his hotel "up-bank," and didn't wish to climb back for it. My mother and her fight to protect and save me from the evil influences of the village; the school, and the immaculately dressed, ear-boxing Slogger; "Boozer" who in a thunderstorm stood on the edge of the village cliff and challenged God, if there *was* a God, to strike him dead. The storms and wrecks; the lifeboat gun rousing the village on a winter's night, the sound of sea-boots hurrying down the cobbled alleys to the dock and the lifeboat house; the red flares lighting up the slipway and the breakwater wall, lined with shawled women, watching the boat being lowered towards the dark sea. The disasters which sometimes overwhelmed the local fishing fleet; cobles capsized hurrying to cross the landing bar, search parties tramping along the beach and scaurs when the tide ebbed; bodies being carried on handbarrows up the slipway, again through a crowd of shawled, silent, hard-faced women. . . .

God—what a book it would make! It would have no plot, of course. It would have less sex interest even than the other two. It might be a disadvantage from the point of public popularity, having its chief character only a boy. But by the time it was out, the second book would have been published and surely if that was as successful as Mr. Mackenzie prophesied, and it had reawakened interest in the first, then this one should go on the strength of their goodwill. And what matter if it did not sell in large quantities? By my contract I'd draw as "royalties" in advance at least one-half of what the previous book had earned in the first six months of publication.

I got up. Choo-i eyed me furtively. I tiptoed into the living-room for pen and paper. Choo-i purred softly (as though to say, "Thank God for that"), and closed her eyes again as I sat down, and stared at a blank sheet and then into the fire; but she needn't have worried, for I was back in Bramblewick, lying in bed, in the attic of my old home, listening to the voice of Boozer Matthews as he staggered down our street from the Dolphin to the Mariner's Arms, to Dad and Mother talking anxiously in the room below me, to the rumbling of the breaking seas on the cliff foot. And soon I had started writing.

Dain was enthusiastic next morning about what I had done, and about the whole idea of the new book; and that I had started writing again. It *was* a blow, she said, losing the collecting job; but after all, apart from the money it brought in, it had been a waste of time. It was far more important that I should write. It didn't matter a bit that we should have to go on economising for a few more months. I was quite right, too, in not bothering as to the new book having no sex interest. I'd made a grand start on it, and it all sounded marvellous, and she wouldn't be very surprised if it proved to be the best of the lot, and even the most popular, and sell like hot cakes. She was just dying to hear the next instalment. Hadn't I better get on with it now, while the fever was on me, instead of our working at the boat?

This, perhaps sounded very sensible, but Dain quickly agreed with me that it would be a mistake to force the thing. We had still a tremendous amount of work to do on the boat. The hours of daylight were getting short. I could write equally well at night, and I wrote better for being physically tired, for then I had no disturbing desire to be doing something I liked better, for no matter how enthusiastic you might feel about your work, writing was an unhealthy occupation. It was hateful, sitting still in a chair, inside a room if the sun was shining outside, and you felt your muscles capable of strenuous work, and there was strenuous and fascinating work to do. Anyway, no matter how fast I worked at the new book, it could not bring us any immediate cash to take the place of the lost job.

We got back to our sheep's head, and fish and vegetable diet again, and there couldn't have been much wrong with it, for we all three, directly or (in Amelia's case) indirectly, thrived on it. There was less sun now, and some of Amelia's tan had gone, but as her hair was almost white, you scarcely noticed the difference, and to our admittedly prejudiced eyes she looked lovelier than ever, for her legs were noticeably growing straighter, she was beginning to hold her head up, and look at things with a most intelligent expression, and without the slightest tendency to squint; and there was one clear sound which she made repeatedly, near enough in its enunciation to convince me that she was doing her best to say "Daddy."

We finished the lengthening of the ribs, and the tying of them; and we shaped the beams, and bolted them, and fitted in the frame of the skylight, and the frame of the after bulkhead, and leaving the planking of the sides for the time being, we started nailing on the deck, which was of course the roof of our cabin. It was a cold, showery day towards the middle of October, when we laid the last plank of it; we'd put Amelia in her bunk, and the bunk inside the cabin, and just as we'd driven in the last nail, it started to rain heavily, and we climbed down and stepped through the doorway in the bulkhead into the cabin, and we had an immense thrill, for we'd tacked temporary strips of sail-cloth along the walls and across the frame of the bulkhead, and we'd glazed the windows of the skylight so that now the whole place was completely shut in. It was warm, and not a drop of rain was leaking through the deck, although it was pattering noisily above us. We had already laid a temporary floor. But we'd left the original thwarts, in position, until the deck was nailed. We cut them now, a little nervously, but there was not a creak from the ribs or the deck beams to indicate that they were protesting against the transferred strain; and the effect was astounding. We found we could walk about, and stand comfortably under the skylight. The size of the cabin was at least half again that of an ordinary two-berthed cabin on a ship.

"It's thrilling—it's thrilling!" Dain cried. "We've got a real boat and a real cabin! Just listen to the rain, and here we are, all three of us, as dry and snug as if we were in the hut. Let's start making the bunks at once. There's going to be heaps of room. There's even going to be room for a tiny cabin in the bow. I don't think it would be a bad idea if we made Amelia's bunk there, or we could make her a little hammock. She'd love that. Later on if we had another baby, then the baby could go there, and Amelia could have her bunk where we planned it first. I don't see that another baby would make much difference. Hang it all, we've simply got to have a son one day."

I was feeling much too excited to start restraining Dain's enthusiasm, and anyway, there was no point in discussing the pros and cons of another baby until our financial position was assured. The really exciting thing was that we had successfully completed the most difficult part of the job— that except for an odd joint or two, where our measurements had gone wrong, it looked professional; that when the sides were finished and the bunks made, we were going to have a liveable-in cabin. All that we needed now was the engine; and I thought that perhaps it was providential that we'd have to wait for that, for the temptation to use it would have been too strong to resist, and we might have hurried and scamped the completion of the hull. I made no remark, one way or another, on the matter Dain had raised, as we took advantage of what remained of the daylight to start on the frames of our own bunks; and, as Dain said nothing either, I assumed it had passed from her mind in the press of more practical thoughts. The problem of design and construction presented by those two full-sized bunks, which had to conform to the horizontal and vertical curve of the hull, was a very tricky one, needing all our wits.

But strangely enough, Dain got a letter from Elsie Fosdyck the very next day. She had given birth to a son, three days before. It weighed eight pounds, and it had dark hair, and very dark eyes and it was the spit and image of Will, and she and the baby were doing very nicely. Will's ship had just been laid up at Liverpool, and he'd been offered the watchman's job, but he'd come home, but the firm had told him he'd get his berth again when things improved, so that was all right. He was so proud of the baby, and he'd actually been doing some gardening, although it was just like his luck, gardening in winter when of course nothing would grow. She hoped that our baby was going on all right, and that we were keeping well, and she and Will did so hope that we'd all meet again some day, because it would be nice to talk about old times and see each other's babies. . . .

I was delighted by that letter which Dain had read aloud. Now that I was a father myself and knew the quiet thrills and satisfaction of parenthood, there was nothing I would rather wish for friends than that they should enjoy the same. Yet I was bothered by a peculiar, far-away look in Dain's eyes as she put the letter down. I was bothered, and frightened too, that my own delight was at least vaguely tinged with jealousy, that Grab's first child should be a son. I thought quickly of our financial position, of the size of our boat, and of the voyages we planned to make in her, and of how in spite of Dain's cheerful suggestions as to the arrangement of her accommodation, another baby might prove an insoluble difficulty. Although Dain said nothing except how pleased she was, and how proud Elsie must be, I knew what she was thinking and feeling, and I couldn't help wishing that Elsie had produced a daughter and not a son.

16

MY FEARS that the second book, the story of my ill-fated patent lobster pot, would be such a success and make so much money, that all our work on the boat would be thrown away, were not justified. True, it was not a complete failure. We got almost as many reviews as from the first, and many of them just as enthusiastic in their praise. We got just as many letters from money-lenders and literary agents, and offers of free sittings from photographers, and even more requests for autographed copies for sale at charitable bazaars. We got a letter from a gentleman in Manchester who said that he had read the book with very deep interest, as the problems of lobster-fishing I described were exactly the same as existed in a small fishing village on the west coast of Scotland where he always spent his summer holidays; and that he thought my patent pot a splendid idea, and he wondered whether I could supply him with a quantity of these at cost price, as he would like to present them to his poor fishermen friends. We got a letter from another man who lived in London, who, however, must have written post haste before he had read the ironic end of the book; for he was himself the inventor of an apparatus for fitting in front of motor cars that simply made it impossible for them to kill any one they might run into—an invention, he said, that was obviously worth a fortune, but he had no money to take out the patents on it and manufacture it, so reading about my lobster pot, he'd thought of writing to me, asking if I'd like to take a financial interest in the thing, to our mutual advantage. He was certain I would be sympathetic, if only to the extent of lending him a pound to take out his provisional patent. And, as evidence that the mild sex interest I had introduced into the book had made a balance to the mechanical details, there was a letter which exuded a strong perfume when we opened it, from a lady who lived in Bayswater, saying that she was charmed by the description I had given of my early love affair. She had never read anything quite so romantic; and as for the invention itself, she *did* think I had been clever to make a thing like that out of odds and ends, that was better than what the fishermen themselves made, and she couldn't understand why the government and all those rich people I had met hadn't helped me. Perhaps (the letter concluded), if ever I came to town, I would call and have tea with her, for she would like so much to meet me, for I must be so interesting, having had so many varied experiences; and she felt, too, that I might be interested in a novel that she had written, but had never been published, which wasn't about fishermen, of course, although the two chief characters in it, an artist and a film actress, first met in an imaginary fishing village on the coast of Devon.

We got several letters, some unsigned, from people who had no axe to grind, who it seemed had genuinely liked the book, and we got one from Marney himself which wholly delighted us, for he said that all of them had liked it better than the other one; that his father had been reading it out aloud to mother, and that he'd fairly split himself with laughing when he read that bit about how we'd got the laugh against the Fosdycks; but again there were no letters from editors offering large sums of money for articles or short stories; no offers for serial or film or foreign rights. The advertisements of the book, in spite that they were at first bold and contained some telling excerpts from the reviews said nothing about its being a success, and the number of printings it had gone into; and by the end of a fortnight we knew by the shrinking of them that it was not, or likely to be a best-seller. Soon our fear was confirmed by a letter from Mr. Mackenzie himself. The book was not selling as he had believed it would; but he trusted that I was pleased and encouraged by what had been said about the book in the press and that I was making good progress with the next one, which he believed more strongly than ever would be a great success and compensate for the comparative failure of the others. The sales of the second (he did not give them) had not yet reached those of the first, but he did not wish me to be embarrassed by a shortage of cash, and he would be delighted to let me have a further advance of fifty pounds if I so wished.

Well, it was no use moaning. The book was a flop, as big a flop, at least financially, as the lobster pot itself. Instead of our being worried as to how we should spend the colossal sum of money we'd thought it would bring us, here we were in the same position as we'd been one year and two years before, except that we had Amelia as an extra responsibility. We had come to the end of our first fifty pounds. There had been no communication from the firm, since their letter of September. The second fifty would have to last us until the third book was finished, and when the advance on that one came there'd be nothing else until publication.

But again there was spring in the air. The sun was getting warmer. The garden, despite our weeks of neglect in the first fever of boat-building, looked more thrilling with its beds of tulips and daffs and wallflowers, and its beds of early broccoli than it had ever done. The birds were starting to sing. Amelia was successfully weaned, and she

could crawl, and sit up by herself, and make quite a number
of distinct sounds; and although for some peculiar reason
she had abandoned her efforts to say "daddy," one of these
sounds was close enough to "Choo-i" to bring our cat
hurrying to her whenever she pronounced it. Choo-i herself
had felt the urge of spring and for one whole week she and
a large black "tom," whom she had mysteriously attracted
either from Porthkerris or from one of the farms, had
disturbed our nights with passionate song. We decided that
for Amelia's sake we'd keep at least one of the expected
progeny of her liaison. I was making good progress with
the book; and apart from the enforced continuance of our
"economy" diet (when we'd been looking forward to roast
beef and steak and chops and an occasional chicken) the only
direct way in which the failure of the book affected our
happiness was the boat; for she was finished, ready for
sea, to take us anywhere we wished, except in that one vital
item of her equipment. She had no engine.

We'd planked the sides, fitted in the portholes; made
the locker bunks, the galley. We had dismissed (or at least I
had) the possibility that we might have to provide accommodation for a fourth "hand," but when we'd completed
the forward bulkhead, the "room" thus made in the bows
looked so attractive, with a tiny porthole on each side, that
we'd decided to make this Amelia's private cabin, and we'd
sewn a sort of hammock bunk out of sail-cloth, big enough to
take the mattress from the cot, and she'd taken quite amiably
to this, and had slept in it while we'd worked. We'd painted
the outside of the hull lifeboat blue, and the deck and top
sides cream, with a line of red along the rubbers. The ceiling
of the cabin was white, and the walls a very pale blue, with
the internal frames of the portholes red again; and, as we
puttied the cracks in all our bad joints before painting them,

the whole job looked in every way professional. We'd called her *Samaki* which was the East African word for fish, and we'd painted this name on the bows; but all this had been finished a week before the book was published, and now it seemed that *Samaki* would have to remain lying on the shore of our beach, immobile and useless throughout the spring, and those hot summer days when we were to have gone on our first exciting cruises.

We thought poignantly of this the morning that Mr. Mackenzie's cheque arrived, for we'd got dozens of catalogues and pamphlets of marine engines, and although our "pre-publication" choice had been a two-cylinder "petrol-paraffin" six horse-power at a complete cost of £85, we had noticed a single cylinder, of three horse-power paraffin burning, which the makers said was capable of driving a twenty-five-foot boat at six knots, and the price complete was only £30. It was awful, to look at that cheque, and think that we could, if we wanted, buy that engine straight away, and perhaps in a week's time have it installed, cast off *Samaki's* moorings, and set off down harbour and for the open sea; and, without any disloyalty to Amelia, it was impossible for me not to think that if Dain and I had been alone, we'd have reckoned the balance of twenty pounds ample for our future needs, ordered the engine and damned the consequences. Yet this thought was a swiftly passing one. Half the fun and excitement of cruising in *Samaki* would be in having Amelia with us, and doubtless if we were cruising in her alone we'd be thinking (or at least Dain would be) that we ought to have a baby, and wishing we had; and of course it was criminal even to think of spending thirty out of our fifty pounds on an engine, when this was all we had to live on for months ahead.

Ironically, the weather was perfect that day the cheque

came: the sun really hot, the sea tantalisingly smooth. We had to go to St. Jude and Porthkerris in the afternoon, to pay in the cheque, and then to pay the rent and settle a small account with Charley, for paint and other items we'd got for *Samaki*. We'd steered clear of the shipyard since publication day for this very reason, and because I had on my last visit spoken very optimistically about the book, and had indeed been foolish enough to tell him that probably I should soon be wanting to discuss with him the buying of the hut. He'd seemed quite pleased about this, yet obviously not so anxious as he had been on the first occasion he'd referred to it. The "gigs" had been a success. All of them had been "converted" and sold, and the "firm" (to what extent the major was behind it now I did not know) had invested in another batch, two of which were moored off the quay as we went in. But on the actual "slip" where the work was done, an entirely different craft was hauled— an old-fashioned, smallish, deep-keeled fishing boat, of the type built primarily for sailing, and equipped later with an engine, as most of our Yorkshire cobles had been. Joe, and his two workmen were engaged burning the black paint from her hull; and close by stood Charley, and a tall, stoutish gentleman dressed in tweeds, who I guessed at once was his wealthy friend.

We had to carry Amelia in our arms, for she had long since passed the stage when we could deposit her in her bunk like a piece of luggage. Charley greeted us politely and at once introduced us to his companion. His name was Major Foster. My first impressions of that gentleman (there was no doubt now that he was the "friend") were not un-favourable. He had a pinkish face, with a white, military moustache, and pale blue eyes which twinkled quite agreeably when he smiled; and his manner was only faintly "haw-

haw," so that I judged that he was not an ex-regular army officer; and I was right, for we found out he had been a manufacturer and that he had held a territorial commission in the A.S.C. during the war. His manner indeed was most genial. He chucked Amelia under the chin, and said what a fine, healthy baby she was, and then he said that he'd heard quite a lot about us, and about the books I'd written— he'd seen something about one of them in *The Times* (wasn't it about a lobster pot or something, he hadn't read it yet, but he was going to); and then he said what an ideal place we'd got up there in the creek. I remembered vaguely Charley telling us that his "friend" actually lived in the south part of St. Jude and I imagined it would be in one of the rather pretentious newly-built houses which looked over the harbour; and I did not see anything of sinister significance in his words when he added:

"A charming little place! I quite envy you. Must be ideal. Charley, here, tells me you've even got your own spring water. Well, it's no wonder you look so healthy, and that baby of yours has got such rosy cheeks."

Nor did I see anything alarming or deliberate then in the way Charley butted in and changed the topic of conversation, by pointing to the boat, and saying:

"What do you think of this? The Major's bought her for conversion into a little sailing cruiser. Fine little craft, isn't she? They're not building any more of her sort now. Came from Penzance. We're going to strip her, and give her a nice little cabin and a new mast, and a Bermuda rig. A new engine, of course, but only as auxiliary. She's for sailing first and foremost. We've just taken the old one out."

We moved closer. Joe turned from his work and said with his customary ironic smile:

"Ah, this be the sort of boat you ought to have got.

Be a real boat, she. As good as anything we ever turned out of this yard before the war, only we never built anything so small. She be a real sailer, or I'm a Dutchman. But damned if I know why they fishermen always wanted everything done with this black paint. Be worse than tar to get off."

We had no particular interest in that boat, which, the Major explained, he was going to have for his own use, as he'd sold his converted gig, and he preferred sailing anyway. What did interest me, but only at first because the shape of it was familiar, was the decrepit-looking two-cylinder engine, and various bits of gear belonging it, that was lying on the ground close by. It was the same make (but clearly a much earlier model), as the one the Lunns had in their coble.

I said to Charley, quite unnecessarily:

"Is this the engine you've taken out of her?"

He laughed.

"Engine! Some people might call it an engine, but I wouldn't! I tell you where that ought to be. In a museum. It's a real antique. It's too rusty to see what its number is, but I shouldn't be surprised if it was number one of its make."

I looked at it more closely. I saw that in many respects it differed from the one I knew, and I recalled that even that one Henry Lunn had purchased second-hand, and it must have been an early model. This one had no clutch or reversing gear; no device for automatic lubrication. The magneto had been dismantled, but I could see from its mounting that its gearing to the engine was different, and there were some gadgets that I could not comprehend at all until Charley, rather in the manner of a museum guide, remarked:

"It's an antique, all right. They hadn't thought of using magnetos on marine engines when that one was built. She'd have a battery for the ignition. But some smart chap must have had the idea of converting her. We've got the magneto. The chap the Major bought the boat from had taken it out of her before she was laid up, otherwise there wouldn't have been much left of that. The engine itself was almost covered in bilge water when we got her, we had her towed down here, of course, and must have been like that for months. It's taken us the best part of a day to get her unbolted from her bed."

It was clear that they had had to use cold chisels for that operation, and there were marks on the crank-case, which suggested that crowbars and even a sledge hammer had been employed, and it was the fact that those marks had a bright gleam, that made me think in spite of the rust the standing part of the engine was not seriously corroded. I gave a turn to the heavy fly-wheel. It moved easily until the invisible pistons reached compression, and then there was a lively resistance; I jerked upwards at the wheel. It moved, showing that the bearings were slack, but they were no slacker than those of the Lunns' engine at the end of winter's fishing, when they'd have to be remetalled. I suddenly thought, My God, *it's still an engine*, and but for the clutch and reversing gear, the same sort as that one which, in my own years of fishing with the Lunns, in all weathers had never let us down. It would burn paraffin, half the price of petrol. If it wouldn't do for our distant cruises, it would be good enough for short ones, and even if we never ventured farther away than the mackerel cove, that would be better than having an engineless cabin cruiser laid up on our beach through all the tantalising summer months.

"What are you going to do with it?" I said to Charley. He laughed again.

"It'll be going on the scrap-heap, I reckon. Only that fly-wheel will make a useful mooring. We'd have had it off, only it's rusted on the shaft too hard."

"Have you got all the parts belonging to it? The silencer and exhaust pipe? What about the shaft and the propeller? Are you using them for the new engine?"

"No. They'll have to come off. All the rest of her gear's there, except the vapouriser and that's rusted to bits, so far as I know. . . . Tanks and everything. Why? You don't mean to say you want her, do you?"

I was not an expert on engines. My knowledge came from once having possessed a second-hand motor bike, and from what I'd picked up from the Lunns, and I said rather diffidently:

"Well, I expect she could be made to go, couldn't she, in spite of her age and everything? Why shouldn't she go? She's not broken, or the wheel wouldn't turn. And if she could drive that boat she could drive ours."

He stared at me incredulously, and I noticed the Major smiling too, but I looked at Dain, and I saw nothing but encouragement; and then Charley said:

"Yes. She'd go all right. She'd drive that boat of yours. You'd probably want some new parts. The vapouriser's a standard gadget, and you could get a spare, or pick a second-hand one up somewhere. The bearings would want tightening. You'd want new piston rings I should think, and new packings on all the joints. If you took her all to bits, and built her up again, I don't see why she shouldn't go. You'd have some fun, anyway."

I looked at Dain and saw that her eyes were positively sparkling.

"Well, how much do you want for her?" I said. "Complete with tanks and propeller?"

Charley grinned, and glanced at the Major.

"It isn't for me to say. She belongs to the Major here."

The Major too was grinning.

"Why. It's no good to me. I don't suppose it's worth ten shillings as scrap. Take it if you want it. Take it by all means. I mean take it as a gift. I'm not much of an engineer myself, but if Charley here says you can get it to go, well, he'll be right. You'll have some fun with it I've no doubt. I'm sure you will."

Curiously, it was in that moment that I had my first instinctive fear of that man; but a fear that I could not immediately analyse. Perhaps I was jealous, of his friendship with Charley, of his wealth, that he had been able to do for Charley and the firm exactly what we would have liked to have done, and would have done if our books had succeeded. But again it may have been only a premonition. I thanked him sincerely enough. And leaving Dain with Amelia, I went up with Charley to his office, to pay the rent and his account. I thought that I had better mention to him that my hopes about the second book had not materialised. He seemed genuinely sympathetic, and in no way perturbed, and, as he did not mention the matter of selling the place, I gathered that it was no longer of urgency so I didn't mention it either. Our lease did not expire until September. He didn't seem in any way annoyed that the Major had given us the engine. Instead he enlarged on the subject of the Major's kindness, and of what a God-send he had been to the firm; and, as we walked back my own fear for him had temporarily at least vanished. For I could think of nothing but that rusty lump of machinery which by a miracle was now ours, and of its exciting possibilities.

17

IT *was* exciting; more exciting than the boat; more exciting even than the first cleaning of the hut, and our first carpentery. The engine of course was too heavy for us to handle by ourselves. But Charley had it transported by boat to our cove; and with the aid of two "unemployed" Porthkerris workmen we carried it into the big room, where we could work on it by night as well as day.

Fortunately it had none of the complicated gadgets of a modern automobile; so that I was not worried, in dismantling it, as to how it should "go back." It consisted simply of the cylinders and water-jacket, in a single casting, the pistons, the crankshaft, the secondary shaft that operated the valves and the very simple water-pump; two gear wheels which connected this shaft to the fly-wheel; that device called the vapouriser which we had to replace; the carburettor, and the magneto, driven by a chain from another sprocketed wheel.

The crank shaft would be coupled direct on to the propeller shaft. The fly-wheel was at the forward end, and to start the engine there was a detachable handle that engaged in a socket in the fly-wheel axle (the forrard end of the crankshaft itself). The whole thing was infinitely less complicated than, for example, an ordinary clock.

Of course there were the fuel feed pipes to the carburettor, one paraffin, the other petrol for starting up. The water inlet pipe from the boat's bottom to the pump; thence to the cooling jacket; another pipe which discharged the water into the silencer where it "baffled" the exhaust gases from the engine, and escaped with them through the exhaust pipe overboard. There was also the propeller shaft, and its tube, and the propeller itself, but none of these things presented serious problems. If the engine would go, the rest was all plain sailing.

Our first job was to unbolt the cylinder casting from the crank-case. This should have been simple, for there were only six bolts. But all of them were "rusted" in, and we had to heat them with a blow-lamp, and then soak them with paraffin, and "tap" them with a hammer and cold chisel before they'd move, and one of them refused to move at all, and it took me the whole of one day, working with a breast drill, to release the two parts completely. But we had a direct reward for our labours when we lifted the cylinders up, and the pistons and the crankshaft were revealed, entirely free from rust; and so far as we could judge by wiping away the filthy oil on them, mechanically sound. It was the oil that had preserved them from the sea-air and wet which had done such damage to the external bolts, and we did not complain that it fouled our hands and clothes, and that no matter how we washed we could not get rid of the smell of it.

We removed the pistons from the crankshaft. We discovered that the bearings, instead of having the usual soft-metal, renewable linings, were of solid bronze, and were very badly worn, but I saw that if I carefully filed the joints of them I could take up most of their slack; and anyway, I did not expect that the thing was going to run like a Rolls-Royce; enough that it would run at all. We stripped the pistons and dropped each part as we removed it into a bucket of paraffin; it was thrilling a few minutes later to pick them out again, and wipe them with a cloth, and see them shining and smooth as though they were brand new.

We stripped the crankshaft. It, too, was badly worn, but there was no suspicion of a crack or other serious mechanical defect in it. The cylinders themselves seemed perfectly sound. The valves, again—their exterior parts were thick with rust—had suffered from wear and neglect, and it looked as though they would need regrinding, but there was nothing else wrong with them or with their springs, or the tappet rods.

With the bearings tightened, the valves reground, to make them positively gas-tight; with all running parts clean and well lubricated, and the whole thing carefully re-assembled, there seemed no reason whatever why that machine should not work and develop at least a good proportion of its original power, and as that power obviously had been great enough to drive the fishing boat, it should be ample for ours.

We could not prove this, however, until it was completely installed in the boat and, despite our feverish desire, the dismantling and cleaning was a longish job, and it was subjected to inevitable restrictions. I had to do a certain amount of regular work on the book. We dare not neglect our garden. We had to do our daily shopping because of the fresh milk we needed for Amelia, and we had to fish, or we'd have had nothing to eat except our sheep's head. Amelia herself was anything but a help. Choo-i had produced her family, and we had kept one kitten for Amelia; out on the lawn they all three got on very well together, and amused themselves intensely. But inside, Amelia and the kitten imagined that our work on the engine was a show put on for their especial benefit, and as Amelia could now crawl anywhere she wished, and at an astonishing speed, it was the devil of a job keeping her out of the way. I'd be busily engaged on a refractory nut, and suddenly find either her or the kitten between my legs, or I'd look round for a greasy spanner I'd laid on the floor, to find Amelia with the end of it in her mouth. Once while both our backs were momentarily turned there was a yell, and a terrified mew, and there was Amelia and the kitten and the bucket of paraffin and dirty oil, which Amelia had overturned on the pair of them.

There was no point in re-assembling the engine in the hut, although we had got a new vaporizer, and all the necessary joints and packings. When we'd got it all to bits, and I'd filed the bearings, and ground in the valves, we started work on the boat, fitting the bearers, the propeller tube and the fuel tanks; and here Amelia was less of an anxiety, for (and we regarded it as a happy sign for the future) she liked being in her hammock bunk, and she would remain content in it for long spells, just watching us; while Choo-i, and the kitten (who luckily had inherited her mother's antipathy to boats) amused themselves on the shore.

But again it was a long job. It took us an entire week to cut and fit the two oak bearers, for they had to be in dead alignment with the propeller shaft. We had to cut through the stern post to insert the tube. We had to cut a piece out of the rudder, for the propeller; and the fitting of the sea-cock (for the water-cooling tube), was a very ticklish operation, for like the stern tube, its joint had to be made completely watertight.

It was already April, and it was only a few weeks to Amelia's birthday when we carried the dismantled crank-case down, bolted it to the bearers, and began the final job of reassembly. Should we be able to complete it in time for that event? I emphasied to Dain the need for meticulous care. An engine was not a thing to take any chances with. Even one of this size could develop terrific power in its combustion chambers, and if that power was not transmitted directly to the moving parts, or the parts themselves were not free, the result might be calamitous. Every bolt and pin must be in its right place and securely fastened; every joint tight. We mustn't hurry anything, and yet we both became obsessed with the idea that it would be ready for the day which, with magnificent appropriateness, we'd celebrate with the maiden voyage of our completely equipped cruiser.

Actually that day fell on a Friday, and it was not until the Thursday afternoon that the job so far as we could tell, was finished: the engine entirely reassembled and "timed," the fuel pipe, the water system, the exhaust, all connected up, and the propeller shaft coupled. I had worked almost continuously on it since dawn, and when I had tightened the last bolt in the propeller coupling, I stood back with Dain (who had Amelia in her arms) in the stern, and we surveyed the job with an excited satisfaction that was only mildly repressed by a fear that we might have left something out.

It certainly *looked* good. No one would have recognised in that engine the piece of rusty machinery that had lain on Hoskins's quay two months before. We had scraped every particle of rust from the casing, and given it and the fly-wheel a coat of aluminium paint. We had polished the heavy brass carburettor, and the copper water pipes, even the exhaust. It looked even more professional than the boat herself.

"Its absolutely thrilling!" cried Dain. "It just looks brand new. . . . And to think we had it given to us, that the whole thing has cost us practically nothing. That we've got an engine and a boat, and that we can *go*. . . . *Do* start it up. . . . I *am* excited! Shall we put Amelia back in her bunk or will it be all right if I hold her here?"

It was a spring tide and about an hour before high water. *Samaki* was still aground forrard, but there was plenty of water aft, and no harm could come of running the engine for a short spell. But I was nervous and, as our little boat was afloat alongside, I thought it better for Dain and Amelia to get into it, and stand well away, until I had got the thing going and proved that all was well. After all, I was not an expert. There was a possibility that I had made a wrong connection somewhere, or forgotten some important gadget.

We had already put lubricating oil in the crank-case; the fuel tanks were full. As soon as Dain and Amelia were clear, I opened the priming ports in the cylinder heads, engaged the starting handle, and gave the fly-wheel a few turns to distribute the oil, and make sure that everything was moving smoothly. There was a gratifying hiss from the "ports," proving that they were releasing a definite compression, and there was a hollow sucking sound from the exhaust pipe, which proved again that the valves were functioning. I squirted some petrol through each "port," closed them, turned on the petrol feed pipe, opened the throttle, and then when the carburettor had started to flood, I shouted to Dain:

"Look out. I'm going to try her now!"

It was a desperately exciting moment, and my heart was thumping, as I engaged the handle again, and then with all my strength swung it round. Nothing happened, except that hollow sound from the exhaust. I swung it again, and keeping up the momentum, went on swinging, for at least a dozen turns. Still nothing happened. I primed the cylinders again, saw that there was plenty of petrol in the carburettor and tried once more without success. I began to feel worried. Surely if there was plenty of compression in the cylinders (and the terrific strain of "swinging" proved there was), and the plugs were sparking all right, there should be at least some sort of an "explosion." I unscrewed the plugs, and laid them on the engine top, and called Dain alongside to watch them while I turned again.

"They're giving a terrific spark," she shouted.

I replaced them, gave the cylinders an even heavier "priming" and swung the handle until I had no strength left. The engine did not give the slightest response beyond that sound in the exhaust, which to me was painfully like derisive laughter. I was tired and swiftly losing my temper. What the hell was wrong with the bloody thing? Was it possible that after all our weeks of labour on it it would not go at all. The compression was there, the plugs were working, the "timing" was right, and whether the carburettor was functioning or not, there was enough petrol in the cylinders to make at least one mild explosion. I stood up, surveying that piece of machinery on which we had built such dreams of happiness, which a few minutes ago we had both thought looked so good, and for a moment I felt capable of attacking it with a sledge hammer. Then I looked at Dain, saw the disappointment in her face, and at Amelia, who (possibly because she sensed that both her parents were unhappy) started to yell bitterly; suddenly I thought, By God, I'm going to make the thing go, even if I've got to swing the handle for the rest of the day! We were not going to be done out of Amelia's birthday cruise.

I shouted to Dain:

"Look here, there's something wrong, something we've forgotten. Probably only a small thing, but I'll find out what it is in time. Leave me to it. I can't concentrate, while the poor kid's yelling like that. Take her up to the garden. You'll know by the noise when I've got the thing to go."

It seemed obvious that the fault was in the ignition. I waited until Dain and Amelia were out of sight (and hearing); then I took out the plugs, cleaned their points and tested them. I got a painful shock from one of them that proved better than sight that it was functioning properly, but there was no response when I swung the handle. I was certain that I had made no mistake in the "timing"; but I disconnected the magneto chain and "timed" it again. I went on "priming" and swinging, and feeling more and more exasperated. The tide had flowed to full, and had started to ebb. *Samaki* was afloat fore and aft. I took a breather and hauled her off to her stern mooring, for it would be more exasperating, I thought, if I did get the engine to go, and she was aground. But when Dain came down to the beach and shouted that she had made tea, *Samaki* was aground forrard again, and I did not haul her off farther. I made one more desperate effort with the handle, then threw the thing down furiously, and shouted to Dain I was coming.

I tried again after tea, and went on trying until dusk; by then my right arm ached, and I had such blisters on my hand that I could scarcely grasp the handle let alone swing it.

Dain did her best throughout the rest of the evening to pretend that she was not disappointed, but she did not make me feel much better when, at bedtime, she said:

"Well, it doesn't really matter. We can be just as happy to-morrow in the little boat. We can go to the sandy cove, and fish and bathe and have our birthday tea, and have a gorgeous time. Won't Amelia love it. I do hope it's a nice sunny day."

I didn't feel like bed myself. When Dain was gone I walked with Choo-i and the kitten to the front door, and stood there looking down at the cove. It was a fine calm night, with the moon nearly full, but hidden in high, floating cloud, which promised a continuance of settled weather. Undoubtedly to-morrow would be an ideal day, not merely for Amelia's birthday picnic, but, I thought with bitter irony, for *Samaki's* maiden voyage. Why the hell wouldn't it go? What was it that was missing? What had I done wrong, or what hadn't I done right? I pictured in my mind every one of the engine's components, and went over the routine of the starting action. Was there any part of that I had left out. I thought of the Lunns' coble and of John (the coble "engineer), starting up after we had launched the coble down to the landing for a fishing trip. Fundamentally there was no difference in the two machines. He'd give it a swing with the "ports" open, to splash the oil into the cylinders. He'd "prime" it, flood the carburettor, give it another swing—and it would go. . . . Then suddenly there came to my mind an occasion when, after John had overhauled the engine, it had obstinately refused to go. We had all taken turns swinging it. Tried every possible position of the throttle lever—in vain. Then, when we had given up hope, Henry had glanced at the leads from the magneto to the plugs, and discovered that they had been crossed, so that the plugs were sparking, not at compression, but at exhaustion point. . . . *God!* Had I done the same?

I presumed that Dain was already asleep, but, anyway, there would have been no point in telling her of my new hope. I didn't bother to get a lantern, for there was plenty of light from the thinly clouded moon. I rushed down to the cove, Choo-i and the kitten following me in high glee.

Samaki was high and dry on the shore. I got into her. There was no need for me to examine the leads. If they were wrong, then I had only to reverse them to have them right. It was only a few seconds' work to do this. The throttle lever, which was at the after end of the engine, was already open. I turned on the petrol, primed both cylinders again; then, grasping the starting handle with my blistered hand, I inserted it in the socket, summed up all my strength, and gave a terrific swing. . . .

My first impression of what happened then was that the whole engine had exploded. I thought indeed that I was fatally hurt; for the handle, a crooked piece of solid steel weighing at least eight pounds, was torn out of my hands and from the socket, and it was flung up with terrific force into my face, catching me across my left cheek and eye. I fell back blinded and at least partly stunned; and a considerable time must have elapsed before I realised that I was alive, that the deafening noise I heard was the engine going—*going like hell*!

I had no sense of pleasure or victory then, however. With one hand clasped to my cheek and eye, I staggered to my feet, and looked dazedly and with growing terror at the shaking, roaring engine. Never had I heard such a diabolical racket. With the boat being high and dry, there was no water circulating through the cooling chambers; the silencer, therefore, was not operating. The propeller (although of course I could not see it) was revolving in the air, so that there was no force to retard the engine, which indeed with the throttle fully open must have been revving at a terrific speed. My terror swiftly grew as I saw the reflection of flames emerging from the exhaust pipe orifice, and smelt blistering paint and felt the sheer heat from the uncooled cylinders, and the boat hull shaking and creaking as though at any moment it were going to split asunder.

"*God*," I thought, "*I must stop it!*"

I took a stride aft, put my hand on the throttle and pushed it back. But the thin rod connecting the handle to the actual throttle valve in the carburettor had somehow or other come loose. Nothing happened. I felt for the valve itself. With the rod loose there was nothing to hold it by. The engine just roared on. I stood back wondering desperately what the devil I could do next to stop it. Then I heard a voice and saw Dain in her pyjamas standing by the boat side, panting, and shouting excitedly:

"Hooray! It's going, it's going! I heard it and rushed down!"

She could not have seen my eye, or my bleeding cheek. I shouted back at her frantically:

"I *know* it's going, I want to stop the bloody thing. I want to stop it."

Then I remembered the petrol feed pipe, which had a cock on the bulkhead. I leapt forrard, found it, and closed it; and after a space of a few seconds, in which the engine seemed to roar and shake worse than ever, in which I stood helplessly waiting for it to burst into flames, or shake the boat to bits, the noise subsided and suddenly stopped, leaving a profound silence, broken at last by Dain, speaking this time with anxiety.

"What's happened? Has anything gone wrong?"

I didn't say anything then about my eye, which by the feel of it was going to be swollen and black for many days to come. With my good eye I surveyed the engine still smoking and stinking with its scorched and blistered paint, but apparently intact and unharmed. Then I looked at Dain, whose scared face was visible over the cockpit gunwale, and I shouted triumphantly:

"No, everything's all right. Everything's splendid. I'd got the plug leads foul, that was why she wouldn't start before. She went with just a touch! And power! My God! She'll drive us like the wind. I've only got to mend that throttle. We're going to have our birthday cruise after all!"

18

IT WAS A perfect day—calm, and sunny, with just a suspicion of a light shore wind. As the tide was down, we spent the morning getting bait, and repairing the throttle and getting the picnic ready. We had lunch, but it was nearly two o'clock before the tide was up to *Samaki's* moorings. We tied the little boat to her stern, cast off, and with a boat-hook, pushed her out to deep water. Dain took the tiller. The engine started at the first turn of the handle. It made a terrific noise for a moment or two. Then, as the pump got into action, the exhaust was muffled. There was less vibration. I opened the throttle slowly, and we began to gather way.

We were too excited in the first few minutes of our maiden voyage to say anything to each other. I took the tiller from Dain, who dashed into the cabin to fetch Amelia, whom we'd temporarily deposited in her bunk. She was wearing her fisherman's guernsey, and a pair of "long" blue serge trousers Dain had made for her, and a little red tam-o'-shanter. She chortled with delight when Dain lifted her on to the deck, and quite definitely (although she might have been meaning something else), cried the word:

"Sea, sea, sea!"

I headed straight down harbour. The flood tide was against us, but even with the throttle only half-open we were travelling at a very good speed and, looking aft, I saw that our little boat had her bows out of the water, and was throwing up two lovely plumes, and I shouted to Dain:

"My God, she's marvellous! Think of it! An engine at

least thirty years old, and going like this and still not full out. And the boat; she feels grand. I can believe she's alive and knows it too."

"We're already half-way to Porthkerris!" cried Dain. "It *is* exciting. After all these months of waiting. Going at last. Where shall we go? Let's go miles and miles along the coast. There's nothing to stop us now. It doesn't matter how late we are getting back. It doesn't matter if we don't get back to-night. We've got heaps of food, and we can get an extra lot of milk at Porthkerris!"

My confidence in and my liking for that engine (despite my painful black eye) was growing every minute, but I thought of our trip to the mackerel cove in our first small boat, and I made a strong resolve, that to-day on our maiden voyage we'd take things easy and run no risks. Our engine, no matter how reliable and efficient it might be for driving the boat, had those two serious disadvantages. It had no clutch, so that it could not run without moving the propeller, and giving way to the boat: having no reverse, there was no means of stopping her forward speed in an emergency, such as might be offered by another approaching boat, or a suddenly perceived rock, or just in the ordinary process of going alongside a quay and landing. Doubtless with practice I should be able to stop the engine, just at the right moment; but practice was essential. Besides, although the boat herself seemed seaworthy, we should need practical proof of this before attempting a really long voyage.

For this reason I did not attempt to land at Porthkerris, but throttled down slow enough for Dain to get into the little boat; and I circled round slowly while she went ashore for milk and bread and the rest of our usual shopping. Then we headed down harbour again for the sea.

My own plan, bred of that cautiousness, was that we should simply go to the sandy cove, drop anchor, go ashore in the little boat, bathe and have our picnic, and then perhaps, if all had gone well, "cruise" for a mile or two along the coast. Dain agreed that this would be wisest, and we turned west from the harbour mouth, keeping the same course as if we had been in our little boat. In ordinary conditions of weather and tide that cove had been about an hour's pull from home. Now, however, it seemed that we had scarcely left the harbour mouth than we were abreast of it; and without any real weakening of my resolve, I agreed with Dain at once that it would be silly to land, particularly as we observed a small pleasure boat already drawn up on the beach, and a man and a girl sitting near the pool where we usually "bathed" Amelia.

The weather seemed more settled even than on that day we had set off to the mackerel cove. The sea was level, without a suggestion of a swell. Even the light shore wind had dropped completely. It was more than a fine spring day. Although the air was not really hot, the sun was quite fierce, and there was a feeling of real summer in the blueness of the sky, and the clearness of the atmosphere. It would be a day like this when we'd be setting off on our first real cruise, with all our stores on board, and everything prepared for days and weeks of happy voyaging and exploration. By then, of course, the capacity of both engine and boat would have been well proved; but we'd already got proof that the engine was more than powerful enough to drive the boat. I could see no risk in carrying on now for another mile or so until we found a cove, which we'd have to ourselves.

The land here, although hilly, was lower than to the east of the harbour. But the cliffs were just as precipitous in places, and the shoreline rock-bound, and with *Samaki's* extra draught to consider, we daren't venture as close in as if we'd been in the small boat. We were, however, close enough for us to have seen any possible landing place. As we did not see one we carried on towards a headland, that reached farther seawards than the one that had hidden the mackerel cove. It was marked with a tall stone beacon; and about a quarter of a mile seawards from its point was a rock with its jagged top just showing out of the water and bearing an iron post with a wood bar fixed near its top. I had tramped along this bit of coast on that Christmas day, when I'd been hunting a place to live in, and I remembered that beyond the headland the coast receded to the north for nearly a mile and formed with a corresponding headland a bay nearly eight miles across. On the farther shore, just inside the bay, was a tiny fishing village with a tidal harbour.

We could not see the bay yet, nor that distant village, but it suddenly became my desire to do so, and point out the village to Dain and, as there was still no sign of a likely cove, I steered seawards to give the marked rock a wide berth, for although there might have been plenty of water between it and the headland itself (seeing that it was nearly high water of a spring tide), I was running no risks. We had no sooner got abreast of it than the "view" opened out. We saw first the western headland of the bay. Then the village itself with its white cottages gleaming in the sunshine and, then, as we steamed on, the whole bay opened out.

I throttled down the engine, for this, I felt must be the actual, as well as the psychological climax and end of our first westerly voyage, but we kept on slowly ahead while we admired the view, which was really very fine; for the northerly shores of the bay were quite low, and beyond them we could see woodlands and farmlands rising up to hills that looked as wild as our Yorkshire moors, and the cliffs on the west side of the bay seemed grander than anything we had seen to the east of St. Jude. But it was the village, lying snug under the farther headland, that excited our interest most. I had not called there on my pilgrimage, for it had no river or creek, and it would have meant a long detour. I said to Dain:

"That place *does* look fascinating, doesn't it? It just shows what a lot of spots we can see, now we've got a motor-boat. We could easily run over to a place like that and back in a day. It wouldn't be a bad idea if we made that our first real cruise."

At once I regretted my remark, for I had not realised to what a pitch of excitement Dain was already aroused.

"It looks thrilling! Just like a foreign place. How far is it? It can't be *very* far. Do let's go, *now*. It would be far more exciting than just landing in a cove; besides, there aren't any coves now those people have bagged ours. Do let's go on. We needn't stay there, we can just land, and have a look at it, and start back straight away. We can have our picnic on board. We've got the primus and we can make tea. That will be real cruising."

I thought of my resolve, and of all the reasons why it would be foolish to make that trip of an extra eight miles across the bay in a boat whose sea qualities were quite unknown, with a thirty-year-old engine that I'd only had running for about an hour, and with a very precious baby on board. Then I looked at that ridiculously tranquil stretch of water and at the cloudless blue sky, and listened to the smooth, quietly chugging engine, and I remembered that both the paraffin and petrol tanks were full. I suddenly thought, well, caution's all right, but it can be a worse fault than recklessness if it's overdone, and it wouldn't be caution, but simply cowardice if I did insist that we should turn back. What could happen, anyway, I asked myself, forgetting just then that at sea, in a boat, what often does happen is the thing one expects least.

I opened the throttle again. I steered direct for those white cottages we saw gleaming across the bay, and even Amelia (for safety's sake we'd put a rope round her waist, and tethered her to the deck) seemed to understand and approve of our decision to go on, for she waved her hands, pointing more or less ahead, and shouted again and again:

"Sea—sea!"

The engine continued to behave well. As we now had no rocks to worry about, we had time to admire the boat herself, to get up on to the "deck" and walk about, to go into the cabin, which seemed completely different to what it had been when *Samaki* was laid up on our beach. You could feel the vibration of the engine, and the actual forward movement of the boat, and look through the portholes at the blue sunlit sea, moving past, and see the dancing reflection of this on the opposite cabin walls. It was so warm inside, we had to open one of the skylight windows. We agreed, enthusiastically, that so far as the living accommodation was concerned, *Samaki* was going to be every bit as comfortable as our expensive dream ship.

We chugged steadily on across the tranquil bay, towards that enchanting-looking village and, ignoring the coast to the north and behind, it was easy for us to imagine that we were making our first landfall after days at sea. It was not until we got really near it that some of its enchantment vanished, when we discovered that some of the white "cottages" were actually stucco villas, built (as in our own Bramblewick) on a hill-top, above the original village, which clustered round the actual harbour, and that what had looked like a very ancient church was really a modern noncomformist chapel, built of white glazed brick, like a public lavatory.

But we were too excited, too pleased with ourselves and our boat, and the conclusion of the first half of our maiden voyage, to be critical or disillusioned. I did not risk trying to take *Samaki* alongside one of the harbour walls, where a group of elderly fishermen stood eyeing us with professional curiosity. We dropped anchor outside, and went ashore in our little boat.

Actually, there was not much in that village to interest us directly. It was clear that as with Bramblewick its fishing trade had declined. There were very few fishing boats, and all the men seemed old. Its main trade obviously was summer "visitors," for there were plenty of laid-up pleasure boats, and in its crooked and otherwise picturesque main street were several shops, all but one still closed, which in the season would sell ice cream and picture postcards, and Kodak films and the usual holiday merchandise. Yet it was novel, and Amelia was thrilled by it all, particularly by the one open shop, where to my secret shame she took a violent fancy to a hideous toy yacht with cotton sails tacked on to its mast, and with a tin keel, and insisted on having it. We loitered and wandered happily about the harbour side for the best part of an hour. Then as it was nearly six o'clock we decided to go back to *Samaki*, have our tea on board while we were at anchor, and start on the voyage home.

All this time the sun, although lowering, had shone brightly, and there was not the slightest sign of a change in the weather. We boiled our kettle on the primus stove, and had our tea in the cockpit, using the engine box for a table. The gulls swarmed round us and, to Amelia's delight, swept down and took the scraps from her hands. Leisurely I hauled the anchor then; started the engine and headed *Samaki* east for the beaconed headland across the bay where two hours ago my resolution for caution had been so easily overcome. The bay itself was still dead calm. The headland looked nearer than the village had looked when we had sighted it. From the headland it was only another three miles home. We had been disappointed in our village but the voyage itself had more than made up for that. It had proved at least what the engine could do, and I did not regret that we had ventured on it. A few more trips like this, some practice in going "alongside," a test in rough weather, which I could carry out alone near St. Jude's harbour when a chance offered, and we'd have no fear in tackling a real cruise, days and perhaps weeks from home.

We chugged on. Amelia started to yawn and, after a half-hearted protest, she consented to being undressed and put to bed in her hammock, but she refused to be parted from her atrocious toy yacht. It was while Dain was in the cabin, giving her a final tuck in, that I first noticed that the seaward horizon line, which had been so clear all day, was blurred; that a thin, indefinite, whitish streak divided the blue of sea and sky. At first I thought that it might be some trick of the light, and I said nothing to Dain when she rejoined me, and we had steamed on for another quarter of an hour, before, glancing astern, I saw that the headland that formed the western extremity of the bay was shrouded with mist. By that time the streak to seawards had definitely grown thicker, and whiter. I said, almost involuntarily:

"My God. I hope we're not in for a fog! Look at that bank to seawards and the cliff astern!"

Dain laughed.

"Well, it wouldn't matter much, would it? We'd be nearly home before then. It's all blue sky ahead. The sun's still shining."

The sun was shining, but getting very low and (I might have been mistaken) it seemed that the air was getting chilly, a common indication on an otherwise fine day of fog "conditions." Yet since we had lived in Cornwall, even in winter, we had never experienced a real fog, of the kind so familiar on the Yorkshire coast; and as there was no sign of it ahead of us, I was not yet seriously alarmed. We were nearly a third of our way across the bay. Once we reached the beaconed headland, and got to eastwards of the rock that lay off its point, we could steer close in to the cliffs which, even in dense fog, in daylight, should be visible and guide us to the harbour mouth.

I opened the throttle, however, and I wished for the first time that our engine was even more powerful. At full speed it looked as though it would take us at least another half-hour to reach and round that rock. There was no doubt soon that the bank to seawards was fog. Looking astern we could see that it was now continuous with the mist that was creeping steadily along the cliffs towards the village we had left. Suddenly we noticed that the hills which rose beyond the north shores of the bay had a thin layer of mist on them.

Inwardly I cursed the fact that we had no compass; that I had not thought of this when I had so easily weakened in my resolve not to venture far from home on our maiden voyage. I made a stern vow that we should never venture outside the harbour again unless we had one; yet I was still hopeful that on this occasion we should not need it. There was not even a wisp of mist on the land or cliffs ahead.

The air was so clear that soon we could distinguish the iron post that marked the rock outside the headland, and a series of smaller rocks showing between it and the cliff. The sight of those rocks which had been hidden at high tide, made me thankful at least that we had been cautious enough to keep seawards of the post on our outward journey.

We chugged on—that iron post our immediate goal. But we were not fast enough. The mist had rolled down the northern hills and had completely obliterated them. The real fog had crept along the cliffs astern, hiding our village. Suddenly we felt a puff of cold wind from the south-west, and we saw what looked like an immense grey-white billow rolling along the surface of the sea towards us. I took a last eager look at the headland and the rock, now not more than a quarter of a mile ahead; and the next moment that billow of fog was upon us, rolling and spreading on. The rock disappeared. The sun and the blue sky had gone. We could see nothing but the shape of our own boat in the grey light of that enveloping vapour.

But in my mind I could still see the iron post of the rock. I kept my eyes and the hand that held the tiller rigidly motionless. I asked Dain to get up on to the deck and get as far ahead as she could, and shout immediately the rock came in sight. My left hand was on the throttle, and I slackened speed gently. The first puff of wind had been definitely from the south-west on my right cheek. It was still blowing, and there was no reason to suppose that its direction had changed, and this increased my confidence that we could pick up the rock all right. But I was immensely relieved, all the same, when Dain gave a sudden shout.

"It's there! Straight ahead of us. I can see the actual post!"

I throttled down to dead slow. I peered ahead, and there was the rock, not more than three lengths away.

"Keep your eyes on it," I yelled. "We daren't go very near. We've got to go seawards of it, then turn in for the main cliff. When we sight that we'll be all right for home."

Very slowly we crept round that rock, which with the tide so low, itself loomed like a cliff through the fog. I kept it in sight until I was confident that the boat was heading direct for the mainland to south and east of it. Then I increased our speed a little, reckoning that as the rock lay about a quarter of a mile "off" we should sight the mainland in about three minutes. The rock quickly disappeared astern of us. I checked the time with my watch. At the end of three minutes I shouted to Dain who was in the bows:

"Look out now. We ought to be sighting something."

Unfortunately the wind had dropped again, but that didn't worry me just then, for almost immediately Dain shouted:

"Land. Ahead of us. . . . Look, a rock, and another iron post, just like the other one!"

I throttled down and climbed up on to the deck for a better view. There was a rock looming ahead of us, and an iron post with a wood bar across the top of it. But it took me an appreciable time to realise why both rock and post were so familiar.

"Good God!" I shouted. "We're back in the same place. There's only one rock with a post on it!"

"But it's impossible. We left that one astern. How can it be ahead of us?"

I didn't know myself, for having left the rock I hadn't consciously moved the tiller. There was, however, not the slightest doubt that it was the original rock, and that instead of steaming straight ahead, we had described a complete circle. That in itself was alarming, but what alarmed me more was that looking now at the rock, I simply could not tell whether we had just approached it from the landward or the seaward side. The post was erect. The walls of the rock were practically the same shape whichever way you looked at them. We might be seawards of it now, we might be landwards, we might be east or west. If we lost sight of it again, the chances were equal of our striking the land, or simply steaming straight out to sea, and travelling until our fuel was exhausted.

I felt angry, deeply mortified. To think that with all my experience of the sea and boats, I should have to admit myself completely lost within a quarter of a mile of land, that I couldn't tell north from south. I think then that if I had been alone my outraged pride at least would have led me to make one more attempt. But I thought of Dain and our baby, fast asleep in her hammock, and I knew instantly we dare not risk it. We must drop anchor, now, while the rock was visible, and simply wait until the fog lifted, and we got a certain sight of land. Already even the dim light the fog let through was failing. In less than an hour it would be night.

I was still more angry than frightened. The sea, apparently, was calm, the wind had completely died away. We had plenty of food on board. We could take no harm, even if we had to remain at anchor all night, and the chances were that the fog would lift long before then. There would be a moon to light us home. It was not until we had dropped anchor, and *Samaki* had tightened on the cable, and our little boat had swung out behind her, that we noticed a very slow swell and heard it breaking gently on the rock, which was now barely visible on our port side. This, however, I thought at first, might be simply the tidal current, which would be running very strong at the corner of the bay.

I said, as cheerfully as I could to Dain:

"Well, we've just got to sit tight and make the best of it. It may lift any minute, and stay clear long enough for us to get into the shore. We may have to stay all night."

"It's fun really," she answered. "Amelia's all right, anyway. Thank goodness we brought her bedding. We might as well try fishing while we're waiting. What a good job we've got the primus and the frying pan. We can have a jolly little supper."

We fished. It was a rocky bottom, with long weeds, and there ought to have been pollack or conger, or at least wrasse, but we caught nothing but a huge spider crab which we put back. Night fell. The fog was as dense as ever, and now the rock itself was invisible. It was impossible even to distinguish the surface of the water into which we dropped our lines, and but for the movement of the boat, and the sound of the swell breaking on the rock, we might have been suspended in midair.

The swell was perceptibly increasing. This did not worry me much, however, until, after we had fished for about an hour, the wind started to blow again. It was a cold, clammy wind as before, and if there was nothing to indicate its direction, I judged it to be from a southerly point. *Was* the swell merely the tidal current, or was it a ground swell, such as we'd get on our Bramblewick "scaurs" sometimes hours before the wind started to blow strongly from the sea. Were we in for a "blow"? I thought, My God, if it did blow we'd be in a tight place, anchored within a few yards of a rock, and only another quarter of a mile from a lee shore, which even in broad daylight offered us no landing place.

I daren't leave the cockpit. If the wind did increase, it might prove dangerous, but it might prove our salvation, by blowing the fog away. Luckily we had a flashlight on board. Dain went inside, got the primus on, and made a pot of tea. We had got some bacon, but the boat was pitching so much that she abandoned her effort to cook it, and we drank our tea, and ate chunks of Amelia's birthday cake standing outside. Dain had taken a peep at Amelia, and announced that she was peacefully asleep, in her swaying hammock. I said nothing of the horrible anxiety that now possessed me; but I did not imagine that Dain was oblivious to our peril, for the wind was increasing, and from the more exaggerated pitching of the boat, and its negligible roll, we knew that it was the wind that was raising the swell.

We finished our tea. We wound in our lines, and we both stood swaying in the cockpit, peering into the darkness that surrounded us. The boat herself made so much noise that soon it was impossible to hear the surf on the rock. Even that one certain clue as to our whereabouts was denied us. The thought struck me that perhaps we were drifting. I climbed up on to the deck and warily made my way forward to the post to which the cable was secured, and felt the cable. It was a brand new, inch manilla (one of our few extravagances), and I was relieved to find it taut and steady, but at the same time I got a full realisation of the strength of the wind and sea, for, hauling with all my might, I could not slacken it a foot. As I turned to go back a wave broke over the bows and drenched me. I was glad to get back into the lee of the cockpit.

"The anchor's holding all right," I said.

Dain, too, seemed glad that I was with her again.

"She's a good boat, isn't she?" she said. "I shouldn't feel a bit nervous, if it wasn't for the fog and not knowing exactly where we were. I'm certain Amelia's all right, but I think I'll just go and have another look at her."

Amelia was still sleeping. She was safer in her bunk, I thought, than if Dain brought her out and held her, and I still daren't really think what would happen if the wind and sea got so bad that we were driven ashore. The cable was stout, the anchor had a good hold, and it looked as though *Samaki* herself had all the qualities we'd imagined of her when we'd seen her first. There was nothing we could do but wait and hope.

The moon must have risen, but we could not see it, or even guess its position, for all it did was to make the darkness less intense, to give a vague luminescence to the fog itself, shortening rather than increasing our range of visibility. With an awful slowness the hours dragged on: nine o'clock, ten, eleven. The swell got worse, but it was not violent enough to be directly dangerous, so long as we were riding in deep water. Just before midnight the wind began to slacken. Indeed it fell completely for a few minutes; but our relief was as short-lived, for suddenly it began to blow again in terrific gusts. Whether it had changed direction or not I could not tell for certain. The first direct effect of it, however, was to increase the pitching of the boat, to start her jerking at the cable like an enraged mastiff at its chain.

I knew that even our stout manilla could not stand that strain for very long. There was the weight of our small boat on it too, jerking almost as violently at the ring in our stern. For a moment I thought seriously of cutting her adrift, taking a chance of her washing up ashore somewhere, in a salvagable condition. Then as *Samaki* gave a savage jerk at the cable that almost shook us off our feet, I remembered that we'd got enough fuel for at least two hours' run, and I decided to start the engine, and keep her steaming against the sea and wind fast enough to take at least some of the strain off the cable. Dain went into the cabin to have another look at Amelia. *Samaki* was rolling now as well as pitching, and spray was coming into the cockpit. I had to lift the lid of the engine box very carefully, to prevent the spray reaching any vital part, and for a full minute my attention was completely engaged with the business of priming the cylinders. I was aware, however, that Dain had come to the cabin door. I heard her say:

"She's still asleep, just as though nothing's happening."

And I was bending down to the carburettor, to see if it was flooding, when she startled me with a shout.

"Look—look! The moon. The fog must be clearing."

I looked upwards, aware at once of a definite lightening in the air above, of a patch in the fog that was growing swiftly brighter, in which suddenly the clear moon emerged. Almost instantly it disappeared again, and the fog seemed denser than before, but only for a space of a few seconds. The patch became visible again, it brightened, the moon rode clear; and then it was as though some huge invisible machine was tearing the fog away from the sky, rolling it back and back in all directions. A flood of moonlight lit the sea. It showed us first of all the rock with its iron post, not more than fifty yards direct to leewards of us, with the waves smashing on to it, and their spray leaping as high as the post itself. Then to leeward of this again we caught first the gleam of broken water at the foot of the mainland cliff up which the tattered remnants of the fog were swirling; we saw the beacon on the cliff top, revealed for a moment, then hidden, then visible again, as the whole headland was swept clear. The coastline to the east, fringed with gleaming breakers, stood revealed to us, and three miles away shone the red light which marked the rocks on the west side of the fairway into the harbour of St. Jude.

We had no time then to ponder on the miraculous change; to think what would have happened if the anchor had not held, or the cable had snapped, and we had been driven into that wave-swept rock so near to leeward of us. I shouted to Dain to hold the tiller. I gave a swing at the handle. The engine started. I leapt on to the deck, hung on to the skylight frame while *Samaki* recovered from a horrible corkscrew dive, and I felt her forging slowly ahead. Then I swarmed forward, pulled in a fathom of the slackened cable, and then realising the futility and danger of trying to haul the anchor in, I loosened the cable end, and cast it off. With luck we might be able to pick it up on some future occasion, but, anyway, that cable had already paid for its cost. I swarmed back into the cockpit, opened the throttle and took over the tiller from Dain, and headed the boat direct for the red light, which for us symbolised not danger, but safety and home.

If we'd had any doubts as to the sea qualities of our boat, and of the reliability of our ancient engine, they were dispelled from that moment. The wind was south, with a little of east in it, abeam to our course. It was blowing as strong as ever, and the waves, white topped, were dangerously steep. But as we could see them I could swing to meet the worst, and *Samaki* rode them in superb style. It was the small boat astern which gave us our only real anxiety now, and I had my knife ready to cut her painter instantly should she fill. But she was light, and our speed kept her head direct to the waves, with her head well out of the water. We forged on towards the light. Dain went into the cabin again, and came back and said that Amelia was still fast asleep.

Steadily the light came nearer. We drew abreast of it, and then it changed to white, giving the bearing for the fairway. We steamed in to the lee of the land. The wind fell, and *Samaki* moved faster on an even keel, as though she scented home. It was not until then that Amelia woke up. We heard her yelling. Dain dashed in, and brought her, swathed in a blanket but still hugging her ridiculous toy yacht, out into the cockpit. The quay-side lamps of St. Jude shone clear and bright across the harbour to our left and made corkscrews on the rippling surface of the water. Amelia stopped yelling and stared dazedly at the lights and said:

" Sea-sea!"

Dain said:

"That's not the sea, dafty! Those are the harbour lights, and we're all safe home. But we've been to sea, and we've had a grand birthday cruise, and we've got a grand boat, and it's all very thrilling now it's over, although I was scared, and I know we shouldn't have ventured so far for our first trip. . . . But she *is* a grand boat, isn't she? I just knew we were safe once the fog lifted."

I looked at Dain and Amelia, and I had a sudden and awful vision of that rock, with *Samaki* crashing into it, and the waves engulfing us, and then I thought, well, a miss is as good as a mile, and what we had risked was really no more than the average motorist risks for himself and his passengers every time he moves round a blind corner on a road. We were safe, and I thought with sudden exultation of how *Samaki* had ridden some of the biggest waves. We'd proved our boat, and the summer lay before us. I put my arm round Dain and Amelia, and hugged them both, and I said excitedly:

"Yes, by God, we *have* got a boat. She'll take us anywhere." But to myself I added with the deep conviction of one who has been sentenced to death, and then reprieved, "Yes, but not outside the harbour mouth again, without a compass."

19

WE THOUGHT that the garden and our little home had never looked so exciting as it did that summer. We had a huge bed of pink and blue and yellow lupins in a bed between the stream and the hut, with scarlet hollyhocks, and sunflowers towering above them. Clumps of giant opium poppies self-sown bloomed again, and they'd got mixed up with some lovely, double, coloured poppies, we'd raised from a penny packet, so that their white did not predominate. We had peonies and phlox and asters, and sweet williams, snapdragons, iceland poppies, and marigolds, and gaillardias, and dozens of things we couldn't identify. One end of the hut was almost entirely hidden by a rambler rose which bloomed so profusely that from a distance it looked as though the hut was on fire. We had a glut of strawberries, and then of rasps and currants. Our potatoes and peas and lettuces did better even than they had done the first year. But for the one too-expensive item of meat, and that we had to go easy on butter, we lived like fighting cocks.

Often we marvelled that all this was costing us only three shillings a week in rent; at our luck in having found it, and such amiable landlords as Joe and Charley May. The firm, although still far from prospering, had had an almost continuous series of "jobs" since the time the benevolent Major had presented us with our engine. The Major's own yacht had been finished (Joe had made a fine job of her), they had done three more "gig" conversions, built several small rowing boats and prams, and there was another fishing smack conversion under way. Charley had never mentioned again the matter of our buying the hut, but I was as determined as ever that we would do this as soon as we were able to. Indeed now that *Samaki* had proved such a success, we decided that this should take precedence over the "dream" cruiser. Wherever we travelled in the future this must always be our home, if for no other reason than Amelia was born in it, and that she was so happy here with the garden and the little stream and the cove; and Choo-i and her kitten, and the robin and all the other birds which sang or cried the whole day long.

True that at times both Dain and I suffered an almost unbearable nostalgia, for the sea and the scaurs and the cliffs and the wild moors of Bramblewick. We longed to hear the roar of breakers in Bramblewick Bay, and the gruff voices of the men speaking Yorkshire instead of this soft Cornish drawl, to see the Lunns again. It was worst of all when I'd finished my day's or my night's spell of writing about my adventures with Chicken or Mike Regen, for it was just like waking from a vivid dream, and it would require quite an effort to get my thoughts and emotions adjusted to reality. When I'd read what I'd written to Dain, it was almost as bad, and we'd talk about our life together there, and our fishing expeditions and our tramps over the moors. But when we began to feel really sad we'd think of all the advantages this place had over Bramblewick; the hut and having our own cove, and the fact that we could use our boats in all weathers, and never have to think about hauling them up, and we could always cheer each other with the thought that one day we'd be going back to Yorkshire in our own boat.

Not this year, we had decided. The book had taken me longer than I had thought. It must be finished, and typed

and packed off to Mr. Mackenzie before we spent even a
night away from home, although we were not going to
worry ourselves about what he was going to think of it.
If he'd liked the others, he'd like this. There was no need
for us to worry about getting the cheque for it, either. We'd
saved about ten pounds, and that should be ample for all
the expenses of our first real cruise. We had pored over the
charts of the English Channel coast, and studied guide-books,
and we finally decided that our first trip should be to
Chardmouth, a small but famous seaport about fifty miles
west from St. Jude. There were many reasons for our choice,
but the main one was that it lay inside an immense, almost
land-locked natural harbour, six times the size of that of
St. Jude, that into this harbour flowed a river navigable
even by ships for several miles inland; and that there were
dozens of tidal creeks branching from harbour and river,
affording a network of waterways, in which we could cruise
for weeks independent of the weather.

Actually it was not until the end of July that I finished
the writing of the book. It took us another ten days to type
it and get it off; but by then all our plans for the cruise
were cut and dried, and *Samaki* was ready. We had carried out
several "improvements" since that nearly disastrous maiden
voyage. I had of course acquired a compass. I had got it
from Charley, second-hand, and it was only the box kind
used by fishermen, but I'd given it a careful testing in the
boat, and it was accurate enough for coastal navigation.
We'd made a light mast too, stepping it far forrard so that
it came down to the keel close to the bulkhead of Amelia's
cabin. I knew that we could not make *Samaki* into a sailing
boat, but a sail of any sort would be useful with a following
wind, or in an emergency. The skylight was too high to
permit the use of a boom, so we simply made a triangle

out of one of the *Amelia Hoskins's* old sails, which furled
round the mast like the fabric of a closed umbrella; and,
unfurled and "sheeted" to a rail I made from side to side
of the after edge of the "deck," didn't look too bad. We made
a little safe to hold our milk and fresh food, just abaft the
skylight. We got a ten-gallon petrol drum, cleaned it and
fitted it with a tap for our fresh water. Although Amelia
yet had not really walked independently, she could move
fast enough if she had anything to touch with her hands;
and we had made her a sort of harness with a fathom of
stout rope to it, by which we could shackle her to a ring
either on the deck or in the cockpit, and so, we believed,
keep her out of danger.

By the night of the day we had packed off the book we
were all ready for sea. We'd arranged with one of the
unemployed men who had first helped us with the engine,
to come out to the hut every day during our absence, and
give food and milk to Choo-i and her kitten, and generally
keep an eye on the place. We had told the postman to keep
any letters that might come for us at the Porthkerris office
until we sent our address; for apart from making Chard-
worth our first port of call, and then steaming up the river,
we could not decide until we had seen them, which of the
creeks we should want to explore first; although Joe, who
knew the district well, had strongly advised us to visit a
certain village which lay at the head of one of the westerly
creeks, where, he said there was a pub which used to sell
the finest cider in the county. Charley had been away on
"business" when we had called at the shipyard to say good-
bye. But we had seen the Major, and he had taken what
had appeared to be a most kindly interest in our plans. He'd
been interested, not only in the details of our trip and in the
boat (and the improvements), but also in the arrangements

we had made about the hut being looked after while we were away.

They were spring tides again with high water round about three o'clock. We were up next morning shortly after dawn, to find the sun mounting in a cloudless sky, the creek like a sheet of glass and everything pointing to a perfect day for our voyage. Amelia was wild with excitement, and while we were doing our final packing, locking all the windows, making certain that there was no food left anywhere to go bad, she scurried about the floors, or climbed up on to the furniture or got hold of our legs, shouting all the time, "Sea, sea, sea!" Choo-i and the kitten followed us down to the cove. I believe that Choo-i with her cat's intelligence knew perfectly well that this was not just an ordinary day's excursion we were bound upon. But I don't think she was bothered. There was a nice comfortable box under the hut where she and her kitten could shelter if it rained, and that there would be plenty for them to eat. It was only Amelia who introduced a note of pathos into our parting, for as soon as we were on board *Samaki*, she looked at the shore and cried her peculiar version of Choo-i's name, and then started to yell; but she stopped the moment I got the engine going and *Samaki* began to move. We took a last glance at our little home, as we headed down harbour, with the early sun shining on the lupins and the hollyhocks and the flaming roses. We saw Choo-i and her kitten already philosophically making their way back up the path. Then our view was shut out by the bluff, and we looked ahead at the harbour crowded with yachts and anchored pleasure craft, most of whose occupants apparently were still asleep, and we forgot our home (and Choo-i and her kitten) in the sudden ecstatic realisation that we were off!

The weather could not have been more propitious. It was

the sort of day that makes it seem incredible that the sky could be otherwise than blue; that the same landscape and seascape could ever be colourless and ugly, that the sea could be violently rough, the air cold. There was a wind, which rose soon after we had cleared the harbour mouth, but it was light and from the land, and all it did to the sea was to stroke its surface into tiny ripples that glittered in the sun. Clouds began to form, but they were high up, compact in shape, and almost stationary, and they promised to make no difference to the sunshine, which already was so powerful that despite the wind we had to strip off our guernseys.

The ebb tide was strong but in our favour. We passed our sandy cove and felt rather disdainful towards it, thinking that as it was August and such a fine day, there'd probably be more than one picnic party there later on. We passed close to the rock where we'd anchored during the fog, and if we didn't feel disdainful then we felt quite merry, re-membering how alarmed we'd been, and that some of our alarm had been due to doubts as to *Samaki's* sea-worthiness.

"I don't think I'd feel worried now, in any sort of weather," I remarked. "So long as we had plenty of sea-room, and, of course, a compass."

"Nor I," said Dain. "But I'd rather it was always like this. Look at the sunlight on the cliffs; and the colour of the sky and the sea. And how hot the sun is! Look at Amelia! Doesn't she look lovely and happy? Isn't it just heaven, chugging along like this in the sunshine, bound for a place we've never seen before, not really knowing where we're going to anchor for the night, and not caring. And the book finished, and absolutely nothing to worry about—not even money! We're going to have a grand time, a simply perfect holiday."

As we cleared the headland and the bay "opened out," the land wind freshened. We lifted Amelia down from the deck into the cockpit, and unfurled the sail. It did not increase our speed by very much, but it made *Samaki* heel over slightly, and it gave us at least the illusion that we were sailing, and added to the exhilaration of our spirits. The gunwale of the cockpit was just low enough for Amelia's hands. She hung on to it, watching the waves curving from the hull, completely fascinated. She had got hold of the words "sail" and added this to the two other most popular words in her vocabulary, and she kept on saying, "Sea, sail, Choo-i" with a decided emphasis on the "Choo-i," but we were sure she was not really pining for our cat, for she seemed far too happy.

We kept a course direct across the bay for the opposite headland, and again we had a feeling of disdain as we looked at the fishing village that had been the goal of our maiden voyage. It seemed so very close to home, to travellers like ourselves. But as we closed on the headland our excitement grew, for beyond it lay an unknown territory. And we were not disappointed in the view that was unfolded when we cleared it. For miles and miles to the west reached a line of cliffs, broken up by lesser headlands and coves, diminishing to where just visible between sea and sky was a cape which from our chart we recognised as marking the western approach to the bay and port of our destination, still about forty miles away.

Yet what excited us more just then was the appearance not very far ahead of a flock of gulls and gannets, swooping over a dark, ruffled patch on the sea. We got out our mackerel lines, put them over, then, as we approached what was so obviously the shoal, slowed down a little, and almost immediately we started hauling mackerel on board.

Amelia was as excited as we were, although she was furious when she tried to get hold of one of them and found she could get no grip on its slippery kicking body. Unfortunately too, she made a quick mental connection between fish and life at home, and she stopped saying "sail" and "sea," and began a chant of "fish, Choo-i, fish, Choo-i," which went on for a long time after we had caught enough of the mackerel for our needs, and I had opened the throttle full again.

The chart gave deep water close in to the cliffs for the whole distance to Chardmouth. So we kept close in and, as there was next to no wind here, we furled the sail, and tethered Amelia on to the deck again. The cliffs were magnificent, and although the nesting season was over, they swarmed with gulls, and shags and cormorants, resting apparently between their onslaughts on the sardine shoals. It was too deep for us to see the bottom but the water was crystal clear, and we saw myriads of small blue jellyfish, and occasionally the monstrous pulsating umbrellas of great medusæ, amber tinted, with yards of stinging filaments streaming behind them in the tide. We passed close to one isolated rock, and saw a grey seal and its cub basking on it. We gave a shout, and the mother jerked her head up, then nudged her cub, and half-pushed it over, but waited until it had dived before she dived herself. Amelia was thrilled. We tried to make her say, "Seal." The word was too near "sail" and "sea," however, but it made her forget "Choo-i" and "fish" for a while.

We chugged on, the engine behaving perfectly. For miles the cliff line was very precipitous; then about midday we came to a tiny bay with a shingly beach. We crept slowly into it, stopped the engine and dropped anchor. We stripped and dived overboard, and swam round the boat, while Amelia watched us from the deck. We took her ashore then in the little boat and let her bathe in the incredibly warm shallow water; then we hurried back to *Samaki*, put the stove on, made tea and fried some mackerel. We had brought some milk pudding in a thermos jar for Amelia's special benefit. She'd no sooner finished her meal than she started yawning and fell instantly asleep in Dain's arms. We carried her into her bunk, hauled the anchor and continued our voyage.

The sky was now bedecked with little puffy clouds, but although you could see where their shadows fell upon the water by the dark purple-tinted patches in its turquoise blue, it seemed that there was never a moment when the sun was not burning fiercely on us, and it was so warm in the lee of the cliff that at last we decided to stand farther out to get the wind again. Having found it we steered straight for the distant cape, but it was not strong enough to be worth while unfurling the sail again. We felt lazy. I leaned against the gunwale of the cockpit, the tiller light in my left hand, for *Samaki* almost steered herself. Dain sprawled on the deck, her chin resting on her hands, her face half-inclined, so that her profile and the cape (blue and quivering in the heat) were in my direct line of sight. Neither of us spoke for a long time. Then I became conscious of the peculiar silence, and I said:

"It's quiet, isn't it, without Amelia?"

Dain laughed.

"I was thinking that too. But you know it's a jolly good thing to have a baby who fits in to things so smoothly. How awful if she didn't like boats, and she was seasick, or just screamed when she saw a live fish! Wasn't she funny, trying to hold that mackerel. But I suppose she's just bound to like the same things that we do. Heredity. It does prove, anyway, that having a baby on a boat isn't a bit of bother.

It just makes everything perfect. . . . You know we've simply got to have another."

The fact that Amelia was proving herself such an admirable cruising companion did not seem in itself to me to be a logical argument for another baby. But it was clear that Dain was not in a very logical mood and I was silent, not feeling too logical myself. She glanced ahead.

"Isn't it all exciting?" she said, dreamily. "I can just imagine that that cape's a tropical island. I wouldn't be a bit surprised if we see coconut palms, when we get closer, and some natives come out to meet us in their canoes. It's all so lovely and exciting. I'm absolutely certain that our next baby will be a son. It can't help but be."

Were we becoming intoxicated again? As a mediæval monk might have muttered prayers when he imagined himself tempted by the devil, I thought swiftly of all the sober reasons why we should not increase our family: our poverty, the uncertainty of the future, the fact that sooner or later we would have to buy the hut, that Amelia herself would be an increasing expense as she grew older. I reminded myself, too, of the scientific fact that you could not pre-determine the sex of a child, that if we had another it was as likely to be another daughter as a son; that if it was a daughter then that would incite us more than ever to continuing the process without, however, any assurance that the result might not be repeated. But I couldn't help remembering that I'd thought very much the same way long before Amelia was born; and thinking what a joy she was, and I knew damn well in my heart that I did want a son and that we'd have to have one some day even if it meant having an enormous family of girls.

I said nothing, however, and shortly there was an indignant shout of " Sea, sea" from the cabin. Dain sprang up and went inside, and brought Amelia on to the deck. She was yawning a bit, but full of beans again after her sleep, and we took good care to see that her harness and her rope were well secured.

We chugged on, with the sun blazing down on us and the sea with scarcely a ripple on it, for the wind had almost completely died. We saw more shoals of fish, and birds attacking them, but we did not trouble to fish ourselves, having got all the food we needed. We passed several motor yachts, and a large cruiser, as luxurious as the one that had excited our envy in St. Jude harbour that first summer, overhauled and passed us, the waves from it rocking us so that we had to hold Amelia tight on to the deck, to stop her rope jerking her. But she enjoyed the motion, and we felt no envy of the people on board, for they could not have been happier than we were.

Slowly the cliffs of that cape grew higher and bolder. We distinguished a lesser headland a mile or two short of it, marked by a gleaming white tower, and from the chart we knew that this marked the actual entrance into the bay and outer harbour of our destination. It was getting on for five o'clock. We made tea, and had it in the cockpit, but we kept on at full speed. Soon we saw a huge tanker appear round the lesser headland, steaming very slowly, and with a pilot cutter made fast close to a rope ladder on its side. It came on towards us, and we were almost within hailing distance when it stopped, and we saw the pilot climb down to his boat. Amelia jumped when the tanker suddenly blew its siren, and got under way again, but as its towering hull moved past us she shrieked:

"Boat, boat, sea!"

She waved her hands, and we saw some sailors, leaning over the rails, wave back. But our interest was soon con-

centrated shorewards, for we had cleared the headland, and
we saw to north of us a wide bay with a breakwater reaching
a quarter of the way across it, and to the west of the breakwater, the houses and buildings and the docks of Chardmouth, with more steamers, and innumerable smaller craft,
and to the east, and much closer (and lying in the same
way as Porthkerris did to St. Jude) a smaller fishing port,
with a harbour that seemed full of yachts and fishing craft.

Our excitement grew more intense as I altered our
course and we steamed in towards the breakwater end, still
about a mile distant. The predominant colour of both the
main port and the lesser one was white, and between the
blue sunlit bay, and the cloud-decked sky, they had the
glamorous aspect of tropical towns approached from the
sea. And this illusion was increased when suddenly we heard
a splash close by the boat, and we saw the dorsal fin of a
huge dolphin, and then saw several of them diving and
gambolling ahead of us, leading us in. It was too much for
Amelia. We pointed to the dolphins and said, "Fish, fish!"
but for the first time since we had left home (except for her
brief interlude of sleep) she seemed to be stricken dumb, and
she just stared at them in complete astonishment.

We neared the breakwater. The fishing port was only
about a quarter-mile inside it on our starboard side, and we
were still nearly two miles from Chardmouth. Technically
we had reached our destination once we were inside the outer
harbour, and as the guide-books we had studied labelled the
fishing port a famous beauty spot, full of quaint streets and
houses, we decided quickly to make it our first call, although
already we had noted that it possessed the usual "residential"
area of villas and hotels; and the predominance of "pleasure"
over fishing craft, suggested that it, too, had moved with
the times.

We steered towards it, the dolphins leaving us as we passed the breakwater end. The villas became more obviously villas, as we drew near. We saw that close on the harbour side was the ultra-modern façade of a cinema, breaking a row of really picturesque whitewashed and grey-slated fishermen's cottages, and that the harbour side itself was thronged with trippers, and in one part packed with gaudy motor charabancs. The harbour was formed by a single L-shaped granite pier. Evidently it was too small to accommodate all the holiday traffic for most of the yachts were anchored just outside the pier end. I throttled down. Dain lifted Amelia into the cockpit to be out of the way. I steered for what looked like a fairly empty space among the yachts close to the pier end which was also crowded with trippers, throttled down until the engine was barely ticking over, then conscious that the people on the pier were looking at us with considerable interest, I stopped the engine, leapt up on to the deck and let the anchor go. *Samaki* pulled up to it. I rejoined Dain and Amelia in the cockpit.

But we did not, as we might have done if we had landed on an empty beach, congratulate ourselves on the successful termination of a voyage. The crowd on the pier, the nearness of so many other people and boats embarrassed us.

"I don't think I like this place very much," said Dain. "I wish we'd gone straight on. What are all the people staring at. There's nothing queer about us, is there, unless it's having a baby on board?"

I glanced at Amelia, who was hanging on to the gunwale, looking at the people with a complete lack of embarrassment, smiling and actually waving one of her hands, but I kept my eyes averted from the crowd, until I heard a shout, and then observed a man in a blue guernsey, and white cheese-cutter hat, waving to us. He shouted again, but I could not make out what he said. Then he pointed, and looking back away from the pier I saw that a big steam ferry boat, its decks packed with trippers, was slowly coming in towards us.

If the man on the pier, evidently the harbour master, had kept cool and shouted clearly that we were in the way of the incoming boat, indicating that we must move and in what direction, I could have weighed the anchor, started the engine and all would have been well. But he was angry, and he shouted with an utterly unfamiliar and unintelligible Cornish accent, and some members of the crowd, evidently imagining that we were deaf, shouted too, and all was confusion. I looked round at the boat, then at the pier. There seemed to be a clear enough fairway between both, and we certainly were not in it.

"Can you make out what the bloody fool's saying?" I said to Dain.

"No. I can't," Dain said desperately. "Every one's shouting at once. Look, the boat's coming straight for us!"

The ferry boat (which evidently had come from Chardmouth) was bearing down on us, and not for the obvious fairway into the harbour. It was not two lengths away. Suddenly its siren blew, and I saw a uniformed man on its bridge waving at us, and then I saw him pick up a megaphone, and his voice boomed.

"You're standing right in our way. We've got to turn there. Get to hell out of it. We're late as it is."

I saw now that the ferry boat wished to turn about and go into the harbour pier stern first, but how the devil was a stranger to have known that? We had not anchored in the actual fairway. I felt indignant, more so because the boat had now brought to only a length from us, and that we had in its passengers another audience whom Amelia chose to greet with a frantic waving of her hands. But I did not

notice that in one of her hands she must even then have
been holding the engine starting handle she had picked up
from the cockpit floor. I leapt on to the deck to haul the
anchor. As I did so I shouted to the skipper on the tug who
was continuing his abuse:

"Why the hell don't you buoy your damned harbour?
There's nothing to show that you want this place clear!"

He shouted back:

"Any one with any sense would know it without any
buoys. Hurry up, and get out of our way."

I hauled the anchor and, incapable of a suitable retort,
I leapt back into the cockpit. And it was then in one awful
second I saw Amelia raise her hand, with the precious
starting handle grasped loosely in it, try to wave it, leaning
it over the side. I made a lightning grab for it. But I was
too late. The handle fell from her grasp. It dropped with a
gentle plop into the water, and as though she imagined she
had done something very clever she looked at me, smiling,
and said:

"Sea, sea."

I did not smile back.

I yelled at Dain:

"Hell and damnation. She's dropped the starting handle
overboard. Why don't you look after her? We can't start the
engine now."

But before Dain had a chance to reply to this very
unfair attack the ferry boat whistled again, and the man
shouted:

"Come on, come on. Are you going to be all day? Have
you got an engine or haven't you? Do you need someone
to come on board and show you what to do?"

I think that if that man had ventured on board us there
would have been a fight, for I could never remember having

been so angry with any one. But I was as anxious to get out of his way as he was and the tide was moving us closer to him. I hauled our little boat alongside, jumped into it, shipped the oars, and started to back with all my strength, towing *Samaki* stern first. She moved very slowly, but she did move, and shortly the ferry began to come ahead into the space we had vacated; to turn and then back into the harbour. But I went on towing, and it was not until we were standing clear away from all that hateful mob of people on the pier that I stopped and got into *Samaki* again, dripping from head to foot in perspiration.

The ferry boat came out again and although we were well off its course I shook my fist at it, cursing its bad-mannered skipper. But Amelia waved happily at the wretched thing and suddenly, although I was very troubled about the handle, I began to see how really funny it had been, even Amelia dropping the thing overboard. We both started laughing, and I said that there was bound to be a blacksmith's or a marine store ashore where we could get another one. Dain said:

"Well, it *was* fun, in spite of that man being so rude. And I'm certain we can get a new handle. I think the place looks quite lovely when you're not so close to it. It's a *new* place, anyway, and we've come all this way in our own boat, and even if it is crowded with trippers there must be dozens of places up the harbour and the river that aren't. We can go on exploring for days and days. I think we ought to anchor here, and wait till some of those people have cleared off in their charabancs. Let's have a meal, and just go on imagining it *is* a foreign place, and romantic, and then go ashore in the little boat, with our minds made up that we're going to like everything. Then, if we do get a handle, we can start off again, and find some nice quiet spot to anchor in for the night. . . . Isn't it exciting to think that we're actually going to sleep in our own boat for the first time?"

We gazed ashore. Perhaps we were tipsy again, with all the hours of our exposure to the sun and the strong sea air, but the place, now bathed in the mellow evening sunshine, did look fascinating and romantic. I had forgotten the embarrassing incident of the ferry boat. It didn't matter a bit about the starting handle. We'd had a glorious voyage. Our holiday was only just beginning. I suddenly picked Amelia up in my arms and hugged her, and I shouted quite tipsily to Dain:

"Aren't we lucky having a kid like this, and a boat, and being able to go just where we like, and do what we like, and not a single worry? I'm in love, with you and Amelia, and our boat and even with that bloody cinema, which does look almost like a Persian mosque from here."

And Dain touched my arm, and she said:

"Didn't I tell you that having a baby just made life perfect? Come on, let's get a meal ready. We'd better have mackerel again. In this heat they won't keep till morning."

20

WE HAD NO difficulty in getting a new starting handle; and if we found that the guide-book had exaggerated the æsthetic attractions of that little port, or rather omitted to say how its original beauty had been spoiled, we had enjoyed our visit ashore.

That beauty, and there were evidences of it left, must have been something deeper than the mere aspect of crooked streets and quaint cottages. As in Bramblewick, it belonged, I imagined, more than anything to the lives of a simple hard-toiling community of men and women, all of whose energies were absorbed in their business with the sea. As in Bramblewick, their cottages were built not with any conscious desire for architectural beauty, but simply and honestly and of local material as homes, their streets conforming to the natural lay of the land, and to meet the conditions of the ways of transport then in vogue, pack-horse or donkeys chiefly, used for carrying fish to the market towns of the farming country beyond.

The coming of the steam trawler, the concentration of the fishing industry in large ports, had spelt gradual but inevitable death to the inshore fisherman's trade. So these small ports and villages had finally become depopulated of their original stock; and as there was capital in their quaintness and in their healthy situation there had been an influx of hotel and boarding-house keepers, and sophisticated tradespeople, to cater for visitors and trippers; selling them picture postcards, Kodak films, Cornish cream or petrol; giving them lobster teas, or motor-boat trips at a shilling a time; and judging by the crowds, doing their trade little harm with the petrol pumps and advertisements that decorated the very streets the guide-books praised.

It was sad, in a way; yet all the holidaymakers we saw (even those whose faces and arms were burnt raw with the sun) seemed happy enough, so what did it matter? We were on holiday ourselves, and if our tastes were different, we had the means to satisfy them. Chardmouth itself was fascinating. Here an original industry of shipping and ship-repairing had moved with the times, and survived. True it had a holiday trade, but its bathing beaches and promenades and its summer hotels were on the south side of a castled hill, out of sight of the old town, where there were crooked streets and houses of unspoilt beauty. Here were shops, but their trade was that of a normal town, and they were dignified. There were docks, and engineering sheds and marine stores and chandlers, and there was a steady noise of hammering and rivetting in the air, and there were ships, and along the waterfront strolled or loitered real sailors, many of them foreign. We saw lascars, and negroes, and even Chinamen. This was what we liked, for it was the real thing.

But there was the river too, and the tidal creeks; and although there was another town at the end of the navigable reach of the river, eight miles inland from Chardmouth, the country through which it ran was chiefly common and woodland, with just here and there an unpretentious village. We cruised leisurely up the river, where we passed, in one deep reach of it, about twenty laid-up cargo steamers, evidence that the slump still continued. We explored the creeks, some of which were as long as the tidal portion of the river, and penetrated far into a secluded and utterly unspoilt countryside. Here, when we went ashore for fresh milk and eggs, we'd find the unsophisticated Cornish agriculturist, speaking an almost unintelligible dialect, but pleasant and merry in manner and kind hearted. To Amelia's delight, two swans attached themselves to us during our leisurely exploration of one of these creeks, and they'd take pieces of bread out of her hand. There were herons everywhere and curlews and wild duck, and in one place where we passed through the park of some large estate, there were deer, browsing among the tall beds of bulrushes at the creek's shore.

The weather continued miraculously fair, yet it was never too hot to be uncomfortable, for we wore very little clothing, and we could jump overboard and swim whenever we liked, or go ashore in the little boat and bathe with Amelia in the shallows, then lounge in the shade of the trees. We had a week of perfect joy in which we lived absolutely in the present. We did not think about our home, or the book; and even Amelia, with so many new words to say like "deer" and "swan" seemed to have forgotten the word "Choo-i" and its significance. It was as though all the time we were partaking draughts of some potent drug, which, however, found us just as bright-eyed and energetic each morning when the sunshine streamed in through the skylight of our little cabin, and Amelia, rampaging in her hammock, aroused with shouts of "Food, food, food."

But when that week was up, although we had not explored one fraction of all the inland creeks, we began to get a nostalgia for the sea itself and, noting on our chart another small fishing port just west of the cape we had steered for on our voyage from home, we decided on making a day's trip to it, if the sea was smooth. We spent the night near the mouth of a creek three miles upriver from Chardmouth, and as soon as we'd had breakfast next morning we got

under way. There was a light shore wind, the sun was
shining bright as ever, and it seemed to promise an ideal
day for our sea-voyage. We decided we would call at Chardmouth on our way, however, for milk and bread, to fill our
tanks, and to post a letter I had written to the Porthkerris
post office, asking that my mail might now be sent to the
Chardmouth post office, for of course we were coming back
here. Not that I anticipated anything important in my mail.
It was too early yet for Mr. Mackenzie to have read the new
book.

It was about nine o'clock when we steamed close into
the boat landing jetty, and dropped anchor. We didn't want
to waste any time, so I thought I'd go alone in the little
boat. As I pulled into the landing steps, I observed that the
ferry boat of vivid memory was just about to leave on its
outward journey across the harbour, and I imagined that
its skipper was staring very hard at me and *Samaki*, but I
kept my eyes averted. I landed and made the painter fast,
and with two empty petrol cans in my hands climbed up the
steps. At the top of it was a small office belonging to the
harbour authority, and close by standing in my way was a
man in uniform, who undoubtedly was staring at me hard.
I wondered whether he was going to ask me to pay some
sort of landing dues, although we'd landed before without
question, and I stopped, and said good-morning. He
continued to stare at me and then at *Samaki*, and then he said:

"Are you from that little blue and white motor launch
called *Samaki*?"

"Yes," I said. "I'm just coming ashore for some oil."

"What's your name?"

I told him.

"And you're from St. Jude's?"

"Yes."

Again he stared, then he said:

"All right then. I've got a telegram for 'e. Came last night care of the harbour master. Would have had to go back to the post office, if you hadn't come in this mornin'. . . . Wait. I'll get it for 'e."

He went into his office and came back with a little buff envelope. I felt a horrible dread inside me as I took it from him. What the devil could it be? No one except Joe and Charley knew that we were here, and in a boat of our name. And why should they wire me? God, I thought, had something dreadful happened, had the hut been burnt down? . . . I ripped it open, and as I read it, I felt that I was going to be physically sick. But I got a grip of myself. I crumpled the piece of paper into my pocket, thanked the man, and stepped back into the boat, and rowed back to *Samaki*. Dain and Amelia were in the cockpit, Dain looking slightly puzzled, and then alarmed as she saw my face.

"What's the matter? Why are you coming back? Are you feeling ill? You do look queer!"

I said nothing while I climbed in, and mechanically made fast the painter of the boat. Then I took out the telegram and read it again, and I said, shakily:

"Dain! it's a telegram from Charley. He's had an offer of three hundred pounds for our place. He's got to accept it, unless we can give him the same, within a week. Wants us to wire him if we can do it. It must be the Major. They've waited until we were out of the way—then. My God!"

I handed her the telegram. I daren't look at her while she read it. But I heard her gasp, and then she clutched my arm, and she cried:

"It can't be true. It can't be true. Charley wouldn't do a thing like that. And I don't think the Major could either. It can't be true that someone could buy our place, and

LOVE IN THE SUN

turn us out. It's our home—ours and Amelia's! Where could we go? There isn't another place on earth that could be like that. It can't—it just *can't* be true."

But I knew that it could be true. I knew that there were forces at work over which Charley or his firm had no control. Something must have happened, making it imperative that the value of the place had to be realised in cash. Yet we knew nothing definite, except that the transaction had not yet taken place. Something might still prevent it.

I said to Dain:

"My God, it's awful. But we can't let it happen. We've got to do something."

"But what? Where can we get all that money from; in a week? And yet we just *can't* let it happen. What *can* we do?"

I glanced in the direction of the breakwater and the sea, which seemed just as calm as on the day when we had left for home. And then, with a coolness which I knew came from desperation, I said:

"We've got to see Charley. I'll not believe that he would deliberately let us down. I'll go ashore for the oil, and I'll send him a wire, asking him to do nothing before he's seen us. . . . No, I'll tell him we will buy the place. We've just got to get that money somehow. We'll start for St. Jude, the very moment I'm back."

21

THE SUN shone as brightly, the sea and sky were just as blue as on our happy outward voyage. The sea was calm, the wind again was gentle and warm and smelling of the land, and Amelia gazed about her, and chattered and laughed as merrily as ever, but our hearts were like lead, as we chugged along, homeward bound for a home which soon might no longer be ours to live in.

That cape, which had lured us on to such delights a week ago, steadily receded astern. We passed the little cove where we had lunch, the rock where we had seen the two seals. We saw innumerable jellyfish, like jewels in the water. We steamed through a huge shoal of mackerel, and again we saw a school of dolphins, and one came so near to the boat that we heard the hiss of it blowing, and Amelia this time did say "Fish, fish," and she would have rolled off the deck in her excitement had it not been for the rope.

But all these sights which had so thrilled us on our outward voyage, and Amelia's present delight in them, made our hearts heavier. Outwardly we both did our best to appear cheerful. We cooked and ate our lunch. We washed up. We put Amelia into her bunk again to rest. We watched the passing coast line, and the headland that marked the bay of our maiden trip draw near, but for the most part, we were silent, and I knew that all the time Dain was thinking, as I was, of our little home, of the cove and the garden and Choo-i and all the happiness it had given us, and, that like I, she was appalled by the thought that we might have to give it up.

We drew abreast of the headland. We passed it and we chugged across the bay. We reached the rock with the iron post, and we saw a large motor cruiser just emerging from the harbour mouth of St. Jude, three miles away, and by then it was nearly five o'clock. Would Charley be "home"? He'd have got my wire. Unless he had been called away on one of his business trips, he would of course wait for me.

We passed our favourite sandy cove, where we'd had so many happy picnics with Amelia. We reached the harbour mouth, and Amelia, who was back on deck, and clearly recognised that she was near home, brought a sudden lump into my throat by suddenly shouting, "Choo-i, Choo-i." But I laughed grimly and I said to Dain:

"We'll go straight into Porthkerris. You'd better stay on the boat, while I'm seeing Charley."

"What are you going to tell him?"

"I don't know exactly. It will depend on what he says. But I'm going to tell him we're going to buy the place, definitely."

"But how *can* we? Where can we get three hundred pounds from?"

I didn't answer, for indeed I did not know. We drew in to the Porthkerris side of the harbour. I stopped the engine, dropped anchor, got into the little boat, and rowed in for the familiar quayside, where long ago I had first seen Joe chopping firewood. As I climbed up the ladder and made my way to Charley's office I could still hear the chugging of our engine in my ears, only it was saying over and over again, "Three hundred pounds—three hundred pounds— three hundred pounds. . . .

Three hundred pounds! I could not get hold of a fraction of that sum within a week, or within a year for that matter, unless my latest book proved to be the success we had hoped and expected the other two to be. Neither of us had relatives or friends from whom we could borrow money. The professional money-lenders who had sent me their circulars, glibly offering to advance amounts up to ten thousand pounds "without security," were of course liars. They'd not advance you half a crown without the dead certainty of getting it back with interest.

My stomach felt like jelly when I knocked at Charley's door, and I heard his voice, saying, come in. He was sitting at his desk (littered with drawings and papers and trade journals), and he rose to greet me and shake hands. I saw instantly that he was embarrassed, and self-conscious; but even then I did not doubt his sincerity and goodwill.

He asked me if we'd had a good trip, and then nervously he looked down at his desk, and began fiddling with a pen. I said we'd had a very good time, and we might have been having one yet if we hadn't got his wire. He looked up at me, smiling self-consciously, then he said:

"Well, I'm very sorry if I've spoilt things for you, but you know I promised to give you first chance of buying the place. It has all been sprung upon us pretty suddenly. The people who hold all the firm's property and estate in trust want cash. It was either your place or the shipyard itself, and the Major offered to buy yours for three hundred, and the trustees have agreed to take that amount. Of course, it wouldn't have made any difference to you. The Major's a very decent sort of chap. He wouldn't want to live in it himself, it's scarcely posh enough for that, of course. In fact, I asked him that when he made his offer. He said he wouldn't dream of turning you out while you continued to be such good tenants. . . . Still, I was glad to get your wire—that you will be able to buy it. You'll feel safer, knowing it's your own for ever."

My stomach still felt like jelly. The Major might be a decent chap. I certainly had no evidence to the contrary. He might have made his offer only as a gesture to get Charley out of a fix. It might be true that he wouldn't wish to live there, that he would keep us on as tenants, as long as we liked, but I knew that we should never feel the same security as we had done with Hoskins as our landlords. I looked Charley straight in the face, and I knew that he was being honest with me, and I felt a sudden compulsion to be as honest with him.

"Look here," I said. "I don't know where I'm going to get that money from. My wire was bluff in a way. You said a week in your wire to me. Can you still hold to that?"

"You mean you can't put the cash down at present?"

"No. But I'm going to do my best to raise it."

"I'm really sorry," he said quietly. "I know you must be very fond of the place. . . . Yes. They'll wait for a week. And I'll tell the Major that. But as I've said before, you needn't worry a bit about being turned out."

We shook hands, on what I knew to be a bargain, but a bargain from which I saw no hope; and as I passed down into the yard I felt sick with the thought that I'd have nothing hopeful to say to Dain. Suddenly I remembered our letters, that these would be at the post office. I turned into the village street and almost bumped into the postman himself who greeted me with more than his customary garrulity. Joe Hoskins had told him that I'd sent a wire to say we were coming back. He supposed I knew that our place was up for sale. What sort of a trip had we had? How had the little maid got on? There were several letters for us. As Joe had told him about the wire, and he'd seen the man who was looking after our place just on his way out about dinner-time, and he'd reckoned that the post office might be closed when we arrived, he'd asked this man to take out the letters and put them in our box. There was one letter from London—only came this morning, but the others looked like circulars. I had long since given up being vexed with our postman either for his garrulity or his curiosity about my affairs. And after all, he had acted for the best. Gloomily I returned to *Samaki*. I weighed the anchor. We started on the last short stretch for home. I said to Dain:

"I saw him. He was quite straightforward about it. It's just as I guessed. They've got to find the money, and the Major's offered to help them out, by buying our place. He says the Major himself is quite decent, wouldn't dream of turning us out, and, anyway, he couldn't until next quarter. I think the Major's straight enough too."

"Yes, but he's a business man. And think how enthusiastic he's always been about it. He'll see all its advantages. He mightn't want to turn us out now, but we could never feel the same about him as about Charley and Joe. . . . Oh, God, we must buy it somehow—did you tell Charley we would?"

"Yes. And he's agreed to wait a week."

We entered the creek. We drew near to our bluff, and Amelia waved her hands and shrieked, "Choo-i, Choo-i!" We rounded the bluff, and the cove and the garden, and the hut came in sight looking even more lovely and desirable than ever before, and Dain's voice broke completely as she hugged Amelia to her, and cried, "Home—home." We made *Samaki* fast to her moorings, and as we got into the little boat we saw Choo-i and the kitten scampering down the path to meet us; and they both seemed wild with a genuine joy when we lifted Amelia out on to the beach, and Amelia was thrilled.

We carried her up the path, Choo-i and the kitten following us close, mewing and purring and doing their best to trip us up. We unlocked the big room door, and walked on into the living-room, and I flung open the windows for it was very hot inside, and the perfume of the flowers came in on the draught of cool air, and it was all as though we had never been away, or that anything terrible had happened.

I plonked Amelia down on the floor. She promptly crawled to a corner where there was a woollen ball that Dain had made for her and the kitten, and she started to roll it, and even Choo-i joined in the game and Amelia grew hysterical with laughter. Then Dain started laughing, but in an awful sort of way, and she cried:

"Oh, my God; just look at that child of ours—nearly busting herself with joy—and us just about broken-hearted!"

Then she flung herself down at the table, and cried:

"I just couldn't bear to leave this place. I love everything —all the things we've made, the table and the stools and the blacksmith's chair, and the fireplace. I just couldn't leave it."

She started to cry, and I'd have put my arms round her and I wouldn't have been far from crying myself, if I hadn't suddenly noticed the letters lying under the trap in the back door, and remembered that the postman had said that one of them was from London. It *was* early for it to be a letter about the book, but I thought, well, perhaps Mr. Mackenzie had given it a very quick reading, and there flashed instantly through my mind a bright new hope. Suppose that he was really thrilled with it, that he was certain that this time I had written a "best-seller." Suppose I dashed up to London, and saw him personally, explained the position, implored him to advance me three hundred pounds on its prospects.

That sum was only a fraction of what a real best-seller might earn. But just as quickly came the thought, suppose he has read it, and he doesn't like it at all, that he has decided to turn it down?

It was not difficult to select the London letter from the several that lay on the floor. The postman had been right. The others were circulars. But at once I was disappointed and relieved to recognise by the shape of the envelope that it was not from Mr. Mackenzie. It was a fattish letter; it felt almost as though there might be a cheque inside in it. I came back to the living-room. Dain looked up at me through tear-filled eyes, and then she laughed ironically, and said:

"What is it? Has someone sent us a cheque for three hundred pounds?"

"Yes," I said; "or it's another money-lender's circular. They seem to have an instinct for knowing who wants money."

I opened the letter. Its bulk was due to its being a double page. I didn't start to read it properly. First of all (because it was printed in red ink and in capitals.) I observed in the text the name of our first book, occurring several times. Then my eyes flashed to the heading and saw that it was the name of a very well-known firm of literary agents. And then, with my heart suddenly thumping, I caught the word *film*, and then, printed in red ink and in figures, £1000!

"My God!" I gasped. "My God!"

Dain shot up.

"What is it; what is it?"

I felt tears swimming into my eyes. I could scarcely see the print, and when I'd read it, I could not believe that I was not dreaming. I gasped again: "My God—my God!"

And I thrust it into Dain's hands, and snatched it back and started to read it again before she had time to glance at it. This time I read it through steadily, for I knew that it was not a dream. It was from the managing director of the firm of agents. In curt business-like terms he referred to our first book. He said that a film company had just been formed with the object of specialising in the making of "open-air" films with a British setting. The directors of this company were very wealthy, and very well-known public figures. They were specially interested in my novel as they gathered that its setting was an actual fishing village on the Yorkshire coast, and that its characters were nearly all living people. They were, therefore, anxious to secure the motion picture rights of it. They would like to make most of the film in the actual village of the book, and if possible use some of the actual characters for certain parts. As this was a new company, and the film must be regarded as an experiment, the sum offered could not be as large as that offered for an ordinary novel. But the whole thing would be produced on a large scale, with well-known actors for the major rolls, and no technical expenses would be spared. They would be prepared to pay the sum of £1000 cash on the signing of the contract, but this would be regarded as an advance on a royalty of five per cent on the gross takings of the film, so that my ultimate profit might be far in excess of this, and I was strongly advised to accept the offer. Would I please give an immediate answer by telegraph or telephone. Could I find it convenient too, to come up to London at once and see the writer, and meet the principals of the company. . . . And there was a postscript to the effect that the company if possible would like to engage my services for the production of the film, as so much of its success would depend on the friendliness and co-operation

of the local people, whom I seemed to know so well. Would
I be prepared to go up to Yorkshire at an early date?

I gave the letter back to Dain. With an extraordinary
and quite unnatural coolness, I picked Amelia up from the
floor, and set her down on the table close to us, and told
her to be quiet. I watched Dain's face as she read, saw her
eyes grow brighter and brighter, and I said:

"Read it all. Carefully. And don't forget the postscript."

Then before she had finished a surge of wild exultation
overcame me. I grasped her arms, and I shouted:

"A thousand pounds. A thousand pounds. Ours, Dain;
ours. And only an advance; only a beginning. A film. A
large-scale production. It's terrific. And to be made at
Bramblewick. God, think how beautiful it can be. Think
of the scaurs and the old village, and the dock and the lifeboat, and the rough seas, and the Lunns. God, won't
Marney and the crowd of them be thrilled? I wonder if
they've still got the old coble. Think of the stunts they can
do with it. We'll have to fetch 'em back from Burnharbour
of course, but they'll not mind that. It'll be a terrific success.
It can't help but be. We'll make pots out of it. It will put
up the sales of the book and the other books, and the new
one. We'll make thousands and thousands of pounds. We
can buy this place twenty times over. We can get our dream
boat built if we want to. We're going up to Bramblewick.
We're going to see Marney and Henry again, and Grab and
Elsie and their new baby. And we've still got our home to
come back to. And we can have another baby, six if you
want, but the next is bound to be a son."

I might have thought then of my patent lobster-pot, of
the books I had written, and how we'd believed that each
one of them was going to be a best-seller and bring us a
fortune; and again I might have reminded myself of that

old proverb that " there's many a slip twixt the cup and the lip," and thought that perhaps after all a film, even with Bramblewick as its setting, might not prove to be a fabulous financial success. But here at least was a thousand pounds, itself to us a fortune. Our home was safe. The future an exciting prospect, and happiness after all was not a state to be attained, but something you encountered on your journey through life. And it was happiness that I saw in Dain's eyes as she clasped Amelia to her, and I put my arms round them both, and we embraced, while Choo-i rubbed herself sensuously against my legs, and her kitten scampered across the floor chasing her woollen ball which she imagined was a mouse.

THE END

THE CORNISH LIBRARY

'Well-chosen works from a literary heritage which is as rich as clotted cream.'

The Times

The aim of *The Cornish Library* is to present, in attractive paperback editions, some of the best and most lasting books on Cornwall and the Cornish, both fiction and non-fiction.

Titles in print, or shortly to be published:

Up From the Lizard	*J. C. Trewin*
A Cornish Childhood	*A. L. Rowse*
Freedom of the Parish	*Geoffrey Grigson*
School House in the Wind	*Anne Treneer*
Rambles Beyond Railways	*Wilkie Collins*
A Pair of Blue Eyes	*Thomas Hardy*
The Owls' House	*Crosbie Garstin*
Twenty Years at St. Hilary	*Bernard Walke*
Troy Town	*Arthur Quiller-Couch*
The Ship of Stars	*Arthur Quiller-Couch*
Hands to Dance and Skylark	*Charles Causley*
High Noon	*Crosbie Garstin*
A Cornishman at Oxford	*A. L. Rowse*
China Court	*Rumer Godden*
Wilding Graft	*Jack Clemo*
The West Wind	*Crosbie Garstin*
Love in the Sun	*Leo Walmsley*
Lugworm: Island Hopping	*Ken Duxbury*
The Splendid Spur	*Arthur Quiller-Couch*
Hawker of Morwenstow	*Piers Brendon*
The Cathedral	*Hugh Walpole*
The Stone Peninsula	*James Turner*
Cornish Years	*Anne Treneer*
The Devil and the Floral Dance	*D. M. Thomas*
Deep Down	*R. M. Ballantyne*
Corporal Sam and Other Stories	*Arthur Quiller-Couch*
The Cornish Miner	*A. K. Hamilton-Jenkin*
Happy Button	*Anne Treneer*
A Short History of Cornwall	*E. V. Thompson*

All the books in *The Cornish Library* are numbered to encourage collectors. If you would like more information, or you would care to suggest other books that you think should appear in the series, please write to me at the following address: Anthony Mott, The Cornish Library, 50 Stile Hall Gardens, London W4 4BU.

Up From The Lizard

First published in 1948 this is a loving celebration of the land
J. C. Trewin knows so well: the County of Cornwall and that part of
it, the Lizard peninsula, where he grew up before the First World
War. Born in sight and sound of the sea, within a few steps of
England's southernmost landfall, he was the son of a sea captain who
had learned his trade under sail and whose voyages inspired the boy's
imagination as much as the shelves of books in Kynance Bay House
which fuelled his love of the dramatic, the literary, and the
fantastical.

Around the story of his childhood in Cornwall, and his days as a
young journalist on the *Western Independent* in Plymouth, Trewin
weaves a fascinating pattern of recollection, anecdote, and
character sketch. One instant he is recalling the Cornish cleric and
antiquarian, Polwhele, who inadvertently caused the odious
Captain Bligh to be locked in an outhouse, the next describing
haunted Pistol's Meadow with its 700 drowned soldiers, then
remembering his excitement as a ten-year-old schoolboy at
witnessing Lady Astor's famous Plymouth election triumph in 1919,
and on to the day when Cornwall's rugby team scored a memorable
victory over the might of Middlesex and narrowly missed the
County Championship.

But always, at the centre of his story, is the sea: in all its changing
beauty and, particularly on the treacherous Lizard coast, its brutal
might. There are extracts from his father's journal of fifty years at
sea which read like Conrad and there is the moving account, which
the young Trewin must have learnt like a litany, of the many
terrible shipwrecks, almost within sight of his home, which The
Lizard counts on its rocks and reefs.

A Cornish Childhood

A Cornish Childhood is one of the most moving and remarkable works of autobiography of our time. First published in 1942 it has sold more than 400,000 copies.

Its author, the distinguished historian, Elizabethan scholar and poet, A. L. Rowse, was born in 1903 in the village of Tregonissey, just outside St. Austell in Cornwall. His father was a china clay worker and his mother kept a small shop to help out. Like D. H. Lawrence the young Rowse was something of an outsider in the tight-knit, simple, and rather primitive community in which he grew up. Like Lawrence he never wholly belonged and lived an inner life of his own, devoted to school and Church, to reading and writing. Through the widening of educational opportunity early this century he found escape. In those days there was only one university scholarship for the whole county of Cornwall; but he won an open scholarship in English Literature at Christ Church, Oxford.

This story of solitary struggle and endurance forms the background to his matchless description of Tregonissey, the village whose customs and characteristics – which all the time the boy was observing – had remained traditional. A good education for the future historian and poet which was to produce this unforgettable portrait of vanished village life.

'There are passages of singular literary beauty. This is a live and courageous book.' *The Daily Telegraph*

School House in the Wind

'The book is Cornwall. The flowers and the wind and sea of Cornwall are always there, conjured up by exquisitely accurate writing which never becomes self-conscious or earnestly literary.'
Compton Mackenzie

When it first appeared in 1944 *School House in the Wind* was immediately recognized as an outstanding piece of autobiographical writing. Time has shown it to be something more than that. It is, quite simply, one of the most enchanting recollections of childhood to have been written in our time.

Anne Treneer was born in Cornwall, towards the end of the nineteenth century, and brought up in the neighbouring parishes of Gorran and Caerhays on the south Cornish coastland. Her father was Headmaster at Gorran, where the large Treneer brood occupied the school house set on a hill in the full force of the Channel gales, and later at the more protected school in nearby Caerhays. Even by the standards of the time these were isolated communities, subsisting on farming and fishing, each with its own character and fierce loyalties. Anne Treneer grew up a bright, energetic, and intensely observant girl, well able to hold her own in a family dominated by sons. She recalls life in Cornwall at the turn of the century in a way which is loving but never sentimental, nostalgic but shot through with rich humour and an unforced perception of people and places.

In its portrayal of the changing seasons, the countryside, and the unique Cornish character this is a book which stands proudly beside those classics of rural life, *Lark Rise to Candelford* and *Cider with Rosie*.